P9-CFV-450

BOOKS BY THE AUTHOR

Medical and Hospital Benefit Plans (with Ruth E. Brecher)

The Consumers Union Report on Smoking and the Public Interest (with Ruth E. Brecher and others)

An Analysis of Human Sexual Response (with Ruth E. Brecher)

The Rays: A History of Radiology in the United States and Canada (with Ruth E. Brecher)

The Sex Researchers

The
Sex Researchers

The Sex Researchers

by *EDWARD M. BRECHER*

WITH A FOREWORD BY

William H. Masters &
Virginia E. Johnson

Boston LITTLE, BROWN AND COMPANY *Toronto*

LIBRARY OF CONGRESS CATALOG CARD NO. 74–83738

FIRST EDITION

Published simultaneously in Canada
by Little, Brown & Company (Canada) Limited

PRINTED IN THE UNITED STATES OF AMERICA

For my Ruth

with whom I lived and worked for a quarter of a century, getting ready to write this book

Observe, probe,
Details unfold.
Let nature's secrets
Be stammeringly retold.

— GOETHE

Sex isn't the best
thing in the world, or
the worst thing in
the world — but there's
nothing else quite
like it.

— W. C. FIELDS

Foreword

This is a highly opinionated book.

It is the natural outcome of an investigative tramp along the highways and byways of sex research by Edward M. Brecher and his late wife Ruth. What Ed Brecher has brought back is a very personal account of what has interested him along the way. He has ignored mountain ranges which might awe others. He has left the highroad to explore long-forgotten cul-de-sacs. He reports at length and with delight on studies which might earn barely a passing footnote in an academic history of sex research. Making no pretense at objectivity, he tells it as he sees it through the lenses of his personal convictions.

Ed Brecher is deeply concerned by the prevailing sexual dilemmas of our time and culture. The aspects of sex research he has chosen to emphasize are those which seem to him to offer hope for change.

As a result, no one is likely to agree with everything in *The Sex Researchers*. We certainly do not. But it both educates and entertains. Indeed, agreeing with and vigorously dissenting from the positions Ed Brecher has adopted are two of the pleasures his book affords; he will not be unduly pleased by agreement nor testily resentful of dissent. What he presents, with investigative diligence and reportorial clarity, is one man's view of the currently visible fraction of the iceberg of sex and sexuality.

The chief virtues of this book are the two demands it makes: a demand for critical consideration and sober reflection on the part of readers, and a demand for generous support of objective research on the part of society.

We join Ed Brecher in missing the participation of his wife and partner Ruth. Though we knew her only briefly, we enjoyed her enormously and always will be warmed by our exposure to her.

William H. Masters
Virginia E. Johnson

Introduction

Three times during my lifetime, the publication of sex research findings has rocked the sexual complacency of our culture:

1948: *Sexual Behavior in the Human Male,* by Alfred C. Kinsey, Wardell B. Pomeroy, and Clyde E. Martin,

1953: *Sexual Behavior in the Human Female,* by Alfred C. Kinsey, Wardell B. Pomeroy, Clyde E. Martin, and Paul H. Gebhard,

1966: *Human Sexual Response,* by William H. Masters and Virginia E. Johnson.

My late wife Ruth and I had the good fortune to be directly involved, as science writers, in the public reception of the second and third of these studies. We read the reports in galley or page proof before publication, interviewed the researchers at length and in depth, and then published for lay readers our own enthusiastic account of their research methods and their findings. But we found the task of making the Kinsey reports and the Masters-Johnson study intelligible and credible to nonspecialists far more difficult than it should have been.

The roots of the difficulty were historical. The Kinsey and the Masters-Johnson findings did not spring full-blown into the world. Rather, they were the natural and perhaps inevitable culmination of at least three-quarters of a century of scientific inquiry by specialists of many kinds, in many lands, using diverse techniques applied to diverse populations. The Masters and Johnson observations of masturbation and coitus in St. Louis, for example, were preceded during the century 1855–1954 by observations published by at least fourteen other observers or observer teams in the United States, France, Germany, and Japan. Readers ignorant of this historical background — and most readers were ignorant of it — tended to misjudge the later studies. One goal of this book, accordingly, is to provide a historical context within which readers who are not specialists can understand and evaluate recent sex research findings, as well as the many additional studies scheduled for publication during the next few years.

In particular, readers of this history should be able to avoid a common pitfall — the complaint that a particular report on sex research is unbalanced or incomplete. Such complaints spring up like weeds after each new study appears. More than one critic of the first two Kinsey reports noted with scorn that there was not a single reference to "love" in the index to either volume. The Masters-Johnson study was often similarly criticized for its concentrated emphasis on the physiology of sex; their work was alleged to be suspect because, in their first book, they had slighted the psychological aspects of the sexual experience.

The suppressed major premise of such criticisms is that each new report must portray the whole truth about human sexuality — and this, of course, is an unrealistic demand. A scientific study of the planets can hardly be reproached on the ground that the moon, stars, and galaxies have received only passing mention.

The present volume seeks to provide the broader scope which many readers have missed in most strictly scientific reports. My purpose here is to present, in nontechnical language and in historical perspective, the entire panorama of what has been learned through the scientific study of sex.

Having announced so immodest a goal, however, let me hasten to beat a retreat. This book falls short of its goal in several crucial respects.

First and foremost, it is concerned primarily with sex research in the United States, Britain, and a few European countries. The vast sexual literature of the Near East, Middle East, Far East, and much European material, including recent studies in the Communist countries, remains outside its purview.

Again, the historical span is short. Starting with Havelock Ellis in England, Krafft-Ebing in Germany, Freud in Austria, and van de Velde in the Netherlands — all men who launched their careers in Victorian times — I have made only casual reference to their numerous predecessors through the centuries.

The study of human sexuality, moreover, is not a completed science.

Little is as yet known on many topics of great interest. This book necessarily shares the shortcomings of the material on which it is based.

Further, as Dr. Masters and Mrs. Johnson have noted above, this is a very opinionated book. It is *my* history of sex research. Studies which failed to arouse my interest are here dismissed in a paragraph or a sentence, or are ignored altogether. The result is neither a textbook nor a reference work. Rather, I have sought to present at unhurried length what seem to me to be the central themes — uncluttered by dry-as-dust summaries of lesser contributions, and unencumbered by the many kinds of nonsense which all too often masquerade as scientific data.

The major theme running through this book is the gradual convalescence of our culture from a debilitating sexual disease. I have called this disease Victorianism, since that is the term most commonly applied to it through the past half-century. It is also known as Puritanism, and as the Judeo-Christian ethic; I have preferred Victorianism because it refers to the historical rather than the religious roots of the disease. Use of the term Victorianism, however, does not imply that the phenomenon is as recent as the name; references will be found in this volume to epidemics of the same disease antedating Queen Victoria by centuries and by millennia.

I particularly regret the absence of a comprehensive separate chapter on one of the most fascinating, significant, and underestimated figures in sex research — the American gynecologist, Dr. Robert Latou Dickinson (1861–1950). Dr. Dickinson was born and raised as a Victorian; but what he learned from his sexually inhibited and frustrated patients, beginning in 1882, soon liberated him from the trammels of Victorianism. It was he who made the scientific study of sex respectable in the United States; and he became in his eighties one of the major consultants to the Kinsey studies at Indiana University. An inspired teacher, he trained most of the leaders in the field of marriage counseling in the United States. His major work on marriage counseling, however, "The Doctor as Marriage Counsellor," remains an unpublished manuscript in the Kinsey Institute Library at Indiana University, and no Dickinson biography has been published. I have therefore had to be content to present selected portions of Dr. Dickinson's work in chapters where they are relevant.

The primary focus of this book is on *human* sexuality; but some of the startling findings from animal research, highly relevant to the human condition, are also presented. The emphasis is mostly on heterosexuality — though homosexuality and many other variant forms of sexual behavior are also dealt with. Especially in the chapters on very recent research, I have sought to select from the large and rapidly growing technical literature those studies likely to throw light on problems of current practical concern rather than those of merely theoretical interest.

Whatever its shortcomings, this is the *first* history of sex research. Before writing it, I consulted with many of America's foremost sex researchers — Frank A. Beach, George W. Corner, Paul H. Gebhard, Sophia J. Kleegman, Robert Laidlaw, William H. Masters and Virginia E. Johnson, John Money, Wardell B. Pomeroy, Christopher Tietze, and others. My talks with them made it clear that the men and women best qualified to write this book were all too busy with their own affairs to take on the peripheral chore of writing a history of their chosen field. Several of them encouraged me in a backhanded sort of way; they assured me of the urgent need for such a panoramic view, and they said they'd be eager to read such a book if somebody else would write it. Thus the assignment fell to me by default.

My personal interest in the scientific study of sex was kindled one sunny afternoon in August, 1921, in a rowboat on Lake Minnetonka, in Minnesota. I was ten years old at the time, and fishing for crappies with a twelve-year-old friend named Max who held forth that afternoon on a variety of interesting topics. I accepted most of his pronouncements at face value until he dogmatically informed me:

"You catch syphilis by screwing a girl you aren't married to."

I didn't argue, but I didn't believe him, either. I just couldn't see how a marriage license or the words of a wedding ceremony could prevent the spread of a venereal disease. How can you catch syphilis, I asked myself, from a girl who doesn't have syphilis, even if she isn't your wife? Such doubts led me to the library, and to the solution of a number of other sex mysteries which I read about with fascination — and continued to study through the years.

Shortly after my marriage in 1941 I was delighted to learn that my wife shared my continuing concern with sex research. Ruth's interest had been kindled at the age of thirteen, when she fell in love with a young physiologist who was at work on an improved type of pregnancy test.

Ruth was privileged to assist him in the laboratory; she found then, and continued to find, both sex research and sex researchers fascinating.

We joined the Society for the Scientific Study of Sex when it was founded in 1957, and attended its early meetings with interest and profit. Studying sexuality with a spouse or beloved, we discovered, pays added dividends of two kinds:

Sexuality, as Masters and Johnson have found, can be better understood when both masculine and feminine insights are brought to bear simultaneously. Thus I learned more from reading Havelock Ellis with Ruth than from reading him alone in college, or from rereading him alone during the preparation of this book. In addition, the fresh insights Ruth and I gained from our reading together, and the lines of communication between ourselves which our reading opened up, constituted a vastly enriching feature of our marriage. We called attention to this in the introduction to a book which we published together in 1966*:

"Many books have had a transforming influence on the lives of their readers. Speaking for ourselves, as a married couple, we can recall at least four that have profoundly altered our own views on sexuality, and have thereby altered the sexual aspects of our lives together. Our own marriage today is different from our marriage of a quarter of a century ago, primarily because of our experience in the interim; but the books we have read together are a significant part of that expanding mutual experience."

This book was begun shortly after Ruth's death in 1966. No doubt it would have been richer if she and I had written it together; but I venture to hope that at least some of her personal insights into the nature of human sexuality, masculine and feminine, have survived in this volume.

West Cornwall,
Connecticut
August, 1969

* *An Analysis of Human Sexual Response,* edited by Ruth and Edward Brecher (Boston: Little, Brown, 1966; paperback Signet edition, New American Library, 1966).

Acknowledgments

My son Jeremy first suggested to me that I write a history of sex research, and made very helpful suggestions as the work proceeded.

Most of the living sex researchers named in this book, and others, helped smooth my way, and corrected at least some of my initial errors; any remaining errors, of course, are my own responsibility.

The chapter on Havelock Ellis has benefited particularly from the suggestions of Professor François Lafitte of the University of Birmingham, the son of Françoise Delisle (Françoise Lafitte-Cyon) and stepson of Havelock Ellis. On a few points, however, my account of Ellis differs from Professor Lafitte's views, which were published in the Spring 1968 issue of *Alta: the University of Birmingham Review.*

I am indebted to Theodoor van de Velde's niece, Mrs. Theo H. Lans, to the Netherlands Information Service, and to several warm friends in that country for heretofore unpublished biographical data on van de Velde.

The resources of the Yale University Library and Medical Library, and the courtesies of their staffs, made this book possible.

My thanks are also due to the Kinsey Institute Library; to my patient secretaries — first Mrs. Marion Burke and later Mrs. Irene Dee; and to the many friends of mine and friends of my sons who read portions of this book in manuscript, suggested additions or deletions, and identified passages needing clarification.

I am grateful in addition to the following:

Basic Books, Inc., New York, for permission to quote from Volumes 1 and 5 of *The Collected Papers of Sigmund Freud,* edited by Ernest Jones, M.D. (copyright 1959).

Ernest Benn Limited, London, for permission to quote from *More About the Sex Factor in Marriage* by Helena Wright (copyright 1947).

The Bodley Head, Ltd., London, for permission to quote from the English translation of *The Book of My Youth* by Hermann Sudermann (copyright 1923).

Delisle Limited, London, for permission to quote from *Friendship's Odyssey* by Françoise Delisle (Madame Françoise Lafitte-Cyon), copyright 1964.

Sigmund Freud Copyrights, Ltd., the Institute of Psycho-Analysis, and the Hogarth Press Limited, London, for permission to quote from the Standard Edition of *The Complete Psychological Works of Sigmund Freud* (copyright 1953–1966).

Paul Gebhard, the Institute for Sex Research, and the W. B. Saunders Company, Philadelphia, for permission to quote from *Sexual Behavior in the Human Male* (copyright 1948) and *Sexual Behavior in the Human Female* (copyright 1953) by Alfred C. Kinsey, *et al.*

Grune & Stratton, Inc., New York, for permission to quote from "Components of Eroticism in Man" by John Money, in *Recent Advances in Biological Psychiatry* (copyright 1960).

William Heinemann Medical Books, Ltd., London, for permission to quote from *Ideal Marriage* by Th. van de Velde (copyright 1930).

Paul B. Hoeber, Inc., Harper & Row, New York, for permission to quote from *Maternal Emotions* by Niles Newton (copyright 1955).

The *Johns Hopkins Medical Journal*, Baltimore, for permission to quote from "Influence of Androgen and Some Aspects of Sexually Dimorphic Behavior," by Anke A. Ehrhardt, Kathryn Evers, and John Money (copyright 1968).

Houghton Mifflin Company, Boston, for permission to quote from *My Life* (copyright 1939) and *Impressions and Comments: Third Series* (copyright 1924) by Havelock Ellis.

The *New England Journal of Medicine*, Boston, for permission to quote from "Psychological Aspects of Lactation" by Niles and Michael Newton (copyright 1967).

W. W. Norton & Company, Inc., New York, for permission to quote from *An Outline of Psychoanalysis* by Sigmund Freud. Authorized translation by James Strachey. (Copyright 1949 by W. W. Norton & Company, Inc.)

Random House, Inc., New York, for permission to quote from *Ideal*

Marriage by Th. van de Velde (copyright 1930), and from *Studies in the Psychology of Sex* by Havelock Ellis (copyright 1936).

Mary Jane Sherfey, M.D., the *Journal of the American Psychoanalytic Association,* New York, and International Universities Press, Inc., New York, for permission to quote from "The Evolution and Nature of Female Sexuality in Relation to Psychoanalytic Theory" (copyright 1966).

John Wiley & Sons, Inc., New York, for permission to quote from chapters by Harry F. Harlow and Paul H. Gebhard in *Sex and Behavior,* edited by Frank A. Beach (copyright 1965).

Williams & Wilkins Company, Baltimore, for permission to quote from the *Atlas of Human Sexual Anatomy* by Robert Latou Dickinson (copyright 1949), and from *A Thousand Marriages* by Robert Latou Dickinson and Lura Beam (copyright 1931).

Contents

The Sex Researchers

1

The First of the Yea-Sayers

Henry Havelock Ellis (1859–1939)

No man or woman, however naïve, approaches sex research naïvely — for each of us brings to the subject his own prior sexual attitudes, experiences, and responses. Most of us also have, or think that we have, a reasonably clear insight into the sexual behavior and feelings of those we love, plus some notion of the sexuality of our friends and neighbors who (we assume) must resemble us quite closely. Out of this material we shape a central intuition of what is sexually normal and usual, reasonable and acceptable. What we thereafter read or hear about the bizarre sexual behavior of Hottentots, hippies, homosexuals, and orgy participants we then arrange around the periphery at a greater or lesser distance from our personal norms — much as the sun, moon, planets and stars were deployed around the earth in Ptolemy's geocentric astronomy.

Henry Havelock Ellis (1859–1939) was one of the first and one of the most influential challengers of this egocentric perspective. He contributed more than any other individual to the overthrow of the Ptolemaic model in the study of human sexuality. In its place he presented concepts of individual and cultural relativism which underlie almost all significant sex research today.

Ellis devoted many decades of his life to mastering most of what had been learned about human sexuality since the days of the ancient Greeks. As a counselor and healer, he studied the sex lives of his contemporaries directly. And he recorded his findings in splendidly flowing prose in a monumental series of volumes, *Studies in the Psychology of Sex,* which he published and periodically revised between 1896 and 1928.

Ellis's erudition was breathtaking; but much of his wisdom can with little loss be summed up in one brief sentence: everybody is *not* like you, your loved ones, and your friends and neighbors.

This theme is implicit throughout Ellis's writings on sex, and it is explicitly developed in a chapter called "The Evolution of Modesty" which he placed at the very front of his *Studies,* as if to make sure that no one who had not already shed his egocentric sexual prejudices would reach the later riches. Throughout the past half-century, reading "The Evolution of Modesty" has been an unforgettable experience for countless men and women (myself included), enabling them to transcend the limitations of the sexual perspective prevailing in their own time and place. As I read it for the first time, decades ago, I felt as if I were emerging from a tunnel into the open countryside. It remains today the best introduction I have found to the scientific study of sex.

Ellis was an English Victorian. He accordingly opened his essay on modesty with the generally accepted Victorian belief that this much-touted virtue consists essentially in keeping the human body, and especially the female human body, adequately clothed. To illustrate this relationship between modesty and clothing, he recounted a visit paid by Jacques (Giacomo Girolamo) Casanova to the public baths near Berne, Switzerland, late in the eighteenth century.

According to the custom of the time and place, Ellis explained, Casanova on arriving at the baths selected a young girl of eighteen from the cluster of attendants awaiting patrons. She undressed him, undressed herself, entered the bath with him, and proceeded to massage him thoroughly all over, "in the most serious manner and without a word being spoken." When the massage was completed, Casanova perceived that the girl expected him to make sexual advances. He felt — strangely enough for a world-renowned libertine — no desire to do so. Indeed, this seducer of scores of women, now near the peak of his career as an international philanderer, felt embarrassed even to examine her nudity below the waist. "Though without gazing at the girl's figure," Casanova had written in his *Memoirs,* "I had seen enough to recognize that she had all that a man can desire to find in a woman: a beautiful face, lively and well-formed eyes, a beautiful mouth, with good teeth, a healthy complexion, well-developed breasts, and everything in harmony. . . . Yet I remained entirely cold. What was the cause of this? That was a question that I asked myself."

Casanova thereupon ventured an answer to his own question. Perhaps modesty in a woman was one of the factors arousing a man's sexual desire. Perhaps, lacking modesty, the Berne bath attendant lacked sexual appeal. But Ellis was not so sure. He went on to demonstrate, from a review of the literature of anthropology, that the relation of clothing to modesty, and of modesty to sexual desire, is in fact far more complex than Casanova had supposed.

In Tierra del Fuego, for example, women once wore only a minute triangle of animal skin suspended between their thighs; yet they were so modest that they never removed it. Even during sexual intercourse they merely raised it. Among the Guaycurús of the Amazon valley, the men went quite naked while the women wore a short petticoat; among the neighboring Uapas the men always wore a loincloth while the women went completely naked. One tribe of North American Indians provided an even more startling example. "Almost to a woman," Ellis stated, citing as his authority an 1892 issue of the *American Journal of Obstetrics*, "the females of this tribe are prostitutes, and for a consideration will admit the connection of any man." Yet they were so modest that one of them, near death during a difficult childbirth, refused to let any man — Indian or white, physician or lover — attend her. At length she consented to be examined by a physician, but first she veiled her thighs and the lips of her vulva with bits of quilt so that only the vaginal opening remained visible.

Example follows example in Ellis's *Studies*, until even the dullest reader must grasp the point. Among the prudish Buganda in Africa, where it was a punishable offense for a man to expose any part of his leg above the knee, "the wives of the King would attend his Court perfectly naked." The Masai in Africa at one time considered it disreputable for a man to *conceal* his penis — "and in the highest degree reputable to display it, even ostentatiously." When a British anthropologist remarked on the nudity of the women of Upoto in the Congo, a chief replied that "concealment is food for the inquisitive." Another British anthropologist commented with respect to Central Africa: "It has been my experience that the more naked the people. and the more to us obscene and shameless their manners and customs, the more moral and strict they are in the matter of sexual intercourse."

For almost all of Ellis's readers, of course, modesty was concerned primarily with covering the male and female genitals and the female breasts. This seems reasonable enough to Europeans and Americans — but others feel differently. For Mohammedans, until recently, the female face was the center of modesty. Ellis described Turkish prostitutes, naked, placing themselves in the position for sexual intercourse with their faces still heavily veiled. "An Englishman surprised a woman while bathing in the Euphrates; she held her hands over her face, without troubling as to what else the stranger might see." Elsewhere the buttocks are central. Thus Moru women once wore a girdle with leaves modestly suspended from it. Yet their genitals remained in plain sight, for the leaves were worn in back instead of front. A Moru woman surprised without her girdle threw herself down on her back to hide her buttocks. In nineteenth-century China, "only the husband may see his wife's foot naked. A Chinese woman is as reticent in showing her feet to a man as a European woman her breasts."

In these and other anthropological examples, Ellis respected his Victorian readers' prejudices (and ours) by concentrating on primitive tribes and non-Europeans — the "lesser breeds without the Law," in Kipling's imperial phrase. These bizarre "natives," according to the prevailing Victorian view, didn't really count; they were for the most part neither civilized, nor Christian, nor white. But Ellis did not stop there. He demonstrated with equally startling data from historical sources that modesty taboos have varied widely from century to century among our own honored ancestors.

He reviewed rapidly, for example, the quite general acceptance of nudity among the ancient Greeks and Romans, and the subsequent early Christian reaction. One early Christian father, Clement of Rome, had urged that even the hands be wrapped in "modest garments." Another, Clement of Alexandria, had complained that women bathing in their own homes "are not ashamed to strip before spectators, as if exposing their persons for sale. . . . Those who have not become utterly destitute of modesty shut out strangers but bathe with their own servants, and strip naked before their slaves, and are rubbed by them, giving to the crouching menial liberty to lust, by permitting fearless handling." A century later the Bishop of Carthage complained that even Christian virgins vowed to chastity were still continuing the nude bathing custom. "You behold no one immodestly," he conceded in one of his epistles, "but you, yourself, are gazed upon immodestly; you do not pollute your eyes with disgraceful delight, but in delighting others you yourself are polluted; . . . the places where you assemble are fouler than a theater. There all modesty is put off [and] virginity is exposed, to be pointed at and to be handled." The pious bishop did not go so far as to prescribe bathing suits or bathing in private for Christian virgins, however. "Let your baths be performed with women," he admonished, "whose behavior is modest toward you."

The Christian view prevailed ultimately — but not promptly, and not completely. "For the German people," Ellis cited one authority as reporting, "the sight of complete nakedness was the daily rule up to the sixteenth century. Everyone undressed completely before going to bed, and, in the vapor-baths, no covering was used." Women wore no underdrawers, and during the dances of the period, both among peasants and townspeople, "it was the chief delight of the dancers for the male to raise his partner as high as possible in the air, so that her dress flew up."

In 1461, when Louis XI made his first royal entry into Paris, "three very beautiful maidens, quite naked, represented the sirens, and declaimed poems before him; they were greatly admired by the public." There was a similar nude display at a public gathering when Charles the Bold entered Lille in 1468, and another when Charles V entered Antwerp. In Denmark in 1658, a Polish army officer was distressed to discover that "everyone sleeps naked as at birth, and none considers it shameful to dress or undress before others. . . . As we blamed their ways, saying that among us a woman would not act so, even in the presence of her husband alone, they replied that they knew nothing of such shame, and that there was no need to be ashamed of limbs which God had created." In Ireland in 1617 a traveler reported that "I have seen with these eyes young maids stark naked grinding corn with certain stones to make cakes thereof." Another traveler at about the same time reported visiting one of the great lords of Ireland. He was met at the door by sixteen women, "all naked, excepting their loose mantles." They led him into the house and sat down by the fire, "with crossed legs, like tailors, and so low as could not but offend chaste eyes." Soon the lord of the region came in, removed his clothes, and "after his best manner in the Latin tongue, desired [his guest] to put off his apparel." The guest, however, "for shame, durst not."

During the hot weather in seventeenth-century Venice and Padua "wives, widows, and maids walk[ed] with naked breasts." At St. Petersburg in 1774, a traveler observed two hundred men and woman naked together in the public baths. Separate places were provided for men and women, "but they seem quite regardless of this distinction, and sit and bathe in a state of absolute nudity among each other." Toward the end of the eighteenth century in Paris, under the influence of rationalism and a revival of Greek fashions in clothing, "women, to the detriment of their health, were sometimes content to dress in transparent gauze, and even to walk abroad in the Champs Elysées without any clothing; that, however, was too much for the public." *

Having thus placed his readers' personal views of modesty in both cultural and temporal perspective, Ellis proceeded to review the current English situation. In 1898, he pointed out, the local clubs associated with the Amateur Swimming Association had considered what costumes should be worn during competitive swimming matches. The regulations adopted "require that the male swimmer's costume shall extend not less than eight inches from the bifurcation downward, and that the female swimmer's costume shall extend to within not more than three inches from the knee. . . . The modesty of women is thus seen to be greater than that of men by, roughly speaking, two inches. The same difference may be seen in the sleeves; the male sleeve must extend for two inches,

* Ellis could have brought his account even closer to his own time and place. Prints made as late as 1817 show men and women bathing nude together at English beaches. In 1856, letters to the editor of the *Times* (London) complained that men still bathed nude at Margate. "The exhibition is truly disgusting," one correspondent wrote, "but what is more disgusting still is the fact that these exhibitions are watched daily by large numbers of ladies who spend their mornings in close proximity to scores of naked men." The following year a physician visiting another English seaside resort, Brighton, reported that when he opened his bedroom window, "the first sight that greeted me, immediately in front of the hotel, was half-a-dozen men, perfectly naked, wading about with the water not much higher than their knees." Also in 1857, Lord Westmeath introduced in the House of Lords a bill which would have prohibited nude bathing. "It is the practice," he told his fellow Peers, "for women to go down to the sea-bathing places and dance in the water without any covering whatever, to the great disgust of the respectable inhabitants and visitors." His knowledge of these scenes, he added, came from reports of local magistrates at Margate, Ramsgate, and other coastal resorts. Women also continued to appear nude in *poses plastiques* on the London stage during the early years of Victoria's reign. For these and other details of sexual freedom in early Victorian England, see Cyril Pearl, *The Girl with the Swansdown Seat* (1955). After about 1860, however, even the memory of this earlier Victorian freedom was erased — and Havelock Ellis, who was born just as it was vanishing, seems never to have heard of it.

the female sleeve four inches, down the arm." One Victorian husband reported that he feared he had corrupted his wife. She had entered the bath in his presence, and had enjoyed his watching as she splashed about nude with her baby in her arms. The husband "was deeply distressed, thinking he must have done her harm and destroyed her modesty."

For readers today, I need hardly labor the point. Modesty is clearly a function of time, place, and status. We laugh at those Victorian women who covered not only their own legs but even the legs of the chairs in their parlors lest innocence be offended. Yet a reminder may still be necessary that *our* modesty is also relative. Indeed, if we dared to parade on our beaches in the 1960's as Victorian ladies and gentlemen did in the 1850's, we would be summarily arrested, tried, convicted, and fined or imprisoned. Another of Ellis's examples drives the point home even deeper.

When his vessel dropped anchor in Tahiti in 1769, Ellis points out, Captain James Cook led his crew in Christian worship, as was then the Sunday custom of the British navy. Following the benediction, however, the mariners witnessed "vespers of a very different kind. A young man, near six feet high, performed the rites of Venus with a little girl about eleven or twelve years of age, before several of our people and a great number of the natives, without the least sense of its being indecent or improper, but, as it appeared, in perfect conformity to the custom of the place. Among the spectators were several women of superior rank, who may properly be said to have assisted at the ceremony; for they gave instructions to the girl how to perform her part, which, young as she was, she did not seem much to stand in need of." Nor was this an isolated occurrence. It was customary in Tahiti, Cook noted, to "gratify every appetite and passion before witnesses" — with one startling exception.

The Tahitians were embarrassed to dine together. Even brothers and sisters had their separate baskets of provisions, and generally sat some yards apart, with their backs to each other, when they ate. Thus the publicly copulating Tahitians were not, after all, without modesty.

How can we account for the fact that modesty, despite its myriad external forms, is so very nearly universal in the human species? Ellis was not a dogmatist. He rarely offered a simple general solution to a problem of human sexuality. Rather, he weighed the pros and cons, described competing theories, and often left his readers to draw their own conclusions. "As a youth," he recalled in 1897, when he was thirty-eight, "I had hoped to settle problems for those who came after; now I am quietly content if I do little more than state them. For even that, I now think, is much; it is at least the half of knowledge. . . . I have tried to get at the facts, and, having got at the facts, to look them simply and squarely in the face. If I cannot perhaps turn the lock myself, I bring the key which can alone in the end rightly open the door: the key of sincerity."

In this spirit Ellis turned from anthropology and cultural history to zoology in search of what he called "the simplest and most primitive element of modesty." That element, he suggested, is *sexual retreat*. It is the gesture of the female who is sexually approached by a male at a time when she is not physiologically receptive to his advances. "Anyone who watches a bitch, not in heat, when approached by a dog with tail wagging gallantly, may see the beginnings of modesty. When the dog's attentions become a little too marked, the bitch squats firmly down on the front legs and hind quarters, though when the period of oestrus comes, her modesty may be flung to the air and she eagerly turns her hind quarters to her admirer's nose and elevates her tail high in the air. Her attitude of refusal is equivalent, that is to say, to that which in the human race is typified by the classical example of womanly modesty in the Medicean Venus, who withdraws the pelvis, at the same time holding one hand to guard the pubes, the other to guard the breast. The essential expression in each case is that of defense of the sexual centers against the undesired advances of the male."

This, of course, was an oversimplification, as Ellis himself was prompt to point out. Even the bitch in heat, so eager for the dog that she now runs after him, turns around and flees again a moment later if she is sure he will follow. "Thus modesty becomes something more than a mere refusal of the male; it becomes an invitation to the male, and is mixed up with his ideas of what is sexually desirable in the female."

Both male and female animals, moreover, need to guard themselves during their sexual activities by hiding from the attacks of enemies or of jealous rivals. "It is highly probable that this is one important sexual factor in the constitution of modesty, and it helps to explain how the male, not less than the female, cultivates modesty, and shuns publicity, in the exercise of sexual functions."

But this, too, Ellis continued, is only part of the story. Another root of modesty is the fear of arousing disgust. The sexual organs are also the organs of urination and lie close to the organ of defecation. Many animals retreat modestly to urinate and defecate — though this form of modesty may be lost in domestic animals. To illustrate the link in the human species between modesty and fear of arousing disgust, Ellis cited an observation from his personal experience:

"Long ago, when a hospital student on midwifery duty in London slums, I had occasion to observe that among the women of the poor, and more especially in those who had lost the first bloom of youth, modesty consisted chiefly in the fear of being disgusting. There was an almost pathetic anxiety, in the face of pain and discomfort, not to be disgusting in the doctor's eyes. This anxiety expressed itself in the ordinary symptoms of modesty. But, as soon as the woman realized that I found nothing disgusting in whatever was proper and necessary to be done under the circumstances, it almost invariably happened that every sign of modesty at once disappeared."

Ritual and magic, Ellis added, tend to perpetuate modesty. "All savage and barbarous peoples who have attained any high degree of ceremonialism have included the functions not only of sex, but also of excretion, more or less stringently within the bounds of that ceremonialism." Finally, there is the economic aspect. The rise of property rights, and the spread of the concept that women are the private property of their husbands, add this economic dimension to modesty:

"Only married women are among some peoples clothed, the unmarried women, though full grown, remaining naked. . . . Before marriage a woman was often free, and not bound to chastity, and at the same time was often naked; after marriage she was clothed, and no longer free. To the husband's mind, the garment appears — illogically, though naturally — a moral and physical protection against any attack on his property. Thus a new motive was furnished, this time somewhat artificially, for making nakedness, in women at all events, disgraceful. As the conception of property also extended to the father's right over his daughters, and the appreciation of female chastity developed, this motive spread to unmarried as well as married women. A woman on the west coast of Africa must always be chaste because she is first the property of her parents and afterward of her husband."

These and other hypotheses drawn from animal behavior, primitive behavior, European history, and personal observation, however, left Ellis still dissatisfied. Something more must be involved in modesty. "It is impossible to contemplate this series of phenomena," he wrote, "so radically persistent whatever its changes of form, and so constant throughout every stage of civilization, without feeling that, although modesty cannot properly be called an instinct, *there must be some physiological basis to support it.*" (Italics supplied.)

More than half a century was to elapse before Dr. William H. Masters and Mrs. Virginia E. Johnson in St. Louis launched their epoch-making laboratory study of the physiological bases of human sexuality. Yet Ellis, astonishingly enough, found physiological evidence in 1897 — and found it in a most unlikely quarter: a paper by a young American student of psychology, G. E. Partridge, in the April 1897 edition of *Paedagogical Seminary,* describing that most Victorian of all physiological responses, the young maiden's blush.

Partridge had collected reports on 254 cases of blushing, 213 of them in girls and young women, and had discovered an astonishing fact. The blush is not just a crimsoning of the face, as is still commonly supposed. Rather, it is a general physiological response in which many other parts of the body may participate. The face-reddening in many or most cases is preceded or accompanied by other specific symptoms which Partridge reviewed in detail — "tremors near the waist, weakness in the limbs, pressure, trembling, warmth, weight or beating in the chest, warm wave from feet upward, quivering of heart, stoppage and then rapid beating of heart, coldness all over followed by heat, dizziness, tingling of toes and fingers, numbness, something rising in throat, smarting of eyes, singing in ears, prickling sensations of face, and pressure inside head."

These responses, Partridge concluded and Ellis agreed — in a remarkable anticipation of the findings of Masters and Johnson during the 1960's — must result from a sexually initiated change in the pattern of blood circulation. The actual blush, the reddening of the cheeks, is but one small feature of the change, and appears rather late in the total response sequence.

Darwin and others, Ellis pointed out, had studied blushing earlier, and had sought to explain why it afflicts only the face. But on this point Darwin was wrong. "Feré once had occasion to examine, when completely nude, a boy of thirteen whose sexual organs were deformed; when accused of masturbation he became covered by a blush which spread uniformly over his face, neck, body, and limbs, before and behind, except only the hands and feet." And even these exceptions may not be universal. "Partridge mentions one case in which the hands blushed."

The sexual nature of blushing, Ellis concluded, is unquestionable. "It occurs chiefly in women; it attains its chief intensity at puberty and during adolescence; its most common occasion is some more or less sexual suggestion." Among the cases reviewed by Partridge, by far the most common cause was teasing, usually about the other sex. "An erection," Ellis quoted an anonymous observer as remarking, "is a blushing of the penis." And he attributed to a nineteenth-century American psychologist, G. Stanley Hall, the view that "the sexual blush is a vicarious genital flushing of blood, diverted from the genital sphere by an inhibition of fear." Thus modesty might be described as behavior designed to forestall a blush.

Here Ellis added a word of caution. The biological, social, economic, psychological, and physiological factors in modesty "do not usually occur separately. Very often they are all of them implied in a single impulse of modesty. We unravel the cord in order to investigate its construction, but in real life the strands are more or less indistinguishably twisted together."

Ellis knew, of course, that he lived in the midst of a pathologically modest society — a society in which even ankles must be shielded from view, and in which guests having chicken for dinner asked for a helping of white meat or dark meat in order to avoid mentioning the chicken's breast or legs. But he ventured to predict a change.

"It is a great mistake," he wrote, ". . . to suppose that in becoming extended modesty also becomes intensified. On the contrary, this very extension is a sign of weakness. . . . It is . . . in a new and crude civilization, eager to mark its separation from a barbarism it has yet scarcely escaped, that we find an extravagant and fantastic anxiety to extend the limits of modesty in life, and art, and literature. In older and more mature civilizations — in classical antiquity, in old Japan, in France — modesty, while still a very real influence, becomes a much less predominant and all-pervading influence. . . .

"Even the most fundamental impulse of all, the gesture of sexual refusal, is normally only imperative among animals and savages. Thus civilization tends to subordinate, if not to minimize, modesty, to render it a grace of life rather than a fundamental social law of life. But an essential grace of life it still remains, and whatever delicate variations it may assume we can scarcely conceive of its disappearance."

What manner of man was Havelock Ellis? What factors in his personal sexual life affected his work, and how did his study of sex affect his personal life? Such questions are often asked about sex researchers; only rarely are reliable answers available. In Ellis's case the answers are frankly set forth in his autobiography, *My Life,* which he began to write at the age of forty and continued to revise at intervals throughout his life. It was published in 1939, shortly after his death. Further details are to be found in *Friendship's Odyssey,* the autobiography of Françoise Delisle, Ellis's mistress during his last years.

Henry Havelock Ellis was born in the town of Croyden in Surrey, ten miles from London Bridge, the son of middle-class parents, in 1859, the twenty-second year of the reign of Queen Victoria. He was forty-two years old when that reign at long last reached its end. Though his writings contain few traces of the sexual blight called mid-Victorianism, that blight was not so readily eradicated from his personal bodily responses. He suffered until the age of fifty-nine from one of the common forms of sexual inadequacy which the Victorian repression of sex was likely to engender in men as well as in women: an inability to enjoy sexual fulfillment with the partners who loved him most deeply and whom he most passionately cherished.

That his early childhood environment contributed to this sexual block can hardly be doubted. The Ellis household consisted of young Havelock, his mother, and his four sisters. His father, a seafaring man, was home only three months a year — and even on these visits, Havelock himself reported, his mother "remained the mistress of the house" and his father "instinctively fell into the position of a guest." Havelock's mother at seventeen had been converted to a pietist, fundamentalist, Evangelical brand of Christianity and retained narrowly Victorian views throughout her life. None of his four sisters ever married, nor is there any evidence that any of them ever entered into any coital relationships. Neither did Havelock until the age of thirty-two.

Ellis's childhood was relatively uneventful sexually. There were only the usual childish gropings with other boys. Havelock's father was captain of the sailing vessel *Empress;* and when Havelock was seven he accompanied his father on a trip around the world. At a South American port a little boy of his own age tried to teach him how to masturbate, justifying the procedure as "a method of promoting the wholesome development of the organs, an object which seemed to me entirely praiseworthy. On his recommendation I attempted, with the best motives, to follow his instructions, but the results were fortunately in every respect completely negative." A boy of fifteen on board the *Empress* during the same voyage "permitted or possibly encouraged me to insert my hand into his trousers and gently to touch his sexual organs; my feeling was simply one of reverent admiration for what seemed to my childish mind their magnitude."

These childhood experiences, Ellis later reported, left little or no trace on his subsequent sexual development. "On the physical side," he wrote, "there was really nothing to say until I had passed boyhood and reached adolescence. . . . Indeed, strange as it may appear to some, throughout the whole course of my school days until they ended at the age of sixteen, I cannot recall that I heard or saw anything that would have shocked an ordinarily modest schoolgirl." Except on that voyage to foreign ports, the Victorian cocoon of his family enwrapped him snugly. The results were sexually disastrous.

The basic Victorian chasm between the emotions of love and the physiological responses of sex was already visible in young Havelock at the age of twelve, when he fell in love for the first time. The object of his affections was a cousin named Agnes, a girl of sixteen, who visited in his home for a week or two one summer. Agnes was "a dark pretty vivacious girl, with long black ringlets," Havelock recalled much later. "Old enough to be a woman in my eyes, and yet young enough to be a comrade and equal, she adapted herself instinctively to the relationship and won my heart immediately. I took not the slightest liberty with her, and never had the slightest impulse to do so, but she, on her part, treated me with an easy familiarity. . . . She would play and romp with me in all innocent unreserve."

Agnes's visit came to an end, and Havelock never saw her again. "I never made any effort to see her," he declared in *My Life*. "I never mentioned her name; no one knew that I even thought of her. But for four years her image moved and lived within me, revealing myself to myself. I had no physical desires and no voluptuous emotions; I never pictured to myself any joy of bodily contact with her or cherished any sensuous dreams. Yet I was devoured by a boy's pure passion. That she should become my wife — though I never tried to imagine what that meant — was a wild and constant aspiration. I would lie awake in bed with streaming eyes praying to God to grant that this might some time be. . . .

"Under the stress of this passion I became a person, and, moreover, in temper a poet. I discovered the beauty of the world, and I discovered a new vein of emotion within myself. . . . The touch of this careless vivacious girl had placed within me a new ferment which began to work through every fiber of my being. It was an epoch-making event in my life."

The essence of that event — love divorced from sexual response — was to recur repeatedly in Ellis's life through the next forty-eight years. Not until middle age did he experience the two together. And Agnes never escaped the Victorian blight. Even at the age of sixteen, romping with young Havelock, Agnes was already thinking about marriage and fantasying an early wedding. Yet this pretty, vivacious, playful, carefree, unreserved, romping girl was in her fifties still a spinster — "an only child who has devoted her life to the care of her aged parents."

A remarkable feature of Ellis's early life was his lack of experience with masturbation.

Victorian physicians of this period were quite generally agreed that willful masturbation caused acne, blindness, impotence, insanity, and countless other pernicious side effects — a doctrine introduced into European medicine by a Swiss physician, Dr. Samuel Auguste André David Tissot (1728–1797), whose two major books, *Onanism* and *Advice to the People in General With Regard to Their Health,* published in Lausanne in 1760 and 1761, were subsequently translated into most European languages. In England and the United States, Tissot's doctrines were spread widely by an eminent London urologist, William Acton (1813–1875), whose textbook entitled *The Functions and Disorders of the Reproductive Organs, in Childhood, Youth, Adult Age, and Advanced Life, Considered in Their Physiological, Social and Moral Relations* went through many editions in both countries. The word spread from Acton to other physicians and then to parents; and Victorian parents spent untold energy trying to save their young children from blindness, insanity, and damnation by preventing them from masturbating.

Acton's textbook was published in 1857, two years before Havelock's birth. There is no reason to doubt that his parents or teachers or both, like other Victorians, took Acton seriously and during Havelock's early childhood tabooed masturbation.

Instead of masturbating, Havelock at the age of thirteen — not long after his summer romps with Agnes — began to experience "copious seminal emissions during sleep, once or twice a week, always without dreams or any sensations, and continued, whenever I was alone, for some thirty years." These emissions aroused in young Havelock the same conflicts which masturbation aroused in other Victorian boys; they were "a source of nervous apprehension, for I vaguely felt that they were something to be ashamed of; I constantly dreaded their occurrence and feared their detection."

Medical opinion was divided during the Victorian era on the harmfulness of such nocturnal emissions of semen. Some physicians believed that "wet dreams," if they did not occur too often, were relatively normal. Havelock Ellis in adolescence had the misfortune to fall afoul of an amazing book which took a far more ominous view. The book was called *Elements of Social Science; or physical, sexual, and natural religion. An exposition of the true cause and only cure of the three primary social evils: poverty, prostitution, and celibacy.* Written by an English physician, Dr. Charles Drysdale, and first published in 1854, it had an enormous influence. By 1904, when the English edition at long last went out of print, it had gone through thirty-five printings, and had been translated into at least ten other languages.

Drysdale was a would-be sexual reformer, and a well-meaning man. He strongly believed that sexual intercourse was not only a delight but also essential to health. He believed that overpopulation was a major cause of poverty, that too many children were the curse of marriage, and that fear of having children or inability to support them was what caused men to patronize prostitutes and contract venereal disease. These views led him to the conclusion that contraception was the only possible cure for poverty, prostitution, celibacy — and unhappy marriages as well. His book described five methods of preventing pregnancy, and urged the need for finding better methods through scientific research.

Most of his contemporaries, of course, believed that continence was the only proper way of not having children. Drysdale detested continence, and in the course of developing his argument against it, he devoted ten eloquent pages to revealing its terrible aftermath — wet dreams (involuntary emissions of semen).

On this point Drysdale was a disciple of the eminent French physician, Claude François l'Allemand (1790–1853), author of *Des Pertes Seminales Involuntaires,* published in Paris in three volumes during the years 1836–1842. L'Allemand considered wet dreams a foul disease resembling gonorrhea or diarrhea; he named the phenomenon *spermatorrhea.* Drysdale agreed, and defined the disease quite frankly for a Victorian:

"By spermatorrhea, or involuntary seminal discharges, is meant the loss of seminal fluid without the will of the patient, which when it occurs frequently, constitutes . . . a most dreadful disease. These discharges may be divided into the nocturnal and the diurnal. In the *nocturnal* ones, the patient has generally a dream on some venereal subject, an erection of the penis, and a discharge of semen, and wakes just as the discharge is taking place." This, of course, precisely described young Havelock's case. Seminal discharge during the day Drysdale considered even more damaging.

At first, Drysdale conceded, little harm is done. But the disease is progressive; "the emissions begin to increase in frequency, and the patient begins to feel his health declining. The emissions may now take place nightly, or even three or four times in the night in bad cases, and this soon brings on a state of great exhaustion. . . . As the disease progresses, discharges take place without a venereal dream or erection." This was what was happening in the case of the adolescent Havelock Ellis. "The patient wakes suddenly from a stupor, just as the discharge is pouring out, which he will try in vain to check; or perhaps, he does not wake till it is over, and then, as a lethargic consciousness, which of itself tells him what has taken place, slowly awakens, he puts down his hand and sickens with despair, as he perceives the fatal drain, and thinks on the gloomy morrow which will follow."

Soon "the organs lose their natural powers of pouring forth a large quantity involuntarily at one time. The semen becomes thinner and deteriorated in quality . . . so as to be incapable of serving for impregnation. The spermatozooids in these cases are sometimes scarcely to be recognized, and do not appear to have their normal development."

Next the nervous system is affected — "a feeling of weakness on rising in the morning, especially after a nocturnal emission, and even more after two or three in the same night; a sort of mistiness or haze in the thoughts, and dimness in the sight, while the eye loses its luster; enfeeblement of muscular power, with irritability of its fibre, often shown by palpitation of the heart" — and so on, page after page.

"As for the termination of the disease: if left to itself, it has a constant tendency to increase. The patient may, after years of suffering, sink into the lowest stage of weakness, and die." Death may be "by a kind of apoplexy, characteristic of this disease, and induced by the exhausted state of the brain. The disease has in many cases progressed to insanity, and idiocy; in one case . . . the patient had lost the knowledge of his friends, and the power of speech."

Many famous men, Drysdale reported, had no doubt suffered from spermatorrhea, including "Sir Isaac Newton, who is said to have lived a life of strict sexual abstinence, which produced before death a total atrophy of the testicles, showing the natural sin which had been committed. It is certain that his matchless intellect declined after middle age, and it is even said, I know not with what truth, that he almost lost his mind late in life."

One treatment for spermatorrhea, Drysdale believed, was use of "the armed bougie. This instrument, intended to cauterize the internal surface of the urethra, consists of a metallic bougie, through which a stilet is passed, containing at its end the caustic nitrate of silver, with which [the physician] slightly touches the tender part of the urethra." This exceedingly painful remedy, however, should in no case be applied more than twice, for frequent use can produce stricture of the urethra, "a disease often more difficult to cure than the spermatorrhea itself."

Sexual intercourse, Drysdale insisted, is the only preventive of spermatorrhea, and it can also serve as a cure. But "we must remember that the organs are in a very feeble state, and hence that an immoderate exercise at first might have an effect directly contrary to our desires. Hence coition should at first be very moderate; once a week, or so; and should be gradually increased with the waxing powers. The signs of its favorable action are, an increase of tone both of mind and body, improved appetite, spirits, and self-confidence. The patient should not be much in the company of women at other times, if they excite venereal desires which are not to be gratified." Above all, he should not consort with prostitutes, for in a patient with spermatorrhea, venereal disease "is ten-fold to be dreaded." It "arrests his cure, greatly complicates his case, and is dreadfully disheartening to one who has suffered so long." Masturbation, too, must of course be strictly avoided.

Sexual intercourse, once a week at first and more frequently thereafter, was hardly a practical prescription for a respectable boy in his early teens in Victorian England. Certainly it lay beyond Havelock Ellis's reach. "I brooded over the unknown problems of my own sexual nature," he wrote, and, under the stress of fear of spermatorrhea, "reached the conclusion that there was no outcome except by death or possibly by becoming a monk." Depressed moods and emotional conflicts of this kind recurred at intervals throughout his adolescence.

When he was sixteen, Ellis set off with his father on another trip around the world. In Australia, however, he left the ship to become a schoolteacher. He remained in Australia for the next four years, during which his sexual education continued at a snail's pace.

On one or two occasions, for example, the youthful teacher was invited to the home of a retired sea captain named Fox, who "had several pretty and charming daughters with whom I was on terms of superficial acquaintance. No more, but without being in love with any one of them I vaguely desired more, yet felt myself powerless, in my inexperienced awkwardness, to attain more. All the obscure mysteries of sex stirred dimly and massively within me; I felt myself groping helplessly among the difficulties of life." It was in this desperately awkward situation that what was to become the central theme of his life first suggested itself to Ellis. He resolved someday to study and write about sex — "penetrate those mysteries and enlighten these difficulties, so that to those who came after me they might be easier than they had been to me."

As a start toward his newfound goal of sex research, Havelock at seventeen began to keep a precise written record of his own nocturnal emissions of semen. No doubt he was waiting for the increase in frequency predicted by Drysdale. This record he continued to keep faithfully for twelve years, and he later published it — though without identifying it as his own — in his *Studies in the Psychology of Sex*. No increase in frequency occurred during those twelve years — thus refuting Drysdale's allegation that spermatorrhea is a progressive disease.

Ellis's seventeenth year was marked by "intervals of unrest, even of misery and despair. . . . I was a teacher in a responsible position, yet still half a child so far as sex was concerned, innocent and virginal. My eldest girl pupil, six years younger than I, was a fascinating, saucy, alert little maiden, in her instincts quite as old as I was, and older. I felt her charm. . . . The little coquette fell naturally into the woman's part, accepted my attitude and the furtive caresses of my hand, and playfully exerted the authority she knew she had acquired over me." It was in connection with this schoolgirl of eleven — though not actually in her presence — that young Havelock experienced his first conscious erections. "Sometimes, after she had snuggled up to my side with her slate of sums, and the hours of school were over, and I started off alone with my Shelley into the bush, I would feel, for the first time in my life during waking moments, the physical presence of the impulse of sex."

Later that same year Ellis fell seriously in love again. He was lodging with a family named Chapman, consisting "mostly of girls, still all unmarried, from the age of about twenty-five down to near infancy." One of these girls — Berta — of Havelock's own age, pretty, and emotionally responsive, became deeply attached to the young teacher. When he later held her hand to say goodbye, "I saw tears gleaming in her tender eyes." But Havelock did not respond to Berta's overtures. Instead, his heart went out to an older sister, May, "dignified and reserved," cool toward him and toward men generally. It was May who haunted Ellis's dreams for the next few years. "To me nothing tangible remains of my adoration," he wrote in middle age, "but a hairpin, once fallen from her hair, which I picked up and devoutly preserved." With a burst of insight he also wrote: "I disdained the women who were within reach; the women I desired, hopelessly, it seemed, were women I had never seen or known."

This Victorian characteristic was even more clearly visible when Ellis took a short boat journey a little later. "One of my fellow passengers — another teacher, if I remember rightly — improved the occasion by flirting with a girl he had become acquainted with on the boat and sat with his arm around her for several hours; toward night, having evidently thus acquired all the satisfaction he desired, he generously introduced her, unasked, to me . . . and left us alone. We walked once or twice up and down the deck, and she remarked to me by way of opening the conversation: 'Ain't the moon lovely?' Such a feeling of loathing rose up within me that in a few moments, after briefly responding, I said it was time to go below, and wished her good night. That was the nearest approach to intimacy with a strange woman during the whole of my four years of adolescence in Australia, where, however, as I had opportunity to observe, the relations of the sexes were often facile."

One further sexual event marked Ellis's Australian years. At nineteen he read a sexually stimulating book — probably Brantôme's *Les Dames Gallantes* — and while he was reading he consciously experienced an orgasm for the first time in his life. The event occurred "without any will or action of my own," Ellis stated, and it rarely happened again. Emissions of semen during apparently dreamless sleep, with no awareness of orgasm, remained his sole — or almost his sole — form of sexual outlet until his marriage thirteen years later.

During his last year in Australia Ellis underwent a mystical experience which he likened to a religious conversion — though he had already abandoned traditional religious beliefs. The outcome of the experience was a decision to live his own life, find his own way, lay his own plans. His adolescent self-doubts and depression thereupon came to an end. A coherent plan for his future was soon laid out. He would return to England. He would study medicine and qualify as a physician — not in order to practice, but to prepare himself for the scientific study of sex. In addition, he would continue his literary interests and become a critic and essayist. This plan he followed without swerving until his death at the age of eighty.

Back in London, however, Ellis's sexual experiences remained shallow and unrewarding. The wife of a headmaster, a young woman of about thirty, came to him one day when her husband was away, "in a tearful mood," and confided her marital troubles. "I was far too shy and awkward and inexperienced to offer her even the most innocent consolation, and even today I am uncertain what kind of consolation she desired or expected. She never came again." Ellis's shyness remained a firmly ingrained character trait throughout his life.

The obverse side of the Victorian cult of purity, of course, was Victorian prostitution. Droves of Victorian males each night saved their wives and sweethearts from pollution by pouring their sexual emissions into London's readily available street women. But this outlet, too, was closed to Ellis — in part, no doubt, by Drysdale's warning that venereal disease is "ten-fold to be dreaded" in a victim of spermatorrhea. Only once in his life, Ellis reports, did he even talk with a prostitute — a woman who accosted him while he was passing a corner near London Bridge. "She was not attractive, scarcely young, and I had no wish to have anything to do with her. But I asked her questions about herself and she answered with simplicity and evident truthfulness. As we walked together talking, she led me, without my being aware of what she was doing, down a deserted side-turning. Then, thinking she knew what I desired, she placed her hand on my trousers at the point with which she was professionally concerned. I instinctively started back, realized the situation, and turned toward the main road, while she gently and soothingly apologized. Then I gave her a shilling and went on my way. . . . I never placed myself in such a situation again."

Ellis entered on his medical studies in 1882, at the age of twenty-three, and qualified as a physician in medicine, surgery, and midwifery seven years later. He practiced medicine only for a few summers. During his student years, he also became known as an editor and literary critic; and it was during those years, too, that the first of the great and enduring love affairs of his life was initiated. The woman was Olive Schreiner, only four years older than Ellis but already famous as the author of the best-selling *Story of an African Farm.* Ellis wrote her in praise of her book, a meeting was agreed upon, and a lifelong intimacy ensued.

Ellis described himself at this time as "a fully developed young man, five feet ten and a half inches in height and weighing . . . around one hundred and fifty pounds. I was in good health, at my best, thanks to the four years I had spent in Australia. . . . At the coming of manhood, I had begun to shave, but I quickly dropped that practice for the simpler plan of allowing my beard to grow. I took to parting my hair in the middle, as it was too thick to lie well when parted at the side." A photograph taken at the time shows a brown beard considerably sparser than the snow-white bush which dominated the familiar photographs of Ellis taken in his seventies; but his deep-set eyes were as direct and as compelling in his twenties as half a century later, and the charismatic quality which men and women — especially women — so often noted in Ellis in later years was already clearly visible. He was a handsome man as well as a shy one.

Within a month after meeting her, Ellis reports, "Olive and I were on terms of friendship so close that she could write of me as 'the person who is like part of me.' We had found ourselves akin in all sorts of essential matters, with common interests and ideals. . . . She loved in those days to call me her 'other self.' "

On Olive's side there was clearly an expectation of more than friendship. She had had two earlier lovers, and she possessed what Ellis called "a powerfully and physically passionate temperament which craved an answering impulse. . . . As I left her one evening to return home she raised her face up to me as we shook hands. I hesitated to realize the significance of the gesture, and we parted. But on my next visit, when the moment to part arrived, the gesture was more significantly repeated; she put her arms around me and from that moment our relationship became one of intimate and affectionate friendship."

Havelock's later reminiscences of Olive provide many sensuous details. "I see her coming suddenly and quite naked out of the bathroom in the house where she was staying into the sitting room where I was waiting for her, to expound to me at once some idea which had just occurred to her, apparently unconscious of all else." Havelock also showed himself nude before Olive, who remarked that his figure reminded her of Christ in a painting by Holman Hunt. "Again I see her at her rooms at Hastings where I had come to spend the week-end with her, bringing at her desire my student's microscope, for she wished to observe living spermatozoa, which there was no trouble in obtaining to place under the cover glass for her inspection, and I see her interest in their vigorous motility." No doubt Ellis was amused to recall Drysdale's prediction of spermatazoal damage from spermatorrhea.

After a few years, Olive returned to South Africa, but the relationship was not broken off; she and Havelock continued to correspond weekly or oftener through the next quarter of a century. The letters are evidence of a transcendent love on both sides. "My Havelock, I want you, I *need you,"* Olive wrote during the second year of their affair. "In some ways I need you more than ever before." Three days later: "My darling, darling comrade, what would I do without you?" And three days after that: "I feel so clingingly tender to you — the one soul that meets mine and touches it. . . . Oh, Henry, how much closer you are to me than anyone!"

Neither Havelock's marriage nor Olive's interrupted this closeness. "Dear, if I could be jealous of anyone," Olive wrote when she heard of his engagement, "it would be of you, you seem so much mine, how could you love someone else? And yet, I want you to marry. No one would be so glad as I, dear, if anything beautiful came to you. If ever you have a little child you must get your wife to call her after me!" Many years later, in the course of his marriage, Ellis journeyed to Italy to spend ten days with Olive in a hotel in Florence.

Yet their relationship was never physically consummated. Having rapidly reached the stage of what Ellis called "intimate and affectionate friendship," it remained there permanently. "We were not what can be technically, or even ordinarily, called lovers," Ellis explained. Nocturnal emissions of semen remained his main sexual outlet through his years of intimacy with Olive, and he entered marriage at thirty-two still a virgin.

Ellis first met Edith Lees, the woman who became his wife, in 1887 when he was twenty-eight and she was two years younger. They were married in 1891, and their union lasted until her death at the age of fifty-five, in 1916.

Readers of *My Life* can hardly doubt that this was a love match of enduring richness. Havelock described their love as passionate, and of this, too, there can be little doubt. They mostly lived outside London, but one or the other was often away — Havelock to pore over esoteric volumes on sex in the Reading Room of the British Museum, Edith in pursuit of her own literary and social career. They wrote to each other daily during these separations and sometimes several times a day. A few quotations from their letters may convey some sense of the deeply emotional commitment which bound them to one another.

"My Wifie," Ellis wrote early in the marriage, "I lay down on my couch this morning, so happy reading over and over my letter that was so full of love. You mustn't have too good an opinion of me, darling, but you may be quite sure I have the merit of loving you! And it's rooted very deep down and I don't know what could tear it up." And again: "I want you so much; I want to come and put my head on your breast and be your child." And a few years later: "All these weeks my whole body has been like a bundle of sensitive nerves throbbing with love of you, every tiniest act of the day has seemed mixed up with love of you, I have had no thought and written no word that wasn't love of you. . . . I am indeed hopelessly in love with you. I fold my arms round you. I seem to be almost grateful to you for enabling me to give you such a proof of my love. I seem to be a mother, and you my fretful babe that I fold and smother in my breast. . . . Lie still, my own, and rest beside me, and grow strong. Always your Havelock." And much later, when the Ellises were in their fifties: "I . . . am feeling very desolate without you. I always seem to see your sweet face. . . . I always seem to love you more and more and your last absence doesn't seem to make this one any easier." And again: "I shall never have any peace or happiness till I can put my arms round you once more. You are never out of my thoughts." And many years later, after Edith's death; "My real self throbs swiftly to any casual contact with the things she once touched, when I kiss her picture as I go to bed, when I cherish tenderly the things she herself had cherished. It is a perpetual revelation that after I had lived with her tempestuously for a quarter of a century, in pain as well as in joy — that more than ten years after she is dead love should retain its fresh original sensitiveness."

Edith's letters bear similar testimony to a lifelong love and devotion. Early in their marriage she wrote, after a minor misunderstanding: "Just kiss me, sweetheart, and know that these things do not hinder but deepen love really." And in a postscript, "I open this again to rock you to me, darling. I *do* love you, Havelock, and need you with my whole woman heart." And two decades later, again after a misunderstanding: "My Precious One, just a line on receipt of your lovely letter. Oh! God! have I hurt you and I love you so — such a love and yet I seem to have hurt you and you me. . . . We will pitch our tent together, my Love, and let no one hurt us. . . . Deep down I am so close that *nothing* can take me away, not even death."

Yet despite this enduring passion, their sexual life together can be described, perhaps a bit too charitably, as unsatisfying, impoverished, and brief. Edith, like Havelock, had come to marriage still a virgin. Neither enjoyed sexual intercourse with one another.

One problem was contraception. Edith was subject to periods of elation alternating with depression, which would today be diagnosed as a manic-depressive syndrome. She had once had a "nervous breakdown." There were several eccentrics among her forebears, including a few who had been diagnosed as "insane." In accordance with a not uncommon Victorian custom, accordingly, the Ellises resolved on eugenic grounds to have no children, so that the defects in Edith's family would not be transmitted to another generation.* They therefore used contraceptives — possibly condoms, though the modern form of vaginal diaphragm,

* Bertrand Russell and his first wife, interestingly enough, reached the same decision on the same grounds at about the same time, though in their case it was so-called insanity in the *husband's* family that caused the Russell family doctor to warn Bertrand against siring children. Thus the nineteenth-century eugenics movement, whatever its other failures, succeeded in saving posterity from the descendants of Havelock Ellis and almost succeeded in the case of Bertrand Russell. Russell, however, recovered from this particular Victorian delusion in time, and had children by his second wife.

invented on the continent during the 1870's, had recently become known in England. Whatever the device, Edith found it objectionable. "She had experienced from the outset a dislike to the mechanical contraceptive preliminaries of intercourse," Havelock later wrote. He, too, was displeased with their sexual life together. "I felt that in this respect we were relatively unsuited to each other, that relations were incomplete and unsatisfactory, too liable to jar on one or the other of the partners." On the first anniversary of their wedding night, Edith wrote to Havelock:

"I look back and it seems years and years ago. I was shy and frightened and cried over my wee babe that was never to be, and you — you made me think of how beautiful men could be."

Within a few years, at Edith's suggestion, sexual relations were discontinued altogether. "I made not the slightest objection," Havelock wrote. Some years later, when Edith proposed that sexual intercourse be resumed, Havelock "allowed the proposal to drop without discussion and she never brought it forward again. The whole matter seemed entirely to pass from our minds; so much remained that it seemed to leave no blank." Their real love, Ellis believed, was not damaged by this sexual denial: "On the contrary, it grew; it grew into passion, and this more than a spiritual passion since the yearning tenderness of the body was not excluded. Only one thing was left out, a real and definite thing, yet so small in comparison to all that was left that we scarcely missed it. Even years after her death and all was in seeming over, I would find myself exclaiming inwardly: My sweetheart!"

In their conscious opinions, as distinct from their physiological responses, Edith and Havelock were almost totally emancipated from Victorian taboos. Their intellects had shed sexual inhibitions even though their bodies had not. They had agreed in advance, for example, that their marriage should not be possessive and that jealousy should play no role in it. Both were contemptuous of what Ellis called "domestic love." Both embarked on extramarital affairs during their second year of marriage — even before their sexual relations with one another came to an end.

Edith's first affair was with a young woman whom she had known from childhood — called Claire in Ellis's autobiography. She promptly wrote to tell Havelock of this development, "with all her native trustful confidence," as Ellis later described her letter. "There was, as I now look back, a pathetic wonder and beauty in that appeal to my comprehending love, as though addressed to a divine being superior to the weaknesses of a human husband." Havelock had some qualms. "It was not so much the mere fact — for I had no prejudices and I well knew she could be guilty of nothing ugly or ignoble — but the realization, as rightly or wrongly it seemed to me, that this new absorption in another person was leading unconsciously to a diminution in the signs of tenderness in her love toward me." Nevertheless he rose to the occasion.

"My own Wifie," he wrote, "my letter was very lovely this morning; I read it over ever so many times. Yes, nothing in the world or out of it will tear you away from my breastbone — unless you want to go. I am perfectly happy that you should be so close to Claire. I feel very tender to her. Give her my love."

Edith wrote similarly: "I told Claire you would be trusted with all and she smiled 'You *are* two odd people!' It is her purity and sweetness which have made me love her; she is so childlike and unprudish, and gives me like a child a love which has rested and comforted and strengthened me in a way that amazes me." And later: "It is so wonderful to have married a man who leaves a woman her soul. I'm utterly satisfied in you, Havelock. It passes all my comprehension, though, why you love me."

After Claire, Edith became the lover of a series of other young women, at least one of whom — Lily — aroused in her an emotionally passionate attachment comparable to her love for Havelock. Indeed, Edith in a conventionally Victorian fashion cherished Lily's memory, and reveled in her mementos of Lily long after her death. Havelock took both the enduring relationship with Lily and Edith's more casual mistresses in his stride. "I never grudged the devotion, though it was sometimes great, which she expended on them," he wrote after Edith's death, "for I knew that it satisfied a deep and ineradicable need of her nature. The only test I applied to them was how far they were good for her. . . . I never had a quarrel with one of them and some of them have been — now more than ever in our community of loss — my own dear friends."

Havelock's first extramarital affair was quite different, and was entered into despite his continuing shyness. Edith had a deadly fear of sleeping alone in a house, and therefore required a companion for nights when Havelock was away. "There was no friend of her own available, and in all innocence I suggested a young lady, an acquaintance of my own, whom I will call Amy. She was found free to come, and she came. Amy, whom I had known from childhood [she was Mneme Barker Smith, the daughter of Ellis's close friend and associate, John Barker

Smith], was at this time twenty-four. I had never paid any special attention to her; with my idealistic and intellectual preoccupations, I had overlooked the gentle, quiet girl who, on her side, had cherished admiration for me from a distance. But in the narrow limits of the bungalow I began to become aware of her sweet, soothing, unselfish qualities. . . . One day I went for a walk with her to a pine-wood near Hindhead; there we sat side by side on a fallen trunk, and there I gave her a kiss. It was but a simple kiss, and for months, even years, afterward there was little further progress in intimacy, for with me relationships developed with extreme slowness, and Amy was much too inexperienced to make, or to invite, any advances." Ellis continued to see Amy from time to time, visited her in Paris, and took several trips with her.

During the twenty-third year of Havelock's affair with Amy, for example, the two went on a two-week ramble through the English countryside. "This little tour at the best season of the year was probably the most beautiful, and almost the last, that we ever enjoyed together," Ellis wrote. "She had now reached middle age and had really begun, however late, to feel the confidence of being complete mistress of her own actions, while I, equally late, had finally conquered an element of misgiving, latent and concealed, which had sometimes marred the joy of our relations. Now we felt a careless and joyous freedom as we went about openly, two independent persons occupying our separate rooms, not ashamed to enjoy each other's society, and indifferent to the speculations of other people."

But it was Ellis's wife who occupied the chief place in his affections. "It is a perpetual source of amusement and wonder to me," he wrote, "to think how from the first, separately and together [Edith] and I had cherished ideals of freedom and independence, both in theory and in practice, and cast contempt on the narrow self-absorption of domestic love, and, as it would seem, had done everything to make such love difficult or even impossible. And yet the love we achieved during a quarter of a century seems to lie beyond even the imagination of those conventional couples who proclaim the duty and the beauty of mutual devotion, never leave each other's side, loathe the ideals of freedom and independence — and in their hearts loathe each other."

Ellis engaged in several briefer extramarital affairs during and following his affair with Amy. One was with Margaret Sanger, one of the leaders of the American birth control movement. Mrs. Sanger in her autobiography recorded the details of their first meeting late in 1914.

"Looking askance at the police station which occupied the first floor," she wrote, "I climbed up the stairs, and, with the shyness of an adolescent, full of fears and uncertainties, lifted the huge brass knocker. The figure of Ellis himself appeared in the door. He seemed a giant in stature, a lovely, simple man in loose-fitting clothes, with powerful head and a wonderful smile. He was fifty-five then, but that head will never change — the shock of white hair, the venerable beard, shaggy though well-kept, the wide expressive mouth and deep-set eyes, sad even in spite of the luminous twinkle always latent.

"I was conscious immediately that I was in the presence of a great man. . . . He lit two candles on the mantel, which flickered softly over his features, giving him the aspect of a seer.

"We sat down and quiet fell. I tried a few aimless remarks but I stuttered with embarrassment. Ellis was still. Small talk was not possible with him; you had to utter only the deepest truths within you. No other human being could be so silent and remain so poised and calm in silence."

Hours later, Margaret made her departure. "I was not excited as I went back through the heavy fog to my own dull little room," she wrote. "My emotion was too deep for that. I felt as though I had been exulted into a hitherto undreamed-of world." Years later Margaret wrote: "I have never felt about any person as I do about Havelock Ellis."

Another of Ellis's affairs was with the American poet, H.D. (Hilda Doolittle; Mrs. Richard Aldington). Ellis himself supplied some of the details of this remarkable relationship in an essay entitled "A Revelation," in his *Impressions and Comments: Third Series* (1924).

"From time to time, at long intervals, she would drift into my room," he wrote, "like a large white bird hovering tremulously over the edge of a cliff, a shy and sinuous figure, so slender and so tall that she seemed frail, yet lithe, one divined, of firm and solid texture. I speak of her as a woman, yet she was in a sense beyond the distinction of sex, at once a married mother and an adolescent virginal youth, and these two together, not by any inharmonious clash, but lifted into the higher unity of a being who belongs to another race."

The affair unfolded slowly, as was usual in Ellis's case. "It was a memorable step in the unfoldment when, one unexpectant day, the tall figure rose and approached and I felt cool kisses, like the rich petals of some tea rose, falling softly on my face, amid murmured words, and the rustle of long cool limbs for a moment gliding gently around my own. Therewith the slow process of my awakening was touched into sudden acceleration."

On a later occasion, "we talked of I know not what grave things in art or in life, and as we talked she rose from the depths of her chair and it seemed by scarce an effort of disentanglement floated into my sight without a single garment left to veil the soft radiance of her form. The room was full of diffused light . . . in which this lofty Person [Ellis's love name for H.D.] shone not only in clear outline, but with all due variations of bright tone and gloom of shaded recesses. All the natural saliences of form were subdued. The shallow inverted bowls of the breasts were of a virginal shape astonishing to see, the firm belly no less, and only the little trace of a droop in the tender globes behind somehow indirectly suggested the touch of maternal fatigue."

More than forty years earlier, when Ellis was a boy of twelve, walking by the side of his mother along a gravel path in an unfrequented part of the London Zoological Gardens, his mother had "stood still, and soon I heard a very audible stream falling to the ground. When she moved on I instinctively glanced behind at the pool on the path, and my mother, having evidently watched my movements, remarked shyly: 'I did not mean you to see that.' " The experience was repeated a little later; this time his mother was not shy but confided in her son beforehand. Havelock "spontaneously played a protective part and watched to see that no one was approaching." Thereafter, Ellis reported in *My Life,* he enjoyed "a slight strain of what I may call urolagnia"—sexual arousal at the fantasy or the fact of a woman urinating, preferably in a standing position. Ellis's urolagnia, he explained, "never developed into a real perversion nor ever became a dominant interest, and formed no distinguishable part of the chief love interests of my life." Nevertheless, "my vision of this function became in some degree attached to my feeling of tenderness toward women — I was surprised how often women responded to it sympathetically."

H.D. was one of those who responded sympathetically. Her "tall form," he wrote, "languidly arose and stood erect, taut and massive it seemed now with the length of those straight adolescent legs still more ravishing in their unyielding pride, and the form before me seemed to become some adorable Olympian vase, and a large stream gushed afar in the glistering liquid arch, endlessly, it seemed to my wondering eyes, as I contemplated with enthralled gaze this prototypal statue of the Fountain of Life, carved by the hands of some daring and divine architect, out of marble like flesh."

I have found no account of this occasion written by H.D.; but Havelock reported that "on the firm austere lines of [her] face one read, not pride, but a shy and diffident smile, the fear lest to the merely human spectator that which is transcendent should be mistaken for what is gross."

In guarded language, "A Revelation" also indicated the manner in which Ellis made love to these women with whom he did not have sexual intercourse. "It was only by intimate contact," he wrote of H.D., "that one might know or divine the scent and the taste of the mysterious salts and essences that distilled from the guarded places of her form."

Ellis identified his beloved "Person" as H.D. in a letter to an American psychiatrist, Dr. Joseph Wortis, in October 1936, after Wortis had discussed the essay with Sigmund Freud. "F[reud] is quite right," Ellis wrote; "there is no coitus, real or assumed, in the narrative. The 'Person' in question, I may now privately mention (though when she last came to see me she said, not long ago, that she no longer minded being recognized in it) is H.D. I had, in the first place, obtained her consent to print it, with some difficulty, though she said, when I read it to her, that it was so beautiful it almost brought tears to her eyes, and it is generally considered by critics my finest piece of poetic prose. H.D. has told me that at that period [her separation from Richard Aldington and her affair with the English novelist Bryher] I was an immense help to her — I have never known why — and she remains an affectionate correspondent."

The dearest companion of Ellis's later years, Françoise Delisle, has more frankly described both Ellis's urolagnia and his mode of making love.

"His lodgings were almost as poverty-stricken as mine," she recalled. "He had hardly a stick of any value, though one or two fine old things. His sofa was a common cheap folding bed camouflaged with brown velvet and cushions; the rest was in keeping: cheap wicker chairs and even junk bought second-, third-, or fourth-hand." Indeed, his flat lacked even a toilet; a chamber pot served instead. On one of Françoise's early visits to these quarters, she had fallen into Havelock's arms. "The touch of his hand had already been 'very quietening,' " she noted, "but so was the closeness of his whole body, just through our clothes. On the first visit we rested as two babes, side by side on his sofa, his arms around me, his lips lightly kissing me, one hand caressing my face, the arms of a man becoming an entrancing home. This I had never known before, nor what treasures of affection dwell in the human hand."

Presently it was time to leave, and Françoise went into the bedroom to use the chamber pot. Havelock unexpectedly "followed me to minister himself to my needs . . . and did this in so unexpected a fashion as to reduce me to utter bashfulness, but delicious bashfulness, wistful and alluring if puzzled, as I stood in front of him, and he, on his knees, let me caress the glorious head fully accessible to my hand. The caress saved me words. Was he not there in full reverence? What best could match this adoration but my hand all over his head? Henceforth we were more than friends, notwithstanding the bashfulness. . . .

"Of the full meaning of his delicate attention I was then ignorant. Nor did he say anything that could enlighten me. Least of all did I know the name given to it in his sexological books. If urolagnia became clearer to me in time, suffices it here to say that, on this our first day of closer friendship, it proved mysteriously soothing to my soul, and thereby restored peace to my body so long bewildered.

"*Honi soit qui mal y pense.* Love's strange ways of expression are far too precious and intimate for me to attempt to convey in words what Havelock's harmless anomaly meant to me in the course of time. This book will nowhere dwell upon it in direct fashion, simply because I dare not risk soiling what was so beautiful by his side that I never considered it abnormal. It was part of our normality."

Following this visit, Françoise's friendship with Havelock "leaped forward at an enchanting pace." Soon "we were naked in each other's arms without my receiving a shock."

Ellis at this time was fifty-eight. Françoise was thirty-two, twice married and the mother of two children. Neither of her husbands — one French and one Russian — had ever aroused her sexually; neither had even tried to; she had never seen either of them naked; they had merely evacuated their semen into her vagina in the dark and fallen asleep. "On the first day [of intimacy with Havelock]," Françoise wrote, "I foolishly expected the marital act I had so far known, but now with a man I truly loved. There was, therefore, a slight dread when this did not happen. A sudden pang of horror went through me. In one swift irrational moment I felt that I was in for another agonizing experience, since he did not seem normal. But instantly came the astounding assurance — as a stroke of lightning before he touched me — that where true love abides everything is perfect. This 'travail' of my soul proved the birth of my new being: woman at last, woman in soul. In that bed, in broad daylight, his hands and his kisses, never jerking me with fear, tenderly brought me to this delight. My body, husbandless, yet spontaneously acclaimed its true rule at the guidance of this other soul: 'Love, and do what you like.' "

Soon Françoise "loved out of his hand without a thought that it could be otherwise," and was moved to write to him: "Havelock, it is bliss, sheer bliss, even more bliss all this happiness. For dread of falling from the clouds I should wish we did not progress further than where we are now. But you instill into me such confidence, you sorcerer, that I picture us going up and up . . . no doubt to heaven." Yet this relationship, too, for the time being remained noncoital; for some time Ellis continued to woo only with "his hands and his kisses."

A psychiatrist reviewing Ellis's case history today would of course consider the possibility that homosexuality might have played a part in blocking his heterosexual fulfillment. Ellis was certainly not an overt or practicing homosexual. He would surely have described in *My Life* any adult homosexual experiences as frankly and with as little embarrassment as he had described his brief homosexual encounters in childhood or his wife's homosexual affairs. But the possibility remains of what Freud and others would call "latent homosexuality."

Evidence can be found for such a view. For more than forty years, for example, Ellis maintained a warm and close friendship with another literary figure of the period, Arthur Symons. They once shared bachelor quarters, though they occupied separate rooms. Both before and after his marriage Ellis made extended trips through Europe with Symons; their mutual interests in art and literature made them congenial companions. And Ellis maintained warm friendships also with other distinguished men of his time, among whom were one or two self-acknowledged homosexuals.

But if "latent homosexuality" — however that term be defined — played a role in Ellis's life, it must have been a modest one. His Victorian inhibitions blocked this road to sexual fulfillment as well as the heterosexual road. His primary attachments, moreover, were without exception heterosexual — to his wife, to Olive Schreiner, to Amy, and in later years to Françoise. And when he ultimately entered a period of full sexual competence, it was a woman — Françoise Delisle — who opened the door for him.

The suggestion has also been made that Havelock Ellis was physiologically impotent. This, clearly, is an error. As we have seen, he was capable of erection and of ejaculation; and after the age of sixty he was potent in coitus as well.

For what it is worth, let me offer my personal view of Havelock Ellis's sexual inadequacy. I have described him as a victim of Victorianism — but Victorianism does not act on individuals solely in vague or amorphous ways. Rather, as subsequent chapters will make clear, its impact on individuals is primarily through the Victorian masturbation taboo. Victorian children were taught that masturbation was nasty, shameful, and disgusting; many of them masturbated despite the taboo — and in later life thought of sexual arousal in general as nasty, shameful, and disgusting. Havelock Ellis's case was different, but no less disastrous in its outcome. In his case, too, I believe, the masturbation taboo became generalized. Just as it kept him from masturbating during childhood, puberty, and adolescence, so, in adult life, it blocked his coital fulfillment in the arms of the women he most warmly loved and cherished. Whether the same factor kept all four of his sisters spinsters until their deaths can hardly now be determined. (I shall have more to say in later chapters on the Victorian masturbation taboo as a major cause of adult sexual inadequacy, and on masturbation as a normal and necessary phase in the development of sexual maturity.)

One final point deserves mention. One of Ellis's mistresses told a friend that Ellis's problem was premature ejaculation. This view is quite consistent with my view that Ellis's problem can be directly traced to his lack of masturbatory experience and to the masturbation taboo. Ellis did not ejaculate prematurely, however, during his later years with Françoise.

The first volume of Ellis's masterwork, *Studies in the Psychology of Sex,* appeared in German in 1896, when he was thirty-seven, and in English the following year. Five more volumes, completing the basic plan, followed between 1899 and 1910. Ellis revised and greatly expanded these volumes periodically thereafter, and added a seventh volume of miscellaneous studies in 1928. A complete edition in four volumes was published by Random House in 1936 when Ellis was seventy-seven. (The two-volume Random House edition currently available is identical in text with the 1936 edition.) There were thirty-two studies in all, listed below in the order in which Ellis arranged them for the 1936 edition; the dates of first publication appear in parentheses:

VOLUME I

Part One (*1899*)
- The Evolution of Modesty
- The Phenomena of Sexual Periodicity
- Auto-Erotism

Part Two (*1903*)
- Analysis of the Sexual Impulse
- Love and Pain
- The Sexual Impulse in Women

Part Three (*1905*)
- Sexual Selection in Man

Part Four (*1896 in German; 1897 in English*)
- Sexual Inversion

VOLUME II

Part One (*1906*)
- Erotic Symbolism
- The Mechanism of Sexual Detumescence
- The Psychic State in Pregnancy

Part Two: Eonism and Other Supplementary Studies (*1928*)
- Eonism
- The Doctrine of Erogenic Zones
- The History of Florrie and the Mechanism of Sexual Deviation
- The Menstrual Curve of Sexual Impulse
- The Synthesis of Dreams: A Study of a Series of 100 Dreams
- The Concept of Narcissism
- Undinism
- Kleptolagnia
- The History of Marriage

Part Three: Sex in Relation to Society (*1910*)
- The Mother and Her Child
- Sexual Education
- Sexual Education and Nakedness
- The Valuation of Sexual Love
- The Function of Chastity
- The Problem of Sexual Abstinence
- Prostitution

The Conquest of the Venereal Diseases
Sexual Morality
Marriage
The Art of Love
The Science of Procreation

The panorama of human sexuality which emerges from these studies startlingly anticipates many of the findings of Kinsey, Masters and Johnson, and other recent researchers. Let me cite just a few examples:

Sexual behavior and sexual responses often appear at a very early age — long before puberty — in both boys and girls.

Masturbation is a common phenomenon at all ages in both males and females.

Boys tend to reach a peak of sexual activity earlier than girls — while still in adolescence. Girls mature earlier physically; but their sexual activity often blossoms and flowers at a later age.

Homosexuality and heterosexuality are not absolutes like black and white; they are present in varying degrees.

The absence of sexual desire among women is a Victorian myth. Indeed, some women are more highly sexed than most men, and take the active role in initiating sex relations. "A well-known physician in Chicago informs me that on making inquiry of twenty-five middle-class married men in succession he found that sixteen had first been seduced by a woman."

The orgasm is remarkably similar in men and in women.

Multiple orgasm is a common phenomenon among women. "There can be no doubt whatever that very prolonged intercourse gives the maximum amount of pleasure and relief to the woman. Not only is this the very decided opinion of women who have experienced it, but it is also indicated by the well-recognized fact that a woman who repeats the sexual act several times in succession often experiences more intense orgasm and pleasure with each repetition."

Male impotence and female frigidity are psychological rather than physiological phenomena in the overwhelming majority of cases.

The repression of sexuality in girls during childhood and adolescence is one of the major factors in adult frigidity. Male clumsiness, callousness, and ignorance — especially ignorance of the importance of the clitoris in female arousal — is a second major factor.

Men and women, under favorable circumstances, remain sexually responsive well past middle age. "In America, Bloom . . . from an investigation of 400 cases, found that in some cases the sexual impulse persisted to a very advanced age, and mentions the case of a woman of seventy, twenty years past the menopause, who had long been a widow, but had recently married, and who declared that both desire and gratification were as great, if not greater, than before the menopause."

Human sexuality is far from a simple phenomenon. In some respects it is mammalian, shared with the other mammals. In some respects it is molded by historical influences. In many respects it is influenced by cultural expectations — the particular customs and beliefs prevailing in the community at the time. Adult sexuality is very profoundly influenced (here Ellis agrees with Freud) by parental attitudes and by early childhood training and experiences. Social class and economic and educational status also play their roles. Underlying all of these influences are the inherited anatomical structure of the body and the physiological functioning of the body at each moment. And all of these factors together fall short of providing an exhaustive explanation.

These themes recur over and over again in subsequent sex research. They illustrate also another significant aspect of Ellis's *Studies* — their primary emphasis on *normal* human sexuality. The *Studies* cover almost all of the generally recognized variations in sexual behavior — male and female homosexuality, sadism, masochism, exhibitionism, voyeurism, fetishism, incest, satyriasis, nymphomania, transvestism, and zoophilia, to mention only a few. Ellis exhibited a sympathetic understanding of even those variations which his contemporaries deemed most repellent.

When writing of incest, for example, he could recall that on his return from Australia, after an absence of four years, he formed with his sister Louie "an intimate friendship which at first was touched by sexual emotion. This could not have happened if the long absence during which she grew into womanhood had not destroyed that familiarity which inhibits the development of sexual interest. This little experience . . . enabled me to understand from personal knowledge how it is that, as a rule, sexual emotion fails to spring up between close relatives or people living together from before puberty, and under what circumstances — by no means of such rare occurrence as is usually believed — it may spring up. I was thereby enabled in later years to give clear precision to my conception of the psychological foundation of exogamy." In addition, of course,

Ellis's personal touch of urolagnia, and his familiarity with Edith's lesbianism, enabled him to understand from the inside a broad range of similar deviations — and to appreciate how they can in some cases enrich rather than impoverish experience. But his primary emphasis was on "normal" human sexuality, with the term "normal" very broadly defined. As he explained in his *Studies:*

"It is a very remarkable fact that, although for many years past serious attempts have been made to elucidate the psychology of human perversions, little or no endeavor has been made to study the development of the normal sexual emotions. Nearly every writer seems either to take for granted that he and his readers are so familiar with the facts of normal sex psychology that any detailed statement is altogether uncalled for, or else he is content to write a few fragmentary remarks. . . . Yet it is unreasonable to take normal phenomena for granted here as in any other region of science."

Everybody is not like you and your friends and neighbors. This, as we have seen, was the central theme of many of Ellis's *Studies*. But a second theme, of almost equal importance, weaves through the volumes in counterpoint to the first: *Even your friends and neighbors may not be as much like you as you suppose*. As Ellis himself expressed it: "So far from the facts of normal sex development, sex emotions, and sex needs being uniform and constant . . . the range of variation within fairly normal limits is immense, and it is impossible to meet with two individuals whose records are nearly identical."

Many of his examples might well be the cases of the man and woman next door. There was the American woman, for example, "a devout church-goer, [who] had never allowed herself to entertain sexual thoughts referring to men." Yet "she masturbated every morning when standing before the mirror by rubbing against a key in the mirror-drawer. A man never excited her passions, but the sight of a key in any bureau-drawer aroused erotic desires."

There was also the ardent sex reformer, devoting her life to denunciations of masturbation, prostitution, and other sexual activities, whose whole life was shattered when she discovered in her forties that the harmless little game she so often played with herself was in fact the masturbating act which she so loathingly described in her public speeches and writings.

Another woman, happily married, "likes her husband to remain entirely passive during connection, so that he can continue in a state of strong erection for a long time. She can thus, she says, procure for herself the orgasm a number of times in succession, even nine or ten, quite easily. On one occasion she even had the orgasm twenty-six times within about one and a quarter hours, her husband during this time having two orgasms. (She is quite certain about the accuracy of this statement.) . . . She acknowledges that on this occasion she was a 'complete wreck' for a couple of days afterward, but states that usually ten or a dozen orgasms (or spasms, as she terms them) only make her 'feel lively.' "

There was also the minister of the gospel, aged fifty-seven, who informed Ellis: "My whole nature goes out to some persons, and they thrill and stir me so that I have an emission while sitting by them with no thought of sex, only the gladness of soul found its way out thus, and a glow of health suffused the whole body."

At the other extreme, Ellis could cite cases of both men and women who had reached middle age without any sexual arousal or experience whatever. He himself was not too far from this end of the scale, at least until middle age.

This enormous variation in sexuality among people who in other respects seem to be quite like us and our friends and neighbors is most clearly visible in the scores of detailed case histories — Ellis called them "histories of sexual development" — which fill hundreds of pages of the *Studies*. Ellis collected these histories in many ways. Some were provided by his friends and mistresses; indeed, his wife's history up to the date of her marriage is included (see below, page 71). Many were the histories of men and women who came to him for help in distress, and many more came from readers of his early volumes who wrote to Ellis, received replies, and thereafter engaged in frank correspondence with him over periods of years or even decades.

These histories were not included in the *Studies* to make theoretical points, or to illustrate specific phenomena. Rather, they present the ebb and flow of human sexuality as it actually occurs, from early childhood to old age, including wishes, desires, and fantasies as well as actual experiences. Many are tragedies; a few have comic overtones. Just as reading Ellis's "Evolution of Modesty" has awakened countless readers to the enormous variations in sexuality from one culture to another and from one historic era to another, so reading Ellis's case histories has alerted many (myself among them) to the enormous variations within a single culture during a single era — a culture and an era which are not so very unlike our own. Ellis's "histories of sexual development" probably influenced Freud and perhaps enabled Freud to correct a major error in his early theories. Two case histories are reprinted here in full to give some notion of their flavor:

History IX. — The subject belongs to a large family having some neurotic members; she spent her early life on a large farm. She is vigorous and energetic, has intellectual tastes, and is accustomed to think for herself, from unconventional standpoints, on many subjects. Her parents were very religious, and not, she thinks, of sensual temperament. Her own early life was free from associations of a sexual character, and she can recall little that now seems to be significant in this respect. She remembers that in childhood and for some time later she believed that children were born through the navel. Her activities went chiefly into humanitarian and utopian directions, and she cherished ideas of a large, healthy, free life, untrammeled by civilization. She regards herself as very passionate, but her sexual emotions appear to have developed very slowly and have been somewhat intellectualized. After reaching adult life she has formed several successive relationships with men to whom she has been attracted by affinity in temperament, in intellectual views, and in tastes. These relationships have usually been followed by some degree of disillusion, and so have been dissolved. She does not believe in legal marriage, though under fitting circumstances she would much like to have a child.

She never masturbated until the age of 27. At that time a married friend told her that such a thing could be done. She found it gave her decided pleasure, indeed, more than coitus had ever given her except with one man. She has never practised it to excess, only at rare intervals, and is of the opinion that it is decidedly beneficial when thus moderately indulged in. She sometimes found, for instance, that, after the mental excitement produced by delivering a lecture, sleep would be impossible if masturbation were not resorted to as a sedative to relieve the tension.

Spontaneous sexual excitement is strongest just before the monthly period.

Definite sexual dreams and sexual excitement during sleep have not occurred except possibly on one or two occasions.

She has from girlhood experienced erotic day-dreams, imagining love-stories of which she herself was the heroine; the climax of these stories has developed with her own developing knowledge of sexual matters.

She is not inverted, and has never been in love with a woman. She finds, however, that a beautiful woman is distinctly a sexual excitation, calling out definite physical manifestations of sexual emotion. She explains this by saying that she thinks she instinctively puts herself in the place of a man and feels as it seems to her a man would feel.

She finds that music excites the sexual emotions, as well as many scents, whether of flowers, the personal odor of the beloved person, or artificial perfumes.

History XI. — Widower, aged 40 years. Surgeon. My experience of sexual matters began early. When I was about 10 years of age a boy friend who was staying with us told me that his sister made him uncover his person, with which she played and encouraged him to do the same for her. He said it was great fun, and suggested that we should take two of my sisters into an old barn and repeat his experience on them. This we did, and tried all we could to have connection with them; they were nothing loath and did all they could to help us, but nothing was effected and I experienced no pleasure in it.

When I went back to school I attracted the attention of one of the big boys who slept in the same room with me; he came into my bed and began to play with my member, saying that it was the usual thing to do and would give me pleasure. I did not feel any pleasure, but I liked the attention, and rather enjoyed playing with his member, which was of large size, and surrounded by thick pubic hair. After I had played with him for some time I was surprised at his having an emission of sticky matter. Afterward he rubbed me again, saying that if I let him do it long enough he would produce the same substance from me. This he failed to do, however, though he rubbed me long and frequently, on that and many other occasions. I was very disappointed at not being able to have an emission, and on every occasion that offered I endeavored to excite myself to the extent of compassing this. I used to ask to go out of school two or three times a day, and retired to the closet, where I practised on myself most diligently, but to no purpose, at that time, though I began to have pleasurable emotions in the act.

When I went home for the holidays I took a great interest in one of my father's maids, whose legs I felt as she ran upstairs one day. I was in great fear she would complain of what I had done, but I was delighted to find that she did nothing of the sort; on the contrary, she took to kissing and fondling me, calling me her sweetheart and saying that I was a forward boy. This encouraged me greatly, and I was not long in getting to more intimate relations with her. She called me into her room one day when we were alone in the house, she being in a half-dressed condition, and put me on the bed and laid herself on me, kissing me passionately on the mouth. She next unbuttoned my trousers and fondled and kissed my member, and directed my hand to her privates. I became very much excited and trembled violently, but was able to do for her what she wanted in the way of masturbation until she became wet. After this we had many meetings in which we embraced and she let me introduce my member until she had satisfied herself, though I was too young to have an emission.

On return to school I practised mutual masturbation with several of my schoolfellows, and finally, at the age of 14 years, had my first real emission. I was greatly pleased thereat, and, with this and the growth of hair which began to show on my pubis, began to feel myself quite a man. I loved lying in the arms of another boy, pressing against his body, and fondling his person and being fondled by him in return. We always finished up with mutual masturbation. We never indulged in any unnatural connections.

After leaving school I had no opportunity of indulging in relations with my own sex, and, indeed, did not wish for such, as I became a slave to the charms of the other sex, and passed most of my time in either enjoying, or planning to enjoy, love passages with them.

The sight of a woman's limbs or bust, especially if partly hidden by pretty underclothing, and the more so if seen by stealth, was sufficient to give a lustful feeling and a violent erection, accompanied by palpitation of the heart and throbbing in the head.

I had frequent coitus at the age of 17, as well as masturbating regularly. I liked to perform masturbation on a girl, even more than I liked having connection with her; and this was especially so in the case of girls who had never had masturbation practised on them before; I loved to see the look of surprised pleasure appear on their faces as they felt the delightful and novel sensation.

To gratify this desire I persuaded dozens of girls to allow me to take liberties with them, and it would surprise you to learn what a number of girls, many of them in good social position, permitted me the liberty I desired, though the supply was never equal to my demand.

With a view to enlarging my opportunities I took up the study of medicine as a profession, and reveled in the chances it gave of being on intimate sexual terms with many who would have been, otherwise, out of my reach.

At the age of 25 I married the daughter of an officer, a beautiful girl with a fully developed figure and an amorous disposition. While engaged, we used to pass hours wrapped in each other's arms, practising mutual masturbation, or I would kiss her passionately on the mouth, introducing my tongue into her mouth at intervals, with the invariable result that I had an emission and she went off into sighs and shivers. After marriage we practised all sorts of fancy coitus, coitus reservatus, etc., and rarely passed twenty-four hours without two conjunctions, until she got far on in the family way, and our play had to cease for a while.

During this interval I went to stay at the house of an old school-fellow, who had been one of my lovers of days gone by. It happened that on account of the number of guests staying in the house the bed accommodation was somewhat scanty, and I agreed to share my friend's bedroom. The sight of his naked body as he undressed gave rise to lustful feelings in me; and when he had turned out the light I stole across to his bed and got in beside him. He made no objection, and we passed the night in mutual masturbation and embraces, coitus inter femora, etc. I was surprised to find how much I preferred this state of affairs to coitus with my wife, and determined to enjoy the occasion to the full. We passed a fortnight together in the above fashion, and, though I afterward went back and did my duty by my wife, I never took the same pleasure in her again, and when she died, five years later, I felt no inclination to contract another marriage, but devoted myself heart and soul to my old school-friend, with whom I continued tender relations until his death by accident last year. Since then I have lost all interest in life.

"The patient," writes the well-known alienist to whom I am indebted for the above history, "consulted me lately. I found him a fairly healthy man to look at, suffering from some neurasthenia and a tendency to melancholia. Generative organs large, one testicle shows some wasting, pubic hair abundant, form of body distinctly masculine; temperament neurotic. He improved under treatment, and, after seeing me three times and writing out the above history, came no more."

These and other Ellis "histories of sexual development" illustrate another point which Ellis repeatedly stressed: the absence of any objective boundary between the normal and the abnormal. "The majority of sexual perversions, including even those that are most repulsive," Ellis taught, "are but exaggerations of instincts and emotions that are germinal in normal human emotions."

Ellis was essentially a naturalist, observing human sexuality rather than judging it — much as another scientist might observe the behavior of gall wasps, hamsters, or chimpanzees. The heterosexual and the homosexual, the celibate and the libertine, the sadist, the masochist, and the fetishist, the lovers of excrement and of corpses — Ellis saw them all as variant expressions of a common human impulse. Few men before him achieved that scientific objectivity. Most contemporary sex research, as we shall see, shares his naturalistic perspective.

Ellis was also a crusader, concerned to introduce reforms in the sexual education of children, in adult attitudes toward sex, and in attitudes toward sexual variations. Having described things objectively as they really are, he went on to draw ethical conclusions. The whole body of his work is richly infused with a sense of human values, and on issue after issue he fought for a realization of those values.

It could not have been otherwise. For in the course of his research, Ellis uncovered in all its poignancy the tragic waste resulting from sexual ignorance and sexual repression. He saw the bachelors and the spinsters, the blighted love affairs and the unfulfilled marriages. He saw the sufferings of the damned imposed by a callous society upon masturbators, adulterers, homosexuals. He saw with an emotional directness arising out of his own personal experience the blight which follows when the normal emotional responses of love and affection are divorced from the "evils" of "lust" — that is, from physiological response. And his studies persuaded him — as most serious students of sex are today persuaded — that this waste and these tragedies are avoidable. Hence he threw himself wholeheartedly into movements for sexual freedom and sexual reform.

He urged, for example, that sexual manifestations during infancy and childhood should be accepted casually, as a routine matter of course. He argued for the frank sexual education of both boys and girls from an early age. He favored greater freedom of sexual experimentation during adolescence, and "trial marriage" as a prelude to actual marriage. He demanded equal rights — including equal sexual rights — for women, greater freedom of divorce, a repeal of the laws banning contraception. And he stated with clarity the legal principles which should govern homosexual and other variant behavior:

"If two persons of either or both sexes, having reached years of discretion, privately consent to practice some perverted mode of sexual relationship, the law cannot be called upon to interfere. It should be the function of the law in this matter to prevent violence, to protect the young, and to preserve public order and decency."

This doctrine of legal immunity for the sexual acts of consenting adults in private has echoed down through the decades. "It is a great injustice to persecute homosexuality as a crime, and cruelty too," Sigmund Freud wrote in 1935. "If you do not believe me, read the books of Havelock Ellis." Ellis's proposal was adopted into law in Britain and in the state of Illinois during the 1960's; and homosexual relations between consenting adults are not subject to legal prosecution in Belgium, Czechoslovakia, Denmark, Greece, Italy, the Netherlands, Poland, Switzerland, and Turkey. But prison sentences are still meted out in all fifty American states. (Despite the change in the Illinois law, the Chicago police continue to arrest homosexuals and judges continue to imprison them; the charge is now usually disorderly conduct.)

Ellis's ability to combine a highly objective naturalism in his scientific study of sex with a deeply committed fervor for sexual reform has also characterized many of his successors.

Havelock Ellis's story had a happy ending. The last twenty years of his life were spent with a mistress who loved and cherished him, whom he loved and cherished, who was wholly devoted to his interests, and with whom for many years he achieved sexual fulfillment in coitus. His beloved was Françoise Lafitte-Cyon, a Frenchwoman who took the pen name Françoise Delisle (formed from the rearranged letters of "de Ellis"). A part of their early relationship has been described above. At his death, Ellis left to Françoise, both as a duty and as a legacy, the privilege of writing the story of their life together. This she accomplished with distinction in *Friendship's Odyssey,* first published in 1946 and later expanded into two volumes, *Françoise* (1962) and *Friendship's Odyssey* (1964).

It was Edith, Havelock's wife, who opened the door to the relationship. During the last months of her life, Edith, fifty-five, was in a manic phase which caused her to launch all sorts of schemes and projects in a final wild burst of pathological energy. While in this phase she met Françoise, aged thirty, separated from her second husband, penniless and with two small children to support. Edith's response was to hire Françoise to translate one of her books into French — for a fee of fifteen pounds — and to woo her as she had long been accustomed to woo young women.

Edith impressed Françoise when they first met as "alive and vivacious, rather ugly I thought (in my pride of youth) when her face was in repose, for it was extremely wrinkled. Also she was rather fat. . . . But . . . that wrinkled face of hers was seldom in repose, and the animation there displayed was not of an old woman but of an eternally young spirit. She plunged so swiftly into my troubles that it took my breath away. Just as one would automatically pick up anything fallen from the mantelpiece, so Edith Ellis picked up any fellow mortal who had grievously fallen on the Road of Life."

Françoise's role as Edith's translator soon "ripened into a friendship with this amazing woman. How I came to love her dainty flat during these evenings when I read her my translation. Most of my free time was spent with her as soon as I had sufficient work ready. . . The translation delighted her; she was lavish in her praise" — though Havelock later commented that he didn't believe Edith knew enough French to follow a translation.

"These evenings," Françoise reported, "were the most interesting I had ever known in my life. . . . I was twenty-five years her junior, and pitifully sore of spirit. She appeared all sunshine in contrast to my darkness.

"She made all sorts of advances to bring me out. She went so far as to invite me to spend a week-end with her and bring my two children. She sent her secretary to meet us; and we arrived on a day when she was to give a lecture on Oscar Wilde, so we found a little gathering in her flat." This was Françoise's first exposure to the theory of homosexuality, and she had not the slightest inkling that Edith herself was homosexual. "All I knew was that she was extremely dear to me."

The denouement rapidly approached. Edith asked Françoise whether, "since she disliked spending the night alone, I would occasionally sleep at her flat when I was free and she had no one with her." Françoise agreed; and on August 25, 1916, Edith wrote her:

> *Dear Lady Translator, could you possibly sleep here on Tuesday? I will then pay you seven pounds ten shillings and the balance when the book is finished. I am sorry I could not pay it before. . . . If you can sleep here, we shall have two hours alone for reading.*

Françoise's poverty at that moment can hardly be imagined. She had already pawned many of her belongings to buy bread for herself and her two children. She left for the rendezvous with Edith with only enough money in her purse to pay her fare one way. "It mattered not, for the morrow would find me rich with seven pounds ten shillings."

But when Françoise reached the flat, Edith was not there. Three weeks later Edith was dead, still owing Françoise those fifteen pounds.

In her despair, Françoise wrote to Havelock, whom she had never met — only to find that he, too, was penniless. The debt to Françoise was one of many which Edith had contracted, and which Ellis paid off willingly — but only slowly and with difficulty — through the subsequent years.

It was under these circumstances that Françoise first visited Havelock, came to know him, received from him a copy of "The Evolution of Modesty," consulted with him on her problems with her husband and with others, told him the story of her life, and, over a period of many months, fell in love with him.

The manner in which Françoise accepted Havelock's urolagnia, and the manner in which Havelock brought her to orgasm with his hand and with his kisses, have been described above. Françoise lived in ecstasy thereafter — and in due course, guided by her intuition, aroused him to full and true sexual potency.

"I had done this in my innocence," Françoise explained much later, "as unerringly as the wave rises to the crest of its power. Though without premeditation, I had taken Havelock a little by assault." And again: "I had, on the one hand, one asset in my youth. Yet I was not so young as not to have acquired much experience of life. He had great wisdom; but I too possessed a little through my hard battle. So that the sorely wandering soul I had been when I met Ellis, if housed in the body of a down-and-out, was yet a determined one. My shy but extreme desperation reached out eagerly toward his extreme if shy wisdom. My spirited vitality acquired a little more wisdom, but also lent him life."

Earlier, in an essay entitled "The Art of Love," Ellis had written: "When . . . the serious and intimate play of physical love begins, the woman's part is, even biologically, on the surface the more passive part. She is, on the physical side, inevitably the instrument in love; it must be his hand and his bow which evoke the music."

Françoise agreed. "With temperaments as heterosexual as ours," she wrote, ". . . what Havelock thus stated was divinely true. I became passive once I had declared my love, and his hand and his bow evoked the music. Constantly new and delightful was his handling of the bow. My heart, therefore, renewed itself for him with as great a constancy, for the music he brought within and without and through me was always his creation."

The remainder of the love story of Françoise and Havelock need not be here retold. I need only add that readers who secure and read in sequence — as Ellis hoped that they would be read — his own autobiography and Françoise's account, have a richly rewarding treat in store.

Both Havelock and Françoise experienced jealousy at times, as *Friendship's Odyssey* frankly describes. But Françoise's was within her control, so that Ellis during his years with her was able to write:

> Today . . . I have more friends, dearer and more intimate friends, than I have ever had in my life before, and they bring me as sweet a devotion, as unmixed a joy, as has ever been brought to me, or perhaps — I somehow imagine — to any man.

And Ellis in his last years also delighted that the Victorianism against which he had so long battled was beginning to fade. "I cannot see now a girl walking along the street," he wrote in old age, "with her free air, her unswathed limbs, her gay and scanty raiment, without being conscious of a thrill of joy that in my youth was unknown. I can today feel in London, as in earlier days I scarcely could even in Paris, that I am among people who are growing to be gracious and human."

No man alive or dead contributed more to that change than Havelock Ellis himself.

2

Sex as a Loathsome Disease

Richard von Krafft-Ebing (1840–1902)

FOR MANY CENTURIES in our culture, sex has been denounced from the pulpits as a sin and punished in the courts as a crime. Richard von Krafft-Ebing (1840–1902) added a third ground for the repression and the suppression of human sexuality. He portrayed sex in almost all of its manifestations as a collection of loathsome diseases.

Others, of course, had held this view before Krafft-Ebing. But his powerful and terrifying masterpiece, *Psychopathia Sexualis* (1886), was and remains today one of the main vehicles for spreading this doctrine of sex as a disease from country to country and from generation to generation.

In Krafft-Ebing's Germany as in Victorian England, most people had what they thought was a very clear concept of "healthy" or "normal" sexuality. A "normal" young man is attracted to a "normal" young woman. She reciprocates the feeling. They fall in love, marry, and live happily ever after. From time to time during the early years of their marriage, the husband inserts his penis into his wife's vagina and experiences an orgasm — but the less said about that the better. Krafft-Ebing's main interest in life was the countless ways in which actual men and women vary from this Victorian norm.

Most of *Psychopathia Sexualis* is concerned with four broad categories of variation — fetishism, homosexuality, sadism, and masochism (though Krafft-Ebing did not present them in that order). He illustrated each with numerous case histories which he had collected from his own patients, from the defendants in criminal courts, from the earlier medical literature, and from medical colleagues who did not dare to publish sexual materials under their own names. These case histories are marred by much pseudo-scientific nonsense, including a stress on "hereditary taint," on "moral degeneracy," and on masturbation as a cause of almost everything unpleasant. But they continue to make fascinating reading, and they cast light into many dark corners of human sexuality. I shall quote from them freely, with the warning that the theories embodied in them (as distinct from some of the clinical observations) are not to be taken seriously.

Fetishism provided Krafft-Ebing with his most bizarre materials. It may be roughly defined as sexual arousal based on something other than a human partner. The sexually arousing object may be a part of a human body, such as a hand or foot. It may be an article of clothing, such as a glove or shoe. It may be a particular material such as fur, velvet, or silk. It may be a particular posture, or action — the possibilities are almost limitless.

Krafft-Ebing's fetishists were all men. Here are two of his many examples:

Case 89. B., of neuropathic family, very sensual, mentally intact. At the sight of the hand of a beautiful young lady he was always charmed and felt sexual excitement to the extent of erection. It was his delight to kiss and press such hands. As long as they were covered with gloves he felt unhappy. By pretexts he tried to get hold of such hands. He was indifferent to the foot. If the beautiful hands were ornamented with rings, his lust was increased. Only the living hand, not its image, caused him this lustful excitement. It was only when he was exhausted sexually by frequent coitus that the hand lost its sexual charm.

Case 111. Z. began to masturbate at the age of twelve. From that time he could not see a woman's handkerchief without having orgasm and ejaculation. He was irresistibly compelled to possess himself of it. At that time he was a choir boy and used the handkerchiefs to masturbate with in the bell-tower close to the choir. But he chose only such handkerchiefs as had black and white borders or violet stripes running through them. At fifteen he had coitus. Later on he married. As a rule, he was only potent when he wrapped such a handkerchief around his penis. Often he preferred coitus *inter femora feminae* where he had placed a handkerchief. Whenever he espied a handkerchief he did not rest until he came in possession of it. He always had a number of them in his pockets and around his genitals.

The vast spectrum of fetishistic variation, visible in Krafft-Ebing's day as today, gave ample scope to his talents for describing the weird and the barely credible. There was the innocent young bride, for example, who was astounded on her wedding night and periodically thereafter to have her husband present her with a bowl of warm water and a bar of soap, demanding that she lather his face as if preparing to give him a shave. This lathering, it appeared, was his sole source of sexual arousal and satisfaction. Another fetish case has an almost poetic quality rare in Krafft-Ebing's stern gallery of sexual deviation:

> *Case 123.* B., thirty years of age, apparently untainted, refined and sensitive; great lover of flowers; liked to kiss them, but without any sensual motive or sensual excitement; rather of *natura frigida;* did not before twenty-one practice onanism, and subsequently only at periods. When twenty-one he was introduced to a young lady who wore some large roses on her bosom. Ever since then large roses dominated his sexual feelings. He incessantly bought roses; kissing them would produce erection. He took them to bed with him although he never touched his genitals with them. His pollutions henceforth were accompanied by dreams of roses. He would dream of roses of fairy-like beauty and, inhaling their fragrance, have ejaculation.
>
> He became secretly engaged to his "lady of roses," but the platonic relations grew colder, and when the engagement was broken off the rose-fetishism suddenly and permanently disappeared. It never returned, even when he again became engaged after a long spell of melancholia.

Homosexuality was another of Krafft-Ebing's four major categories of variation; he called it "antipathic sexual instinct" and described many cases among women as well as men. In one sense the homosexual is closer to the Victorian norm than is the fetishist; for at least the sexually arousing object is a human being rather than a handkerchief with a black border or violet stripes. Here are two of his cases:

> *Case 156.* S. J., age thirty-eight, governess. Came to me for medical advice on account of nervous trouble. . . . From the earliest youth she was subject to sexual excitement and spontaneously practiced masturbation. At the age of fourteen she began to menstruate. . . . With the age of eighteen she gave up masturbation successfully.
>
> The patient never experienced an inclination towards a person of the opposite sex. Marriage to her only meant to find a home. But she was mightily drawn to girls. At first she considered this affection merely friendship, but she soon recognized from the intensity of her love for girl friends and her

deep longings for their constant society that it meant more than mere friendship.

To her it is inconceivable that a girl could love a man, although she can comprehend the feeling of man toward woman. She always took the deepest interest in pretty girls and ladies, the sight of whom caused her intense excitement. Her desire was ever to embrace and kiss these dear creatures. She never dreamed of men, always of girls only. To revel in looking at them was the acme of pleasure. Whenever she lost a "girl friend" she felt in despair.

Patient claimed that she never felt in a defined role, even in her dreams, towards her girl friends. In appearance she was thoroughly feminine and modest. Feminine pelvis, large mammae, no indication of beard.

Case 135. V., age twenty-nine, official; father hypochrondiac, mother neuropathic; four other children normal; one sister homosexual.

V. was very talented, learned easily and had a most excellent religious education. Very nervous and emotional. At the age of nine he began to masturbate of his own accord. When fourteen he recognized the danger of this practice and fought with some success against it; but he began to rave about male statuary, also about young men. When puberty set in he took slight interest in women. At twenty, first coitus . . . but though potent, he derived no satisfaction from it. Afterward only *faute de mieux* (about six times) heterosexual intercourse.

He admitted to have had very frequently intercourse with men. . . . He took either the active or passive role.

At the consultation he was in despair and wept bitterly. He abhorred his sexual anomaly, and said that he had desperately battled against it, but without success. In woman he found only moderate animal satisfaction, psychical gratification being totally absent. Yet he craved for the happiness of family life.

Excepting an abnormally broad pelvis (100 cm.) there was nothing in his character or personal appearance that lacked the qualities of the masculine type.

Along with these homosexual cases, Krafft-Ebing similarly presented case histories of transvestites (men or women who feel an urge to dress in the clothes of the opposite sex) and transsexuals (men and women who feel an urge to be transformed into the other sex, including a change in sexual organs). He mistakenly assumed that these are all successive stages in a single disease, antipathic sexual instinct. (For current views, see Chapter 7.)

Sadism was another main category or variation reviewed in *Psychopathia Sexualis*. It may be defined as sexual arousal and orgasm from inflicting pain. This, Krafft-Ebing most generously illustrated with a broad selection of case histories ranging from the most brutal "lust murders," accompanied by the butchering of the corpses, to such relatively mild examples as the following:

Case 38. D, agent, age twenty-nine years, family heavily tainted, masturbation at the age of fourteen, coitus at twenty, but without pronounced desire or satisfaction, thereafter masturbation preferred. At first these acts were accompanied by the thought of a girl whom he could maltreat and subject to humiliating and infamous actions.

Reading of acts of violence on women excited him sexually. But he did not like to see blood either on himself or others. He hated the sight of a naked woman.

He never felt inclined to put his sadistic ideas into actual practice for he disliked unnatural sexual intercourse.

He could not account for his sadistic ideas. These statements he made at a consultation for neurasthenia.

Women as well as men, Krafft-Ebing noted, may be sadistic:

Case 48. A married man presented himself with numerous scars of cuts on his arms. He told their origin as follows. When he wished to approach his wife, who was young and somewhat "nervous," he first had to make a cut in his arm. Then she would suck the wound and during the act become violently excited sexually.

Krafft-Ebing's fourth major category, masochism, he defined as "the opposite of sadism. While the latter is the desire to inflict pain and use force, the former is the desire to suffer pain and be subjected to force." Like sadism, masochism is found in both men and women. An example:

Case 54. A patient of Tarnowsky's had a person in his confidence rent a brothel during his attacks, and instruct its personnel (three prostitutes) in what was to be done with him. Whenever he came there he was undressed, manustuprated and flagellated as ordered. He pretended to offer resistance, and begged for mercy; then, as ordered, he was allowed to eat and sleep. But in spite of protest he was kept there, and beaten if he did not submit. Thus the affair would go on for some days. When the attack was over he was dismissed, and he returned to his wife and children, who had no suspicion of his disease. The attacks occurred once or twice a year.

Krafft-Ebing noted, however, that in many cases of masochism the actual suffering of pain was involved only incidentally or not at all. One masochist, for example, reported that women, "no matter how ugly, always excited him sexually whenever he discovered anything domineering in their character. An angry word from the lips of such a woman was sufficient to give him the most violent erections. Thus one day he sat in a café and heard the (ugly) female cashier scold the waiters in a loud voice. This threw him into the most intense sexual excitement, which soon induced ejaculation. Z. required the women with whom he was to have sexual intercourse to repulse and annoy him in various ways." Other masochists are actually concerned with *bondage* rather than pain; they are aroused by thinking of themselves as enslaved to a person of the other sex. Still others seek to be degraded or debased by the partner — demanding, for example, that a woman urinate on them before they can become sexually aroused.

In addition to these four major categories, *Psychopathia Sexualis* presents cases of satyriasis and nymphomania (excessive sexual desire in men and in women); exhibitionism and voyeurism (sexual arousal from exhibiting one's own body or from viewing the bodies or the sexual activities of others); zoophilia (sexual acts with animals), kleptolagnia (sexual arousal through stealing); sexual arousal stimulated by urination or defecation; and what might today be called Lolitaism (sexual arousal in relations with young girls approaching or experiencing puberty). Relatively few variations of sexual response are known today which cannot be found in Krafft-Ebing; and all of Krafft-Ebing's examples have their counterparts today.

The author of this comprehensive work had, of course, devoted his life to the study of such phenomena. He was the oldest of four children born into the aristocratic Krafft-Ebing family in Mannheim, Germany, and he inherited the German title of *Freiherr,* translatable as baron. His mother was a Mittermaier, the daughter of a renowned Heidelberg lawyer. Young Richard lived with the Mittermaiers during his university studies at Heidelberg; and he promptly developed an intense interest in the criminal cases involving deviant sexual behavior with which his maternal grandfather was concerned. This interest led him to study medicine and to qualify as a neurologist and psychiatrist. For the rest of his life he served as "alienist" — psychiatric consultant — to the courts of Germany and Austria; on many occasions he was also called as an expert witness on sexual crimes by the courts of other countries. He became professor of psychiatry at the German University of Strassburg at the remarkably early age of twenty-nine, and published an influential textbook on the legal aspects of insanity when he was only thirty-five. The work on which his fame chiefly rests, *Psychopathia Sexualis,* first appeared when he was forty-six; revised editions and translations poured from the presses of many countries throughout his lifetime, and continue to appear today.

Krafft-Ebing married late in life, and had two sons and a daughter. Beyond that I have found no surviving record of his personal life, tastes, or sexual predilections. A careful reading of his works reveals not a single form of sexual behavior concerning which he displayed any sympathy, personal interest, or personal knowledge. His rejection of sexuality was very nearly complete. Certainly no hint of scandal touched him. For the last ten years of his life he held what was generally considered "the most important professorship of psychiatry in the world" — at the University of Vienna. There, we are told, "honors and recognition were showered upon him, not only by his own country, but by many professional bodies and associations abroad."

Yet for the history of sex research, Richard von Krafft-Ebing represented an unmitigated disaster. An untold proportion of the confusion which continues to surround the subject of sexual variation today stems directly from his writings.

Consider, for example, your personal reaction to newspaper headlines such as these:

RAPIST SLAYS CHILDREN, 6 AND 8;
MUTILATED BODIES FOUND IN SEWER

NUDE MODEL STRANGLED
IN BATHTUB: ESCAPED
MENTAL PATIENT SOUGHT

Such stories arouse horror, of course, and we hasten to buy the paper in order to read the gruesome details. But our horror does not stop there. It spills over from these ghastly lust murders and other bloodcurdling phenomena — sexual intercourse with corpses, cannibalism, sexual arousal from the eating of excrement — to the relatively harmless sexual variations which Krafft-Ebing described as if they were all on a par — the collector of violet-striped handkerchiefs, the man who loved to smell roses, the girl who longed to kiss and embrace other girls. There can be little doubt that Krafft-Ebing sought deliberately to achieve this confusion; but even if he didn't seek it, he certainly did achieve it.

He accomplished this in part by the order in which he presented his material. Instead of starting with a relatively unthreatening phenomenon such as fetishism, as I have done above, he presented the milder variations against a background of the most horrifying case histories he could find — lust murders accompanied by butchery and even cannibalism. Here are three of the early cases which he used to set the stage for a generalized rejection of all sexual variation:

Case 15. A four-year-old girl was missing from her parents' home, 15 April, 1880. On April 16th, Menesclou, one of the occupants of the house, was arrested. The forearm of the child was found in his pocket, and the head and entrails, in a half-charred condition, were taken from the stove. Other parts of the body were found in the water-closet. The genitals could not be found. . . . The circumstances, as well as an obscene poem found on his person, left no doubt that he had violated the child and then murdered her. M. expressed no remorse, asserting that his deed was an unhappy accident.

. . . Convulsions at the age of nine months. Later he suffered from disturbed sleep; was nervous, and developed tardily and imperfectly. With puberty he became irritable, showed evil inclinations, was lazy, intractable, and in all trades proved to be of no use. He grew no better even in the House of Correction. He was made a Marine, but there, too, he proved useless. When he returned home he stole from his parents, and spent his time in bad company. He did not run after women, but gave himself up passionately to masturbation, and occasionally indulged in sodomy with dogs. His mother suffered from *mania menstrualis periodica.* An uncle was insane, and another a drunkard. The examination of M.'s brain [after his execution] showed morbid changes of the frontal lobes, of the first and second temporal convolutions, and of a part of the occipital convolutions.

Case 16. Alton, a clerk in England, went for a walk out of town. He lured a child into a thicket. Afterward at his office he made this entry in his notebook: "Killed today a young girl; it was fine and hot." The child was missed, searched for, and found cut into pieces. Many parts, and among them the genitals, could not be found. A. did not show the slightest trace of emotion, and gave no explanation of the motive or circumstances of his horrible deed. He was a psychopathic individual, and occasionally subject to fits of depression with *taedium vitae*. A near relative suffered from mania with homicidal impulses. A. was executed.

Case 22. A certain Gruyo, aged forty-one, with a blameless past life, having been three times married, strangled six women in the course of ten years. They were almost all public prostitutes and quite old. After the strangling he tore out the intestines and kidneys *per vaginam*. Some of his victims he violated before killing; others, on account of the occurrence of impotence, he did not. He set about his horrible deeds with such care that he remained undetected for ten years.

Of these many lust murders, Krafft-Ebing himself described as "the most horrible" the case of one Andreas Bichel, who violated little girls, killed them, and butchered them. "With reference to one of his victims, on his examination he expressed himself as follows: 'I opened her breast and with a knife cut through the fleshy parts of the body. Then I arranged the body as a butcher does beef, and hacked it with an axe into pieces of a size to fit the hole which I had dug up in the mountain for burying it. I may say that while opening the body I was so greedy that I trembled, and could have cut out a piece and eaten it."

Having thus stretched his readers' terror, disgust, and contempt to their utmost, Krafft-Ebing went on to review in much the same tone the cases of the fetishists attracted to white kid gloves or high-heeled shoes, the cases of masochists who liked women to tread on them, and the cases of homosexuals attracted to partners of their own sex.

From our horror at the details of lust murder it is but a step to horror at all sexual variations, and then but another step to horror at all manifestations of sexuality. Krafft-Ebing does his best to lead us down those steps.

He rightly points out, for example, that even the simplest and most harmless acts of sexual love are related to aberrations. He notes that it is not uncommon for husband and wife during sexual foreplay or intercourse to "strike, bite, or pinch each other." He notes that kissing sometimes "degenerates into biting. Lovers and young married couples are fond of teasing each other; they wrestle together 'just for fun,' and indulge in all sorts of horseplay." Havelock Ellis in his treatment of precisely this subject used such examples to help his readers understand from their own experience the more extreme pathological forms which these impulses sometimes take in others. Krafft-Ebing, in contrast, uses these commonplace examples to arouse forebodings of the most terrible kind. The simple tussling and the gentle love bite, he warns, may be a prelude to lust murder. "The transition from these atavistic manifestations to the most monstrous acts . . . can be readily traced."

But it was in his insistence on masturbation as a factor in the development of all sexual deviations from fetishism and homosexuality to lust murder that Krafft-Ebing accomplished the most harm. Indeed, for Krafft-Ebing masturbation becomes the soil out of which all of the sexual variations seem to grow. Against the background of the lust murders, for example, he tells the story of "a girl eight years old, who was devoid of all childlike and moral feelings, and who had masturbated from her fourth year; at the same time she consorted with boys of ten or twelve. She had thought of killing her parents, that she might become her own mistress and give herself up to pleasure with men."

In such cases, Krafft-Ebing generalizes — without a shred of evidence — "the children begin early to masturbate; and since they are greatly disposed constitutionally, they often sink into dementia, or become subjects of severe degenerative neuroses or psychoses." These evils, moreover, may be visited upon subsequent generations as well. Thus one young girl who began to masturbate at eight "continued to practice masturbation when married, and even during pregnancy. She was pregnant twelve times. Five of the children died early, four were hydrocephalic, and two boys began to masturbate — one at the age of seven, the other at the age of four." The outcome of the twelfth pregnancy he did not record.

Even heroic measures, Krafft-Ebing stressed, could not deter these children from their obstinately degenerate behavior. Thus he tells what he calls "the disgusting story" of a girl who began to masturbate at seven, taught her sister to masturbate also, and "at the age of ten was given up to the most revolting vices. Even a white-hot iron applied to the clitoris had no effect in overcoming the practice."

Sexual manifestations in old age, like sexual manifestations in children, Krafft-Ebing viewed with dire suspicion. His message may be simply paraphrased: beware of sexuality in your parents as well as in your children and your neighbors. Even though an old man may appear honorable and rational in all other respects, the appearance of sexual desire should warn you against him, for sexual desire "may be the precursor of senile dementia, and may make its appearance long before there are any other manifestations of intellectual weakness." The aftermath can prove disastrous. "A lustful old man killed his daughter out of jealousy and took delight in the dying girl's wounded breast."

No useful purpose would be served by prolonging this discussion of Krafft-Ebing. Indeed, this whole chapter might have been omitted altogether were it not for a distressing circumstance. Krafft-Ebing's *Psychopathia Sexualis* is still amazingly popular in bookstores and from mail-order houses in many countries. Two typical advertisements from 1969 American mail-order book circulars follow:

> Krafft-Ebing's *Psychopathia Sexualis*. 624 pages. Startling case histories of unnatural sex practices, weird auto-erotic methods, sex — lust — torture — much, much more! Many of the hundreds of sex case histories are from secret files and hushed-up court proceedings. Monstrous strange, almost unbelievable sex acts! For mature adults only! $1

> *Psychopathia Sexualis* [by] Richard von Krafft-Ebing. Nearly every book ever written about abnormal sex has used this book as a reference. It is presented here, for the first time, in its complete unexpurgated and authoritative translation into English. Previous editions had important phrases and paragraphs in Latin or French, but this classic edition is now entirely in modern English. Orig. published at $10.00. Hardbound collectors edition — Over 400 pages. $5.49

Some physicians still keep a copy of Krafft-Ebing on their shelves and refer to it on occasion. Two new editions were published in the United States in 1965. Both carried new introductions by reputable psychiatrists — introductions which casually conceded that perhaps Krafft-Ebing was a little out of date, but which failed to alert readers sufficiently to the deeply damaging nonsense (such as the alleged relation between childhood masturbation, lust murder, and homosexuality) with which his pages are filled. The cauterization of a little girl's clitoris with a white-hot iron has gone out of style, but the ideas which provoked such savagery still circulate widely.

In subsequent chapters I shall present the saner attitudes toward sexual variations developed by subsequent researchers.

3

The Child as Father of the Man

Sigmund Freud (1856–1939)

ONE of the many contributions to modern thought made by Sigmund Freud (1856–1939), the founder of psychoanalysis, was the concept of ambivalence. It is a mistake, Freud taught, to believe that the small child who exhibits love for a parent does not also hate that parent. Similarly we adults do not merely love or merely hate the significant figures in our lives — our wives and husbands, mistresses and lovers, employers, political leaders, psychoanalysts. Rather, all such emotionally charged relationships are compounded of simultaneous love and hostility in varying proportions. We may *think* that we are experiencing pure love or pure hate; but deeper analysis reveals that the opposite emotion is also present. It may be banished from the conscious mind — repressed; but it survives and continues to function in the unconscious.

The present chapter clearly illustrates this Freudian concept of ambivalence. I both love and hate Sigmund Freud. I view his doctrines with admiration tinged with awe — yet also with distrust and even contempt. To illustrate, let me briefly summarize a typical psychoanalytic theory: Freud's explanation of fetishism.

By fetishism, Freud meant exactly what Ellis, Krafft-Ebing and others had meant — the sexual arousal of certain males* by some object such as a shoe, foot, underclothing, or handkerchief, or by objects made of some material such as velvet or fur, rather than by living women. Freud had treated a number of typical fetishists during his half-century of practice

* Very few cases of female fetishism have been reported.

as a psychoanalyst. He presented his mature explanation of the phenomenon in a paper which he published in 1927, when he was seventy-one.

"In all the cases," he wrote, "the meaning and purpose of the fetish turned out under analysis to be the same. It revealed itself so unequivocally and seemed to me so categorical that I should expect the same solution in all cases of fetishism." In simple words, "the fetish is a penis-substitute." It is not however, "a substitute for any chance penis, but for a particular quite special penis that had been extremely important in early childhood but was afterward lost. . . . To put it plainly: the fetish is a substitute for the woman's (mother's) phallus which the little boy once believed in and does not wish to forego."

Three factors are involved, Freud declared, in this selection of a fetish as a substitute for the mother's penis. First, the little boy aged three or four values his own penis very highly as a source of sexual gratification. Second, he has an unconscious fear that his father will cut off his penis to punish him for masturbating or for some other offense. (Freud called this the "castration complex," though castration usually means cutting off the testicles rather than the penis.) Finally, the little boy assumes, in the absence of evidence to the contrary, that females as well as males have these treasured appendages.

In such circumstances, the little boy's sudden discovery that his mother, or some other female, does *not* have a penis leads to disastrous consequences. The boy leaps to the unconscious conclusion that someone — perhaps his father — has cut off his mother's penis. Thus the experience reinforces his own castration fear. The little boy, Freud explained, "no longer ventures to doubt that his own genitals may meet with the same fate. Thenceforward he cannot help believing in the reality of the danger of castration."

Nor is this a rare experience among a few unfortunate little boys. "Probably no male human being," Freud bluntly asserted, "is spared the terrifying shock of threatened castration at the sight of the female genitals."

One natural consequence of this "terrifying shock" is that little boys develop a horror of the female pubic region — that gruesome reminder of the awful threat that hangs over them. In later years this unconsciously motivated dread may lead to homosexuality as a means of avoiding altogether any sight of or contact with the loathed female genitalia.

The little boys who grow up to be fetishists react in a different way to the same traumatic experience. They "ward off" the abhorrent sight by concentrating instead on the object which occupied their attention a moment before the castrated female genitals came into view. This prior object thus takes on a very special significance and becomes the fetish.

"We cannot explain," Freud conceded, "why it is that some [boys] become homosexual in consequence of this experience, others ward it off by creating a fetish, and the great majority overcome it. . . . We must be satisfied when we can explain what has happened, and may for the present leave on one side the task of explaining why something has *not* happened."

The heart of Freud's theory, however, was its ability to explain why one boy becomes a shoe fetishist and another a handkerchief fetishist. It all depends on "the last impression received before the uncanny traumatic one" — the sight of the castrated female. "Thus the foot or shoe owes its attraction as a fetish, or part of it, to the circumstance that the inquisitive boy used to peer up the woman's legs toward her genitals. Velvet and fur reproduce — as has long been suspected — the sight of the pubic hair which ought to have revealed the longed-for penis; the underlinen so often adopted as a fetish reproduces the scene of undressing, the last moment in which the woman could still be regarded as phallic."

Krafft-Ebing once remarked, after hearing Freud propound an explanation of the sexual origin of hysteria, "It sounds like a scientific fairy tale." Many readers may be tempted to echo that comment here. Yet Freud's explanation of fetishism has a haunting attraction, even for skeptics.

Surely the fetishist whose lust is aroused by a handkerchief with violet stripes did not *inherit* this particular predilection. Nor did he *learn* it in the usual way — by trial and error, or through a series of rewarded experiences. *Something* must have happened to him at some crucial and unique moment in his life, something which in some sense or other "imprinted" the fetish on him. And since in adult life he retains no recollection of the imprinting event, the suspicion arises that it *must* have occurred in early childhood. How else, moreover, can the curious fact be explained that there are no (or very few) female fetishists? Thus even readers who scorn the details of Freud's "scientific fairy tale" must concede that there may, after all, be a little something of value in it.

It is this "little something of value," as we shall see, which leads even ardent anti-Freudians to reveal a curious ambivalence toward his views, and to make use of Freudian concepts in the very act of rejecting his theories.

Havelock Ellis, you will recall, stressed two major insights into human sexuality: *Everyone is not like you, your loved ones, and your friends and neighbors;* and *your loved ones, friends, and neighbors are not as much like you as you commonly suppose.* To these Freud added a third: *Deep down inside, your own personal sexuality is not at all what you suppose it to be.* Your infantile love, hate, and fear of your parents, your infantile fear of castration if you are a man, your infantile envy of the penis if you are a woman, and countless other feelings, fantasies, and experiences left over from early childhood, survive in your unconscious, to mold both your feelings and your behavior throughout your adult life.

Freud reached his startling opinions by a long and arduous road.

"I was born on May 6th, 1856, at Freiburg in Moravia, a small town in what is now Czechoslovakia," he wrote in *An Autobiographical Study.* "My parents were Jews, and I remained a Jew myself. . . . When I was a child of four I came to Vienna, and I went through the whole of my education there. At the 'Gymnasium' I was at the top of my class for seven years; I enjoyed special privileges there, and was required to pass scarcely any examinations. Although we lived in very limited circumstances, my father insisted that, in my choice of a profession, I should follow my own inclinations."

Freud chose to become a scientist, and during his twenties, at the University of Vienna, he made a number of contributions to anatomy and physiology, based mostly on the microscopic study of nerve cells. He took an M.D. degree when he was twenty-five as an almost incidental milestone on his path toward laboratory research.

At twenty-six, however, Freud fell in love with a cousin, Martha Bernays — and belatedly faced up to the fact that he could not afford to support a wife and family on the pittance available for laboratory work at the university. During the four stressful years of engagement to Martha that followed, the two were separated most of the time by hundreds of miles. They were married in 1886, when Freud was thirty, and he reluctantly hung out his shingle as a physician in private practice, specializing in neurological diseases.

Few of the patients who came to his waiting room were suffering from the specific nerve conditions which his university training had prepared him to treat. Rather, like other neurologists then and now, he found himself consulted primarily by neurotics — men and women whose symptoms were compounded of "nervousness," anxiety, frustration, phobias, obsessions, compulsions, and emotional conflicts, often accompanied by vague or shifting headaches, stomachaches, backaches, tinglings, dizziness, nausea, vomiting, diarrhea, constipation, breathing difficulties, and countless other bodily afflictions for which no plausible physical explanation could be found. These neurotic patients, in accordance with the medical custom of the time, Freud at first divided into two major categories: the neurasthenics and the hysterics.

The neurasthenics, Freud readily concluded, were masturbators. In this he was following a familiar tradition. One symptom of neurasthenia is a feeling of weakness or debilitation; the French authority Tissot nearly a century earlier had announced his finding that the loss of one ounce of semen through masturbation was as debilitating as the loss of forty ounces of blood. Krafft-Ebing and others had in addition attributed to masturbation a long list of other diseases. Freud accordingly concluded that persuading patients to stop masturbating might cure their neurasthenia. He reported some successes. When persuasion failed, he did not hesitate to resort to stronger measures. Thus one adolescent girl, on Freud's prescription, was placed under prolonged round-the-clock surveillance so that she would have no privacy for masturbation.

Not all cases of neurasthenia, however, could be explained or cured in this way. Some male neurasthenics insisted, despite Freud's skepticism, that involuntary nocturnal emissions of semen were their only sexual outlet. This led Freud to the same conclusion announced a generation earlier in France by l'Allemand and in England by Drysdale: nocturnal emissions must be as damaging as masturbation, and must lead to the same baleful results.

Thus Freud's patients, like Drysdale's, were caught between the Scylla of masturbation and the Charybdis of nocturnal emissions. The almost suicidal despair induced in the adolescent Havelock Ellis when he stumbled upon the same doctrine in Drysdale's book has been noted above. (Let me assure any adolescents who may happen upon this book that all this is utter nonsense, as they will learn in later chapters. Indeed, though Freud continued to hold this dismal view of masturbation and nocturnal emissions until 1925, when he was sixty-nine, he abandoned the view in 1926.)

For yet another group of patients ordinarily diagnosed as neurasthenics, Freud found that the symptoms could be explained neither by masturbation nor by nocturnal emissions. Some of these patients were chaste and in love, perhaps engaged to be married. Others were already married or were engaging in nonmarital intercourse, but were practicing *coitus interruptus* — withdrawal of the penis from the vagina prior to ejaculation — as a form of birth control. Freud concluded that these patients were not in fact neurasthenic as had been supposed. They suffered instead from a previously undiagnosed condition centering around anxiety and featuring acute anxiety attacks; Freud named this syndrome *anxiety neurosis.* (He had initially diagnosed his own difficulties during his long and stressful engagement to Martha Bernays as neurasthenia, but later decided that they were anxiety attacks.) Anxiety neurosis, Freud concluded, is caused by repeated experiences of sexual arousal terminating in frustration rather than fulfillment. He also believed that intercourse with a condom produced a tendency toward anxiety neurosis, but he deemed condoms less harmful than withdrawal prior to orgasm. He cited no evidence for these views except his own limited clinical experience.

To illustrate his approach to the diagnosis of what he called "the actual neuroses" — those due to current sexual practices — Freud reported the case of a young neurasthenic who had been sent by another physician to a hydropathic sanitarium in the hope that rest and bathing in medicinal waters would relieve his symptoms. "In this establishment his condition at first improved so much that he was justifiably expected soon to depart, as a grateful convert to hydrotherapeutic methods. In the sixth week a change occurred; the patient 'couldn't stand the water any longer,' became more and more nervous, and finally left the establishment after two more weeks, dissatisfied and unrelieved of his trouble." On his return to Vienna, the patient came to Freud for help.

Freud asked a few questions concerning the precise nature of the original symptoms — and of the symptoms which had developed during the course of treatment. "He had come to the sanitorium complaining of cranial pressure, lassitude, and dyspepsia; the disturbances in the course of the treatment had been excitement, attacks of dyspnea, locomotor vertigo, and troubled sleep."

These were the only clues Freud needed. The initial symptoms were neurasthenic; the subsequent ones indicated anxiety neurosis. Freud accordingly proceeded to enlighten his patient concerning the causes of his difficulties.

"You fell ill, as you know, on account of long-continued masturbation," Freud began. "In the sanitarium you gave up this form of gratification and therefore improved rapidly. But when you felt well you unwisely sought the company of a lady, let us say one of your fellow-patients, and started a relationship with her which without normal satisfaction could only lead to excitement. The beautiful walks in the neighborhood of the institution gave you many opportunities. Your relapse is due to this relationship, not to a sudden inability to tolerate hydrotherapy. From your present condition I should conclude, by the way, that you are continuing this relationship here in town as well." And Freud's account of the case concluded: "I can assure the reader that the patient confirmed my supposition point by point."

Freud was thus well on his way to an important insight. Going one step farther than Krafft-Ebing, who viewed human sexuality as a collection of loathsome diseases, Freud was gradually reaching the conclusion that sex is the cause of diseases which do not at first blush appear sexual at all. And he applied the same approach to the other very large class of neurotics who came to him for treatment — the hysterics.

Since no *current* sexual practice could be incriminated in their illness, Freud — following clues provided by one of his teachers, Jean-Martin Charcot of Paris, and by his Viennese friend and associate, Josef Breuer — began to explore the memories of these hysterical patients in a search for traumatic *past* experiences. In many of these early cases Freud hypnotized the patients in order to bring to consciousness memories which could not otherwise be recaptured.

Soon his hysterical patients were obligingly bringing to the surface traumatic sexual factors of the kind Freud sought. Freud published several examples in *Studies of Hysteria* (1895). In the case of Fräulein Lucie R., a young Englishwoman employed as a governess, it turned out that she had years before been in love with her employer — a love she could not consciously face until aided by Freud's analysis. Thereafter her symptoms improved. Fräulein Elisabeth von R. was quite similar; she improved when Freud revealed to her the fact that she had long loved her sister's husband.

The case of Fräulein Katherina came a little closer to Freud's later views. Katherina was a young waitress at a resort in the Alps; and while serving his meal one day she asked Freud if he could help her with her breathing difficulties — "sometimes it catches me so that I believe I am choking." Close questioning revealed that Katherina's uncle had made attempts to seduce her when she was fourteen, attempts which she did not at the time recognize as sexual. Then, at the age of seventeen, Katherina had accidentally seen her uncle through a window, in bed with another of his nieces. Her symptoms had set in soon thereafter. She breathed more easily after this revelation.

In the fourth published case, that of Frau Emmy von M., Freud conceded that he found no overtly sexual factor; but he nevertheless concluded that there must be one. The patient was very modest, and had no doubt held back the sexual portions of her life story.

By 1895, when these cases were published, however, Freud already felt dissatisfied with such relatively superficial explanations of hysteria, and was trying to push his patients' recollections farther and farther back into early childhood. In this effort he began to use the characteristic method of psychoanalysis which he called "free association." Patients lay stretched out and relaxed on a couch, with Freud sitting a little behind them, out of their line of sight. They were instructed to report "whatever came to mind" — no matter how trivial or irrelevant the random thought might seem to be, and no matter how objectionable or embarrassing it might be. Eventually the chain of associations thus evoked might stretch back to the child's second or third year. And there Freud found at last an explanation of hysteria that satisfied him. *In every case,* he reported, *these hysteric patients recalled a scene of seduction or of sexual assault made upon them in very early childhood.*

Decades might elapse between the infantile sexual trauma and the onset of hysterical symptoms — years during which the memory of the experience was wholly repressed until revived by psychoanalysis. Yet Freud thought the connection between the early assault and the later symptoms was undeniable, for the nature of the assault *determined* the nature of the symptoms. "Thus in one of my cases," Freud reported in 1896, "the circumstances that the child was required to stimulate the genitals of an adult woman with his foot sufficed for years to fix neurotic attention on the legs and their functions, and finally to produce an hysterical paraplegia [paralysis of the legs]."

The assaults were often heterosexual but occasionally homosexual;

and often it was the child's mouth or anus which was sexually abused — leading in adult life to such symptoms as "painful bladder pressure, painful sensations in defecation, intestinal disturbances, choking and vomiting, indigestion and nausea." Sometimes a stranger, nursemaid, or other attendant perpetrated the assault; but when the victim was a little girl, Freud found, the attacker was almost always her own father.

Freud presented these views, in slightly expurgated form — he neglected to mention that the father was usually the little girl's seducer — at a meeting of the Society of Psychiatry and Neurology in Vienna on May 2, 1896. The effect on his fellow psychiatrists and neurologists may be imagined. Many of their own patients, of course, were hysterics; indeed, there were those who saw at least a touch of hysteria in everyone. The number of sexual seductions and assaults on small children needed to account for the widespread prevalence of the disease must have leaped to mind. And the audience must also have shuddered at Freud's statement that, while most of these sexual assaults were made upon two- and three-year-olds, one-year-olds were not immune from them.

Professor Krafft-Ebing was chairman of the meeting, and it was on this occasion that he made the comment quoted above, "It sounds like a scientific fairy tale."

Freud held his ground. "I believe this to be a momentous revelation, the discovery of a *caput Nili* of neuropathology," he wrote at the time to a friend, Dr. Wilhelm Fliess of Berlin.

Even the realization that his own brother and several of his sisters showed hysterical symptoms did not shake Freud's faith. As he wrote Fliess in February, 1897, this led to the conclusion that Freud's own father had perhaps engaged in homosexual and heterosexual practices with his children.

Further confirmation appeared in a dream one night in May, 1897. Freud was then just beginning to include the interpretation of dreams among his psychoanalytic methods — a major feature of his later technique — and he dreamed one night about his niece Hella. He interpreted this dream as masking an incestuous desire for one of his own daughters — and he wrote Fliess on May 13 that he considered this a further verification of his theory. The fact that fathers have such desires made it easier for him to believe that fathers often sexually assault their very young daughters.

Four months later, however, Freud abruptly abandoned the theory on which he had publicly staked his career. Krafft-Ebing had been right; those infantile seductions and assaults had never in fact occurred.

"If the reader feels inclined to shake his head at my credulity," Freud wrote forty years later, "I cannot altogether blame him; though I may plead that this was at a time when I was intentionally keeping my critical faculty in abeyance so as to preserve an unprejudiced and receptive attitude toward the many novelties which were coming to my notice every day. . . . However, I was at last obliged to recognize that these scenes of seduction had never taken place, and that they were only fantasies which my patients had made up or which I myself had perhaps forced upon them."

Yet there remained that same "little something of value" in Freud's abandoned fairy tale. Children really do have sexual desires, sexual experiences, and sexual fantasies. Where Freud (like his entire generation) had initially erred was in supposing that babies are born asexual and remain sexually inert until puberty. Instead, as he learned a little later, even two- and three-year-olds are tiny bundles of sexual energy. Most of the remainder of Freud's life was to be devoted to the intensive study of the impact of prepubertal sexuality on adult life.

Havelock Ellis, however, preceded Freud in this respect. Beginning in 1894, Ellis published a series of articles on homosexuality in English, German, and Italian journals. These were later collected in book form — in German in 1896 and in English the following year. Here are some excerpts from Ellis illustrating prepubertal sexuality, all in boys and girls who later became homosexual, and all published in German in 1896 or earlier:

> *Case XVII, male.* Soon after 5 he became so enamored of a young shepherd that the boy had to be sent away. He practiced masturbation long before the age of puberty. . . .

> *Case XXV, male.* Sexual consciousness awoke before the age of 8, when his attention was directed to his own penis. His nurse, while out walking with him one day, told him that when little boys grow up their penes fall off. The nursemaid sniggered, and he felt that there must be something peculiar about the penis. . . . About the same time he became subject to curious half-waking dreams. In these he imagined himself the servant of several adult naked sailors; he crouched between their thighs and called himself their dirty pig, and by their orders he performed services for their

genitals and buttocks which he handled and contemplated with relish. [It was childhood imaginings such as this that Freud had confused with memories.]

Case XLII, female. At the age of 4 she liked to see the nates of a little girl who lived near. . . . Her first rudimentary sex-feelings appeared at the age of 8 or 9, and were associated with dreams of whipping and being whipped. . . . [This little girl, incidentally, was Edith Lees, who grew up to be Mrs. Havelock Ellis.]

Nor were such prepubertal sexual experiences a monopoly of children who later became homosexuals. Ellis collected similar accounts from heterosexual adults. Many of them have what today sounds like a Freudian ring, as the following excerpts from the series of "histories of sexual development" which Ellis published in 1903, will show:

History I, male. T.'s earliest recollections of ideas of a sexual character are vaguely associated with thoughts upon whipping inflicted upon companions by their parents, and sometimes upon his own person. At the age of 7, occasionally depicted to himself the appearance of the bare nates and genitalia of boys during flagellation. . . . The sight of a boy being whipped upon the bare nates caused erection before the age of 9. . . . T. knew a boy and girl of about his own age whose imaginations dwelt somewhat morbidly upon whipping. The three used to talk together about such chastisement, and the little girl liked to read "stories that had whippings in them."

History II, female. The first time I can remember feeling keen physical pleasure was when I was between 7 and 8 years old. I can't recollect the cause, but I remember lying quite still in my little cot clasping the iron rails at the top.

History IV, male. I can remember trotting away as a youngster about 5 with another boy to "see a girl's legs"; the idea emanated from the other boy, but I was vaguely interested. . . . When 6 or 7 I remember being put to bed with the nurse girl and feeling her bare arm with undoubted sexual excitement; I remember, too, gradually feeling along the arm very quietly, fearing the girl would awake, and being bitterly disappointed to find it was merely the arm.

History VII, male. About the age of 7, a German nursery governess, B., took charge of me, and I soon became devoted to her. . . . B. would sometimes take me into her bed and soothe me with kisses, etc. These I returned, and can remember that I was particularly fond of kissing her breasts.

Sometime later, probably when I was about 9, something led up to B. saying that she was not built like I was, that she had no penis, etc. . . . I was incredulous, and demanded to be allowed to see if it was true; this was refused, and I made many plans to gratify my curiosity, such as slipping into her room when she was dressing, tipping up the chair she was sitting in, and trying to thrust my hand up her skirts. I did not succeed. . . .

History VIII, female. When I was about 8 years old . . . with several other children, we used to play in an old garden at being father and mother, unfastening our drawers and bringing the sexual parts together, as we imagined married people to do, but no sexual feelings were aroused, nor did the boys have erections.

History X, female. The very first [sexual manifestation] was at the age of 6. I remember once sitting astride a bannister while my parents were waiting for me outside. I distinctly remember the pleasurable sensation. . . . From that year until the age of 10 I simply reveled in the idea of being tortured. I went gladly to bed every night to imagine myself a slave, chained, beaten, made to carry loads and to do ignominious work. One of my imaginings, I remember, was that I was chained to a moldering skeleton.

History XII, female. The first sensations which she now recognizes as sexual were experienced at the age of 3, when her mother gave her an injection [enema]; afterward she declared herself unable to relieve her bowels naturally, in order to obtain a repetition of this experience, which was several times repeated.

History XIII, male. When I was about 4 or 5, I was constantly chaffed by my older companions about putting my hand down my trousers and playing with my privates. I don't remember getting an erection, nor at what age this first occurred to me. At one time my brother and I used to play with my sister's underclothing, and took great pleasure in it, but we never saw her genitals. She told us that on carefully examining herself one day she was glad to find a small penis like boys had—doubtless the clitoris. When in France at the age of 8 to 10, I began to notice the sexual parts of animals and was very keen to know what mares kept between their hind legs. Later on I took great pleasure with another boy in feeling the teats of a she-ass, and, by myself, the penis of a donkey, as I had seen the French grooms do; but I took no interest in my own penis. I used to put my finger as far up the anus as it would go, and got a vague satisfaction from it.

History XV, male. Before or soon after I was 7 years old, the example of an older brother . . . initiated me into the mysteries of masturbation, which seemed to me then as harmless as it was fascinating; and the novel pleasure was almost daily indulged in. . . . Almost from the first [we practiced] fellatio and approximation of the organs . . . and it appeared to me quite as natural and as right for us to amuse ourselves together in that way as for a married couple.

History XVIII, male. My earliest recollection is of being punished for "playing with myself" when I could not have been more than 3 or 4 years of age. I distinctly remember my exultation on discovering that I could excite myself (while my hands were tied behind my back for punishment) by rubbing my small penis against the carpet while lying on my stomach. At this time, of course, I knew nothing of sex or of what I was doing. I did what my desires and instincts at that time prompted me to do. However, punishments and lectures failed utterly to break this habit, and, though I always wished and tried faithfully to obey my parents, I soon grew to indulge quietly in bed when I was thought to be asleep. . . . My recollection of the sensations is that there was a short period of excitation, usually by rubbing, which was not particularly, often not at all, pleasurable, and this was followed by a single thrill of pleasure that extended all over my little body. The curious thing was, however, that there seemed to be no limit to the number of times I could consecutively produce this sensation. My recollection is perfectly clear of how I would lie abed of a morning and thus excite myself time after time. As I grew older this condition, of course, changed. . . . I enjoyed it and felt that in it I had a means of entertainment when other sources of enjoyment were not at hand.

By the time I was 6 or 7, I had figured out the difference in sex in animals and suspected that "all was not as it should be" in some portions of a girl's anatomy. This suspicion was suddenly confirmed one never-to-be-forgotten morning when I induced my dearest play mate, a little girl, to urinate in my presence. I was more thunderstruck than excited over this discovery, and it led to no results in any other way, nor did we ever again unveil ourselves to each other.

In a word, Ellis's early "histories of sexual development" revealed in great detail not only the existence but also the varied nature of prepubertal sexuality in both boys and girls. Anal and oral eroticism, sadism and masochism, masturbation, exhibitionism and voyeurism, homosexual and heterosexual incest, even zoophilia — the whole long list of Krafft-Ebing's perversions was present long before puberty. Yet few of these children grew up to be "perverts" in Krafft-Ebing's sense. In a very telling phrase which Freud introduced a little later, and which he often stressed, all small children are by nature "polymorphously perverse."

Freud regarded his own discovery of childhood sexuality as one of the "principal findings" of psychoanalysis. He summarized these findings as follows:

> (a) Sexual life does not begin only at puberty, but starts with clear manifestations soon after birth.
>
> (b) It is necessary to distinguish sharply between the concepts of "sexual" and "genital." The former is the wider concept and includes many activities which have nothing to do with the genitals.
>
> (c) Sexual life comprises the function of obtaining pleasure from zones of the body [erogenous zones] — a function which is subsequently brought into the service of that of reproduction. The two functions often fail to coincide completely.

Freud reached these conclusions, however, along a route quite different from Ellis's. In 1897 he began to psychoanalyze himself; this practice he continued at intervals throughout his life. It was primarily through exploring his own memories, dreams, fantasies, slips of the tongue, and other cues to his own unconscious that Freud gained his initial insights into infantile sexuality and many other phenomena.

A vast body of psychoanalytic doctrine emerged from Freud's self-analysis, and from his subsequent analyses of the patients who flocked to Vienna from all over the world during the later years of his fame. Many of the concepts which he elaborated during those years have entered into our thinking and into the very fabric of our language: the ego, the id, and the superego, the conscious, the preconscious, and the unconscious, sexual energy (libido), erogenous zones, ambivalence, Narcissism (a term borrowed from Ellis), bisexuality (a concept he owed to Fliess), repression, resistance, transference, countertransference, fixation, wish fulfillment, regression, sublimation. But one concept, Freud himself insisted, stood at the heart of his entire doctrine. It arose directly out of his self-analysis, and it took the place of the assaults on small children central to his earlier theory. This was the Oedipus complex.

"I venture to assert," Freud wrote the year before he died, "that if psychoanalysis could boast of no other achievement than the discovery of the repressed Oedipus complex, that alone would give it a claim to be counted among the precious new acquisitions of mankind."

As a fair sample of his mature views in general, accordingly, let me present at some length Freud's account of the Oedipus complex, in his own words, and in the final form in which he cast his theory for his *Out-*

line of Psychoanalysis — written when he was eighty-three, and published after his death.

"A child's first erotic object is the mother's breast that feeds him," Freud began, "and love in its beginnings attaches itself to the satisfaction of the need for food. . . . This first [love] object subsequently becomes completed into the whole person of the child's mother, who not only feeds him but also looks after him and thus arouses in him many other physical sensations pleasant and unpleasant. By her care of the child's body she becomes his first seducer. In these two relations lies the root of a mother's importance, unique, without parallel, laid down unalterably for a whole lifetime, as the first and the strongest love-object and as the prototype of all later love relations — for both sexes."

The subsequent pattern of development, however, is different for boys and girls.

> When a boy, from about the age of two or three, enters upon the phallic phase of his libidinal development, feels pleasurable sensations in his sexual organ and learns to procure these at will by manual masturbation, he becomes his mother's lover. He desires to possess her physically in the ways which he has divined from his observations and intuitive surmises of sexual life, and tries to seduce her by showing her the male organ of which he is the proud owner. In a word, his early awakened masculinity makes him seek to assume, in relation to her, the place belonging to his father, who has hitherto been an envied model. . . . His father now becomes a rival who stands in his way and whom he would like to push aside. If when his father is absent he is able to share his mother's bed, and if when his father returns he is once more banished from it, his gratification when his father vanishes and his disappointment when he reappears are deeply felt experiences. This is the subject of the Oedipus complex, which Greek legend translated from the world of childhood phantasy into a pretended reality. Under the conditions of our civilization it is invariably doomed to a terrible end.

The boy's Oedipus complex by itself, Freud conceded, can sometimes be handled in ways which are not necessarily disastrous. But all too often the boy must master simultaneously both his Oedipus complex and his castration complex — described briefly above in my account of fetishism. Here is Freud's account of how the two complexes interact:

> The boy's mother understands quite well that his sexual excitement refers to her. Sooner or later she thinks to herself that it is wrong to allow this state of things to continue. She believes she is acting rightly in forbidding

him to manipulate his genitals. The prohibition has little effect and at the most brings about some modification in his method of self-gratification. At last his mother adopts the severest measures: she threatens to take away from him the thing he is defying her with. As a rule, in order to make the threat more terrifying and more credible, she delegates its carrying out to the boy's father, saying that she will tell him and that he will cut the penis off. Strangely enough, this threat only operates if another condition is fulfilled, either before or afterward. In itself it seems quite inconceivable to the boy that anything of the sort could happen. But if, when he is threatened, he is able to recall the appearance of female genitals, or if shortly afterward he has a glimpse of them — of genitals, that is to say, which really lack this supremely valued part, then he takes what he has heard seriously and, coming under the influence of the castration complex, experiences the severest trauma of his youthful existence.*

The effects of this trauma are tragic.

They affect the whole of a boy's relationship with his father and mother and subsequently with men and women in general. As a rule the child's masculinity is unable to stand up against this first shock. In order to preserve his sexual organs he gives up possession of his mother more or less completely; his sexual life often remains permanently under the weight of the prohibition. If a strong feminine component, as we put it, is in him, its strength is increased by the threat to his masculinity. He falls into a passive attitude to his father, of a kind such as he ascribes to his mother. It is true that as a result of the threat he has given up masturbation, but not the activities of his imagination accompanying it. On the contrary, since they are now the only form of sexual gratification remaining to him, he practices them more than ever, and in these fantasies, while he continues as before to identify himself with his father, he also does so, simultaneously and perhaps predominantly, with his mother. Derivatives and modified products of these early masturbatory fantasies usually make their way into his later ego, and play a part in the formation of his character. Apart from this encouragement of his femininity, fear and hatred of his father gain greatly in intensity. The boy's masculinity withdraws, as it were, into a defiant attitude toward his father, which in a compulsive fashion dominates his later behavior in human society. A residue of his erotic fixation to his mother is often left in the form of an excessive dependence upon her, and this persists as an attitude of subjection to women. He no longer ventures to love his mother, but he cannot risk not being loved by her, since in that case he would be in danger of being betrayed by her to his father and handed over to castration.

* Some analysts today add that the fear of castration may arise even in the absence of overt threats from parents.

This whole drama of love, hate, and renunciation, enacted at the age of three or four, is soon forgotten — that is, repressed. But "all of the contending emotional impulses and reactions . . . are preserved in the unconscious, ready to disturb the later development of the ego after puberty." Thence, as the boy with a castration complex matures, his "sexual life will be disclosed as inhibited, incoherent and fallen apart into mutually conflicting impulses."

To many readers, this may sound like yet another "scientific fairy tale" different from, yet strangely reminiscent of, Freud's earlier doctrine of infantile seduction and assault. Yet, once again, there is surely at least a germ of truth in it, visible even to the most skeptical. It really isn't a wise procedure, almost everyone must agree now that Freud has called it to our attention, to warn a three-year-old boy that his father will cut off his penis if he doesn't stop playing with it.

Meanwhile, what of little girls? "A female child has, of course, no need to fear the loss of a penis," Freud conceded; "she must, however, react to the fact of not having received one. From the very first she envies boys its possession; her whole development may be said to take place under the influence of her envy for the penis. She begins by making vain attempts to do the same as boys and later, with greater success, makes efforts to compensate herself for the defect — efforts which may lead in the end to a normal feminine attitude." There are pitfalls ahead, however. "If during the phallic phase [about the age of three] she attempts to get pleasure like a boy by the manual stimulation of her genitals, it often happens that she fails to obtain sufficient gratification and extends her judgment of inferiority from her stunted penis [clitoris] to her whole self. As a rule she soon gives up masturbating, since she does not wish to be reminded of the superiority of her brother or playmate, and turns away from sexuality altogether.

"If a little girl adheres to her first wish — to grow into a boy — in extreme cases she will end as a manifest homosexual, and in any event will show markedly masculine traits in the conduct of her later life, will choose a masculine vocation, and so on. The other road leads by way of an abandonment of the mother she has loved: the daughter, under the influence of her envy for the penis, cannot forgive her mother for having sent her into the world so insufficiently equipped." This blaming of the mother leads to the *feminine* form of the Oedipus complex — sometimes called the Electra complex. "In her resentment she gives her mother up and puts someone else in place of her as the object of her love — her father. . . . The little girl puts herself in her mother's place, as she has always done in her games; she tries to take her place with her father and begins to hate the mother whom she has hitherto loved. . . . Her new relation with her father may begin by having as its content a wish to have his penis at her command; but it culminates in another wish — to have a baby from him as a present. The wish for a baby takes the place of the wish for a penis or at all events branches off from it."

The male and female versions of the Oedipus complex are thus different but related. "In males, as we have seen, the threat of castration brings the Oedipus complex to an end; in females, on the contrary, we find that it is the effect of their lack of a penis that drives them into their Oedipus complex."

The survival of the Oedipus complex, however, does little harm to a woman. "She will in that case choose her husband for his paternal characteristics and will be ready to recognize his authority. Her longing to possess a penis, which is in fact unappeasable, may be satisfied if she can succeed in completing her love for the organ by extending it to the man who bears that organ, just as earlier she progressed from her mother's breast to the mother as a whole."

No man or woman, however naïve, approaches sex research naïvely — as I noted at the very beginning. Faced with theories like Freud's, we immediately seek to apply them to the history of sexual development we think we know best — our own. Freud fails this particular test. Few readers, I am sure, will respond to the passages I have quoted by crying out, "Exactly! That's just what happened to me when I was three years old!" Nor do parents generally recognize the applicability of the Freudian *schema* to their three-year-old children.

Freud, of course, had an explanation ready. The Oedipus complex, the castration complex, and penis envy are not only forgotten but *repressed;* and any effort to revive them in consciousness is strenuously *resisted.* Indeed, even in the course of a psychoanalysis, resistance makes the recovery of the Oedipus complex exceedingly difficult. "The whole occurrence, which may no doubt be regarded as the central experience of the years of childhood, the greatest problem of early life and the most important source of later inadequacy, is so completely forgotten that its reconstruction during the work of analysis is met by the adult's most determined skepticism. Indeed the objection to it is so great that it is sought to silence any mention of the tabooed subject, and the most obvious reminders of it are met with the strangest intellectual blindness."

But if this intellectual blindness prevents us from recognizing the truth of Freudian doctrines in our own lives (short of being psychoanalyzed ourselves), then how are we to judge of their validity? Freud discussed this problem and did not hesitate to announce his conclusion.

"The teachings of psychoanalysis," he stated, "are based on an incalculable number of observations and experiences, and no one who has not repeated those observations upon himself or upon others is in a position to arrive at an independent judgment of it."

I shall not attempt to map here all of the other highways and byways which Freud and his associates and successors explored by means of psychoanalytic techniques. Readers who want to know more are referred to the twenty-four volumes of Freud's collected works, and in particular to his brief and clear *Outline of Psychoanalysis;* to Ernest Jones's three-volume biography of Freud; and to a readable little volume, *Elementary Textbook of Psychoanalysis,* by an American analyst, Dr. Charles Brenner. But I do want to comment here on a very strange phenomenon:

Despite the flavor of scientific fairy tale which characterizes Freud's mature theories as well as his early errors, the powerful resistance we all feel to accepting the applicability of his views to our own situations, and the fact that Freud's views can be adequately evaluated only by psychoanalysts or by patients who have themselves been analyzed, Freud is widely honored today as one of the great pioneers. His discoveries are often ranked with Darwin's theory of evolution and Einstein's theory of relativity among the major achievements of the human mind. Let me suggest a few reasons for this admiration and awe, felt even by skeptics like myself:

Freud was one of the first physicians in history who *listened* to patients. (Havelock Ellis was another.) Freud also talked to patients, and in the process he demonstrated the therapeutic effectiveness of psychotherapy. Modern psychotherapy of all kinds, non-Freudian and anti-Freudian as well as Freudian, must trace its origins to Freud's stumbling and misguided efforts during the 1890's with Emmy von N., Lucie R., the Alpine waitress Katherina, Elisabeth von R., and those other early patients who improved after sessions with Freud.

Freud discovered and stressed the overwhelming significance of unconscious forces in our daily lives, in our decisions, and in our emotional conflicts. Once made aware of these unconscious forces, we see evidence of them in people all around us — in our loved ones, friends, and neighbors, in our political leaders, in our psychoanalysts. Our understanding of the social world in which we live is thus enormously enriched. Some of us, through being psychoanalyzed or in other ways, even learn to recognize some of the unconscious motivations implicit in our own thoughts and behavior — and our personal lives are thereby enriched.

Freud called dramatic attention to the crucial importance of a child's first few years, and of his relations with his parents during those years. Perhaps he overstated the case. Perhaps he misinterpreted the details. But in broad outline his emphasis on those early years is almost universally accepted today. Children in many countries are being brought up a little differently — even by parents who have never heard Freud's name — because Freud's central view has seeped so convincingly through our society.

His popularity benefited, of course, from the fact that, as interest in sexuality revived following the Victorian repression, there were few places to turn for sexual enlightenment except to Freud. But the reverse was also true; the growing interest in Freud's doctrines was one of the factors leading to the revived interest in sex and the increased willingness to think and talk about sex. Even those who publicly denounced Freudianism were contributing their share to a breakdown in the taboos against frank sexual discussion.

Freud's doctrines have also been a factor in the somewhat less vengeful attitudes common today toward those who deviate from Victorian standards of normality, especially toward homosexuals. Essentially Freud held that "perversions" are signs of immaturity — failures to repress on schedule the polymorphously perverse sexual heritage common to all young children. Being stigmatized as immature is hardly a form of praise — but it is surely better than being denounced as a sinner, punished as a criminal, or feared as the carrier of a loathsome disease.

Many Freudian doctrines are by their very nature not amenable to verification or disproof by means of scientific methods other than psychoanalysis. As a result, sex research today tends to remain divided into relatively isolated compartments — psychoanalytic research on the one hand and all other research on the other. On a few issues, however, it is possible to compare or contrast Freudian findings directly with those of other disciplines. In subsequent chapters I shall call attention to points at which other forms of sex research tend to confirm, extend, or refute Freud's psychoanalytic findings.

4

He Taught a Generation How to Copulate

Theodoor Hendrik van de Velde (1873–1937)

THEODOOR HENDRIK VAN DE VELDE (1873–1937) was a Dutch gynecologist. Raised in the Victorian sexual tradition, he never completely got over it. He gave his most important book, first published in 1926, a title which might equally well have graced a Victorian best seller — *Ideal Marriage;* and he interlarded its pages with platitudes which would surely have earned him the praise of the good Queen herself had he published them a generation earlier:

> *"A common hobby keeps mutual sympathy warm and active."*
>
> *"Marriage is sacred to the believing Christian."*
>
> *"Children are the strongest mental link in normal married life."*

Yet it was from this prim and proper Dutchman* that an entire generation (my generation) of Europeans and Americans learned that there are more than two ways of performing sexual intercourse — and that such activities as cunnilingus and fellatio are not only enjoyable but permissible preliminaries.

Many hundreds of "how to" sex manuals had been written before *Ideal Marriage,* of course — some of them thousands of years before. Many more have been written since. Van de Velde's was neither the

* Prim and proper in his published writings; in private life he is described as being warm, witty, affectionate, lighthearted, and very flirtatious.

frankest of these coital guides, nor the most comprehensive, nor the most trustworthy. Its limitations and shortcomings were many. Yet it was precisely its limitations, strangely enough, which made *Ideal Marriage* so important to an entire generation. For van de Velde was able to speak to his contemporaries, the post-Victorian victims of Victorian repression, in language which neither alarmed nor repelled them. He intuitively sensed how far they could be led along the path of sexual responsiveness without unduly arousing their qualms and inhibitions — and he very skillfully led them just that far.

"This book will state many things which would otherwise remain unsaid," van de Velde announced in a Personal Introductory Statement to his *magnum opus*. "Therefore it will have many unpleasant results for me. I know this, for I have gradually attained to some knowledge of my fellow human beings and of their habit of condemning what is unusual and unconventional." Yet he felt a duty to "write down what I have learned to be true and right; I could not face the evening of my life with a quiet conscience if I omitted to do so. There is need of this knowledge; there is too much suffering endured which might well be avoided, too much joy untasted which could enhance life's worth. . . .

"My advice and suggestions are offered here in a wholly responsible, *i.e.*, ethical, spirit, and would lose half their moral purpose if proffered anonymously or under an assumed name.

"So I will meet all blame and annoyance arising therefrom with untroubled mind, and in the hope — nay the *certainty* — that many men and women, even if they dare not say so, will breathe their thanks in the privacy of their nuptial chamber."

Van de Velde, however — like many physicians today — misjudged the readiness of his contemporaries to welcome sexual enlightenment. Far from suffering for his boldness, he promptly reaped both worldwide renown and financial rewards beyond his fondest imaginings. Written simultaneously in Dutch and German, and promptly translated into most civilized languages, *Ideal Marriage* went through forty-two printings in Germany alone between 1926 and 1932 — but was suppressed in 1933, when Hitler came to power. The English translation, published by William Heinemann in 1930, has gone through forty-three printings totaling an estimated 700,000 copies. Figures for the American edition, published by Random House, are not available for the years from 1930 to 1945 —

but more than half a million hardcover copies have been sold since 1945. A revised edition, published in 1965, is being read today by the grandchildren of van de Velde's original readers.

Van de Velde was a specialist. He aimed his book squarely at legally married husbands and wives embarking on a presumably permanent sexual relationship. He ignored all of the practical problems, emotional stresses, and incompatibilities which provide the fodder for many contemporary marriage manuals. He assumed as a preliminary condition that his readers were mature, loving men and women eager to cherish one another and to give one another joy. He concerned himself solely, moreover, with forms of sexual behavior which he considered physiologically normal, aesthetically acceptable, and ethically justifiable according to his personal standards. And even within these restricting limits, he focused his primary attention on two quite specific aspects of conjugal copulation:

How can a sensitive, considerate, loving bridegroom introduce his eager but inhibited and virginal bride to the delights of sexual responsiveness?

How can a married couple, after years of mutual erotic fulfillment, prevent the coital experience from becoming routine, humdrum, repetitious? How can the freshness, enthusiasm, and excitement ordinarily associated with a change in sexual partners be achieved *within* an enduring marriage?

Much of what van de Velde had to say on these matters has a quaintly old-fashioned flavor. Yet readers today will still find three insights of enduring significance.

First, van de Velde correctly diagnosed the major sexual problem of the generation just emerging from Victorianism — a problem still often met with. His generation no longer believed that sex was inherently evil. It accepted in principle the view that a couple bound in an enduring commitment of love and affection could enjoy sexual fulfillment with a clear conscience. But the delusion still survived that where love and affection reign, sex will take care of itself. Van de Velde's patients illustrated the disastrous consequences of this delusion. He learned from them that no matter how loving a couple may be, sexual response is *not* automatic. He therefore prescribed in detail the specific bodily techniques — the kisses, the caresses, the thrusts — by means of which his patients and his readers could translate their emotional commitments into physiological responses and orgasms — mutual, simultaneous orgasms.

It was a prescription urgently needed by the first post-Victorian generation, and many of them welcomed it wholeheartedly. It remains a useful prescription today.

Van de Velde's second major insight can be paraphrased from a popular saying of his time: "it takes two to tango." He concentrated neither on the male nor on the female role in the sex act, but on the myriad subtle interweavings of sensation and emotion which bind the two together. This theme may seem almost too obvious to be worth noting; yet an amazing amount of writing about sex both before and after van de Velde concentrates so intently on frigidity in the female, or on impotence in the male, or on other familiar problems of the individual, as to obscure altogether the proper focus of concern: the reciprocally functioning human couple. Two generations later, Masters and Johnson were to achieve remarkable therapeutic results by reviving van de Velde's focal concern with the couple as the sexual unit.

Finally, and as a sort of corollary, van de Velde stressed the reciprocal joys of simultaneously giving and receiving within the sexual context. To love and to be loved, to arouse and to be aroused, to stroke the partner's clitoris and to feel one's clitoris being stroked, to suck the beloved's penis and to feel one's penis being sucked, to thrust and to receive the thrust, to bring one's beloved to orgasm and to be brought to orgasm by one's beloved — all such individual actions and passions van de Velde presented as inextricable parts of a single transcendent experience. Surely it is blessed to give, and surely it is joyful to receive; but for van de Velde the ultimate blessing and joy were the merging of the giving and the receiving in the ecstasy of simultaneous orgasm.

Van de Velde left no personal account of his own sexual development comparable to Havelock Ellis's; but from readily available clues we can reconstruct at least a part of the story. He was born into a solid family of Dutch burghers, the son of a military man and the grandson of a physician, whose "inhibition of thought and speech" in sexual matters, may be judged from a story he once told:

> In my youth . . . I was present at a wedding breakfast; the host, a man respected by all, was the adoptive father of the bride, and in his speech of

goodwill and congratulations to his foster-daughter and her bridegroom, he wished them the blessing of children in terms of touching emotion, for he had himself suffered deeply because this blessing had been denied him. Among the younger guests, many of them medical men with their fiancées, there was general indignation and resentment at such freedom of speech. Reference to the natural results of married union was considered indecent!

Van de Velde attended medical school in Leiden and Amsterdam, and thereafter won recognition as director of the Haarlem Gynecological Clinic and as author of some eighty papers on various aspects of obstetrics and gynecology. His patients were mostly respectable Dutch matrons, healthy in body, good wives in a conventional way, good helpmates, faithful partners — but in far too many cases sexually unwakened. That, at least, was how van de Velde envisioned them. Their husbands were mostly healthy men, good providers, good fathers, good citizens, loyal and stable in their devotion to their homes through the first years of marriage — but unable, in far too many cases, to preside effectively over the sexual awakening of their wives. That, at least, was how van de Velde envisioned them.

And that, in all probability, is how van de Velde saw himself and his first wife, Henrietta van de Velde-ten Brink, whom he married in 1899 when he was twenty-six and she was three years older. The marriage was not a happy one. There were no children. After ten years, van de Velde eloped with one of his patients — a socially prominent married woman, Martha Breitenstein-Hooglandt, eight years his junior. Even van de Velde's closest friends were alienated; he was forced to give up his practice and for several years he and Martha wandered through Europe, "living in sin." On June 3, 1913, Henrietta divorced him; and five days later he and Martha were married in Corfu, Greece. Thereafter they moved to Switzerland, eventually settling near Locarno. Theodoor and Martha remained inseparable until van de Velde's death in 1937, at the age of sixty-four. There were no children. Surviving witnesses report that, despite its unorthodox beginnings and the exile it entailed, the union of Theodoor and Martha was in all visible respects an ideal marriage; no doubt readers whose lives have been enriched by *Ideal Marriage* (myself among them) owe much to Martha as well as to Theodoor.

Ideal Marriage, published thirteen years after van de Velde's marriage to Martha, was dedicated to her. The two key problems on which the book is focused — the effort to initiate a virginal bride into her proper erotic heritage and the maintenance of erotic freshness between loving partners through the decades — may well have been the central themes of his own first and second marriages respectively.

Van de Velde described his qualifications for writing a sexual handbook in these terms:

> I have now attained a suitable age and experience for this task. The scientist who has studied theory and practice for more than a quarter of a century; the man of letters who has expressed many thoughts in diverse forms; the experienced gynecologist; the *confidant* of many men and women; the man to whom naught human, and naught masculine, has remained alien in the domain of feeling; the husband who has experienced all the joys and griefs of married life; and, finally, the man of fifty, who has learned to contemplate life with a certain serene detachment, who is too old for "youthful follies," but still too young to have lost all desire — all these various entities have been called to contribute to a work written by one pen alone.

Some of van de Velde's data came directly from his patients and their husbands. "In cases where I have been consulted on matters connected with the sexual side of married life," he wrote, "I have found it a valuable help . . . to request each partner to furnish me with as full a report as possible of their sexual life. These reports must, of course, be written separately." Husbands and wives were assured that neither would learn of the other's statements.

In addition to these written reports, and to verbal questioning of his patients, van de Velde seems to have engaged in a limited amount of direct observation of female sexual response in the course of performing gynecological procedures. When describing the action of the uterus and cervix during orgasm, for example, van de Velde adds: "It need hardly be explained that it is absolutely impossible to observe or verify this process during communion [i.e., coitus]. Thus we are compelled to refer to and rely on observations of the uterus, and especially of the *portio* [cervix], *during orgasms produced by intensive stimulation of the clitoris, vagina, or portio, without actual coitus*. There are only rare opportunities for such observations. Nevertheless, in the course of years sufficient data have been collected from various sources to form an idea of the uterine action and response in the orgasm." Thus van de Velde no doubt deserves a place among the many predecessors of Masters and Johnson in the direct observation of human sexual response.

Much of the detail presented in *Ideal Marriage,* however, must have come from a more intimate source. Consider, for example, this account of coitus with the husband lying on his back and his wife astride, facing him:

> In the astride attitude, there is no possibility of mutual embrace or kisses. On the other hand, the full unimpeded view of each other's bodies, especially of a finely formed feminine body seated upright and leaning backward, has a strongly stimulant effect. And the opportunity, often missing in other attitudes, of gazing face to face, into one another's eyes, of beholding, in the reciprocal play of expression, the rising tide of excitement to its ecstatic culmination, greatly enhances all the other stimuli of this attitude.

Here and in many similar passages, surely, van de Velde was not writing as a gynecologist. Nor was he describing at second hand the experience of his patients and their husbands. He was reporting as a man and as a lover.

After the worldwide success of *Ideal Marriage,* van de Velde turned out a series of additional volumes on related topics, including *Sexual Tensions in Marriage, Fertility and Sterility in Marriage,* and *Sex Efficiency: Exercises for Women* — the last designed to teach women how to strengthen and control their vaginal muscles and other muscles useful in sexual intercourse. These books added little to his reputation, and need not concern us here.

An anecdote told about van de Velde at a meeting in New York of the Society for the Scientific Study of Sex illustrates the precarious compromise between conventional morality and physiological responsiveness which he sought to maintain. A young man just starting out in the field of sex research, it seems, visited the van de Veldes at the country home which they maintained near Locarno.

> "Maestro, I am puzzled by one aspect of your great work," the young man began.
>
> "Yes, my son."
>
> "You believe, if I understand your book rightly, that the bride should be a virgin on her wedding night?"
>
> "Of course, of course."
>
> "But you think that a husband should come to marriage sexually experienced?"
>
> "Precisely so. We must not entrust a young filly who has never been mounted to a rider who has never ridden before."
>
> "Further, you oppose adultery?"

"It is the destroyer of marital bliss."

"And you denounce consorting with prostitutes?"

"Vehemently."

"Then with whom," asked the young man triumphantly, "is the groom to secure his premarital experience?"

Van de Velde was nonplussed, and stroked his chin thoughtfully. At length an answer came to him.

"Il y a toujours les veuves," he responded. "There are always the widows."

Ideal Marriage begins, inauspiciously enough, with a series of low-keyed sections: "Reasons for Retention of Marriage," "The Four Cornerstones of Marriage," "The Husband as Permanent Lover of his Wife," "Ideal Marriage Demands Study and Thought," "The Present Treatise as a Manual on this Subject." The next 134 pages are devoted to the anatomy and physiology of sex, both female and male. Much of what van de Velde has to say on these topics is outdated, and there are errors of detail. Robert Latou Dickinson's copy of *Ideal Marriage,* which I have examined, bristles with marginal question marks, exclamation marks, and statements about van de Velde's physiological naïveté — such as his belief that the vagina is lubricated during sexual arousal by mucus entering through the cervix from the uterus, or his statement that a woman experiences an ecstatic yet soothing sensation as she feels the male ejaculate strike the lining of her vagina.* For unsophisticated readers, nevertheless, van de Velde supplies in broad outline the necessary information about the breasts and nipples, the penis, clitoris, labia, and vagina, and their ways of responding to sexual arousal.

The next hundred pages, forming the heart of his work, are concerned with sexual intercourse. "But let us first of all make unmistakably clear," he writes, "that by 'sexual intercourse,' unqualified by any adjectives, we refer *exclusively to normal intercourse between opposite sexes.* If we cannot avoid occasional reference to certain abnormal sexual practices, *we shall emphatically state that they are abnormal.* But this will only occur very seldom, for . . . it is our intention to keep the Hell-gate of the

* But perhaps van de Velde was right on this point after all. In 1949 a woman sex researcher, Dr. E. W. Hardenberg of Pennsylvania State College, reported on thirty-six married women who were asked to agree or disagree with the following statement:

"The sensation of the ejaculate increases the pleasure of the climax."

Twenty-four of the women agreed, two disagreed, and the remaining twelve stated that the sensation of the ejaculate did not influence their climax.

Realm of Sexual Perversions firmly closed. On the other hand, Ideal Marriage permits normal, physiological activities the fullest scope, in all desirable and delectable ways; these we shall envisage without any prudery, but *with deepest reverence for true chastity*. All that is morbid, all that is perverse, we banish: for this is Holy Ground." (The italics and the capitals are van de Velde's.)

Opinions disagree, of course, on what is "normal," "morbid," and "perverse," and opinions change from generation to generation. Van de Velde himself had no doubts. Though he admired Havelock Ellis and often quoted him, the cultural relativism at the heart of Ellis's teachings failed to get through to van de Velde. He bluntly defined "normal" intercourse as "that intercourse which takes place between two sexually mature individuals of opposite sexes; which excludes cruelty and the use of artificial means for producing voluptuous sensations; which aims directly or indirectly at the consummation of sexual satisfaction, and which, having achieved a certain degree of stimulation, concludes with the ejaculation — or emission — of the semen into the vagina, at the nearly simultaneous culmination of sensation — or orgasm — of both partners."

Every word in that definition was carefully selected, and almost every contingency allowed for. Nowhere have I found a more specific statement of precisely what was deemed "normal" by the first post-Victorian generation.

The sex act itself van de Velde subdivided into four overlapping phases: prelude, love-play, sexual union or communion (coitus), and after-play or epilogue (postlude).

The prelude begins "as soon as the first stirrings of the impulse of approach are perceptible." This is the phase of coquetry and flirtation. "Looks and words have the main roles in the prelude, for *they* can best utter the feelings at this early stage when the soul is more stirred than the body. . . . The most important instrument in the prelude to sexual intercourse is — conversation; the exchange of impressions and ideas. Its most effective subject is — Love."

So far, we are on safe Victorian ground. But now, gently and almost imperceptibly, van de Velde the physician takes over from van de Velde the romanticist. "The best realization of what this prelude *means*," he writes, "may be formed if we consider its bodily influence. . . . *Through purely psychic stimuli, it produces an unmistakable physical symptom in both man and woman — at least in the normal erotically experienced woman.* This symptom is *distillation,* or the lubrication of the genitals which physically expresses the desire for closer contact."

The prelude gradually matures into the second phase of the sex act, love play. "It is obvious that they merge into one another in delicate gradations. . . . Nevertheless, it seems most helpful to indicate a dividing line, a natural Rubicon, between these two phases of the love drama. And it is not difficult to recognize; for the *erotic kiss* or *lover's kiss* is the prototype of all erotic contact, and initiates a new grade of tension." This erotic kiss is different from mere social kissing, for it is mutual; "it is given and received *from mouth to mouth with mutual pressure.*" Moreover, "the *tongue* is indispensable in the erotic kiss, and 'plays lead' in its most important variations." "From its lightest, faintest form, it may run the gamut of intimacy and intensity to the pitch of *Maraichinage** in which the couple, sometimes for hours, mutually explore and caress the inside of each other's mouths with their tongues, as profoundly as possible."

The erotic kiss, however, need not be mouth to mouth. "Kisses on various parts of the body are also appropriate and acceptable at this stage of approach . . . from forehead and temples downward over the cheeks and throat; from fingertips along the palms and arms; from the insteps and ankles, up the calves and thighs, [sensitivity] steadily increasing as the genital organs are approached." Here as elsewhere van de Velde stresses mutuality. "The bodily kiss gives a very different kind of pleasure, according to whether it is given or received. Both feelings can be erotically delightful, and the more so if each partner can be, simultaneously, kisser and kissed."

Kisses lead, of course, to caresses, especially of the breasts and nipples — "sexual organs with high erotic value. We may again stress the extreme sensitivity of the nipples (including the areolae) to contact by the tongue, or finger, or by definite suction. These caresses give special delight when a certain degree of excitement has already been reached. And this effect is further enhanced when the nipples themselves have become *erect* — for they are just as capable of erection (proportionately) as the clitoris and penis. . . . The sensation afforded is strongest if it coincides with stimulation of another erogenous zone. When the nipple and clitoris are simultaneously and delicately caressed, they mutually enhance each

* A mode of kissing named for a district in Brittany where it was commonly practiced.

other's stimulation, and this double contact gives to many women the maximum of possible pleasure outside coitus."

And again, the theme of mutuality. "The man's nipple . . . is much less sensitive sexually. But it is capable of receiving sexual sensations and becoming erect (or turgid or tense)."

A discussion of genital caresses comes next. In the case of the woman, "these will be chiefly bestowed on the *Glans clitoridis,* the tiny organ which projects in the center; all the more so as excitement will have already congested the clitoris, leading to its expansion and the *retraction* of its prepuce. Thus the finger cannot miss the most sensitive spot of all (where the *frenulum* or rim is attached) and this sensitiveness is multiplied by the erection of the tiny organ. This form of contact — almost inadvertent at first — is acutely delightful to the wife and increases her desire incalculably. And the man's increases in response, as he feels her pleasure at his touch. And then there follow, spontaneously and as a matter of course, the prolongation of clitoridal titillation and friction, and of the adjacent structures: the inner lips, the orifice . . . and the whole shaft of the clitoris; but the main focus of pleasure is in the Glans clitoridis. And this local (genital) stimulation, to the accompaniment of kisses and words of love, with a crescendo of emotion, whose most effective instrument is the *exchange of manipulation,* continues and accelerates itself till the male member, or *phallos,* is introduced into the vagina." At that point, the love-play phase merges into the third phase, coitus or sexual communion.

Van de Velde emphasizes the importance of love play, and especially of precoital stimulation of the clitoris, with all the eloquence at his command. If the wife is not sufficiently aroused "to cause swelling of the labia, dilation of the vulva, and erection of the clitoris — then, as these manifestations are normal and desirable *before coitus, it is both stupid and grossly selfish of the husband to attempt it if they are absent.* For it means that he will leave her ungratified. Prolonged local stimulation is the only means to save the situation here, for it is the only way to give the wife the requisite degree of local congestion and expansion and psychic readiness." If all else fails, moreover, and especially if the wife's vagina is not sufficiently lubricated, van de Velde recommends "what I prefer to term the *kiss of genital stimulation,* or *genital kiss:* . . . gentle and soothing caresses with lips and tongue."

The male should usually be the bestower of the genital kiss, van de

Velde declares, because his wife usually lags behind him in tempo of sexual arousal. But "on occasions when the man's reactions are less rapid, the woman may with advantage take the more active part during the second act of the love-drama, and *herself, most successfully, give — instead of receiving — the genital kiss.*"

No matter who is the bestower, van de Velde sees the benefits as mutual. "For the *active* partner, the pleasures of the genital kiss are *wholly psychic.* They center around the joy of giving joy to and rousing desire in the beloved, and the imaginative realization of this pleasure and desire. (Of course, this psychic and emotional pleasure may be intense, and transmit itself . . . in the form of increased tumescence.) The feelings of the passive partner, on the other hand, however strong their emotional undertones, are predominantly . . . physical."

The genital kiss, van de Velde adds, "is particularly calculated to overcome frigidity and fear in hitherto inexperienced women who have had no erotic practice, and are as yet scarcely capable of specific sexual desire."

But wait a bit: what of van de Velde's initial promise that he will expose the reader solely to "normal" behavior, and that he will "keep the Hell-gate of the Realm of Sexual Perversions firmly closed," maintaining the "deepest reverence for true chastity." Are not cunnilingus and fellatio in fact perversions?

Van de Velde thought that they were — if by cunnilingus and fellatio we mean "the attainment of orgasm through bucco-lingual contact with the genitals." Orgasm achieved in this way he described as "pathological." But bucco-lingual contact with the clitoris or penis *for the purpose of pre-coital arousal,* and *stopping short of orgasm,* he described, in italics, as "*absolutely unobjectionable and legitimate,* ethically, aesthetically, and hygienically." He demanded only that, in bestowing the genital kiss, "the husband must exercise the *greatest gentleness, the most delicate reverence!*" As for the wife —

"*Is it necessary . . . to emphasize the need for aesthetic delicacy and discretion here?* To advise her to abstain entirely from [mouthing of the penis] during the early stages of married life, and only to venture on them later, and experimentally? To remind her that she runs greater risks than he does, in approaching that treacherous frontier between supreme beauty and base ugliness? I think there is *no* need; she knows this intuitively, she feels it with all a woman's instinctive modesty." Thus did van de Velde reconcile his Victorian reverence for women with his equally firm belief in the need for adequate clitoral and vulvar engorgement, adequate vaginal lubrication, and the fullest possible erection of the penis prior to the onset of coitus.

The third phase of sexual intercourse — sexual union or communion — begins with the introduction of the penis into the vagina and ends immediately following orgasm. In van de Velde's view, the orgasm should be simultaneous or almost so, for husband and for wife. Much of his discussion is concerned with ways to achieve this simultaneity.

The most important way has already been noted: by postponing the introduction of the penis until foreplay has fully aroused the wife. *"If absolutely necessary,"* van de Velde concedes, "the woman can . . . begin the coital act without special preparation." Indeed, if she is sufficiently ardent and experienced, she can reach orgasm simultaneously with her husband even though initially unaroused. This she can accomplish in a way that deserves emphasis here — *"by conscious intention to enjoy all the stimuli received;* a psychic process in which both the active will and the unconscious and subconscious factors of experience and practice cooperate, under the sceptre of sympathy and love."

Van de Velde's prescription that the wife exercise a "conscious intention to enjoy all the stimuli received" plays a significant role in the subsequent history of sex research. During the 1960's, when Dr. William H. Masters and Mrs. Virginia E. Johnson were first reporting at medical meetings on their program for treating sexual inadequacy in married couples, the first question from physicians in the audience was almost always the same: "What do you teach the wife?" Virginia Johnson's answer baffled some of her hearers: "We teach her sensate focus." Yet students of van de Velde understood what she meant quite readily: Forget your worries and cares. Forget your doubts and fears. Concentrate instead on purely sensory awareness; adopt "a conscious intention to enjoy the stimuli received."

Van de Velde believed that a woman experiences two separate kinds of sexual stimulation — clitoral and vaginal. "We must clearly understand," he wrote, "that the sensations caused by stimulation of the vagina are quite distinctive and dissimilar from those due to stimulation of the clitoris. In both cases there is pleasure, and characteristically sexual pleasure, or *voluptas*. But the sensations differ as much between themselves as the flavor and aroma of two fine kinds of wine — or the chromatic glories and subtleties of two quite separate color schemes. And even the orgasms induced by clitoridal or vaginal stimulation respectively are curiously, though not widely, *different*. . . . Perfect and *natural* coitus would give the woman a blend of both types of sensation. Such a blend would involve supreme pleasure and probably very rapid orgasm."

Simultaneous stimulation of clitoris and vagina, van de Velde pointed out, can be achieved through "the obvious method of combining vaginal friction by the phallos with . . . clitoridal friction by the finger." He believed also — a controversial point — that in certain positions of intercourse, the clitoris is directly stimulated by friction against the thrusting penis. He did not think such direct clitoral stimulation during coitus necessary, however. In most cases, "stimulation . . . focused on and in the vagina . . . will be fully adequate for such a variety and intensity of sensation as will culminate in the orgasm."

Though it is the wife, in most cases, who lags behind the husband in their progress toward simultaneous orgasm, van de Velde recognized exceptions. "In very passionate and excitable women, [orgasm] may have been experienced several times before the man's discharge."

Van de Velde further believed that when both partners are on the brink of culmination, it is generally the onset of the man's orgasm which triggers the onset of the woman's orgasm. This can happen in either of two ways. "The final reflex in the woman may receive its signal from her realization of the muscular contractions of the man's orgasm, or from the impact of the vital fluid" on her vaginal lining. The wife's response, in turn, enriches the husband's orgasmic response. There follows "the glorious consciousness of having experienced the supreme pleasure, and the soothing, complete relaxation."

It sometimes happens, of course, that the husband experiences his orgasm without triggering his wife's climax simultaneously. Van de Velde considered this most distressing, and attributed it primarily to lack of adequate stimulation before coitus began. But he recommended a simple remedy when the female orgasm fails to occur. "To be precise, if . . . the man has had his ejaculation without producing orgasm in his partner, he should immediately caress and stimulate her to 'concert pitch' by genital friction and manipulation — unless, indeed, he should have inclination and potency to start afresh, on a new love-play, communion, and orgasm."

Finally, if the husband is unable to secure his wife's orgasm by his manual caresses, *"autotherapeutic measures"* — that is, self-masturbation by the wife — "are probably better than none at all."

Van de Velde recognized that this last recommendation raised moral issues for many of his readers, and especially for the Catholics among them. But he was ready with chapter and verse to justify his proposal: a statement by Vicar-General D. Craisson in a clerical treatise, *De rebus venereis ad usum Confessariorum* ("On Sexual Matters for the Guidance of Fathers Confessors"), published in Paris in 1870. On page 172, Van de Velde reported, the learned Vicar-General considered, from the Roman Catholic point of view, the question, "whether, if the husband should withdraw after ejaculation, before the wife has experienced orgasm, she may then lawfully at once continue friction with her own hand, in order to attain relief." The Vicar-General's reply was that "certain moral theologians deny this, but the greater number permit it. . . . In the same manner, it is lawful for the woman to prepare herself by genital stimulation for sexual union, in order that she may have orgasm more easily." *

But orgasm, in van de Velde's view, is not the end of the drama of love. There follows "a sensation of profound gratification, of mental and physical peace, balance, self-confidence, and power which is hardly attainable in such perfection through any other experience." Indeed, "the most profound and exquisite happiness which human beings can taste is tasted by couples who truly *love* one another during this pause of respite and realization, after completed communion. Far, far more closely than even the rapture of mutual orgasm does this bliss and content of the *after-glow* unite true lovers, as they lie embraced, side by side, while nature recuperates, and their thoughts, in a waking dream, once more live through the joys they have experienced, and their souls meet and merge, even though their bodies are no longer linked.

"This is the first stage of Epilogue — the After-play."

To some youthful readers today, all this may sound like an advertising

* Van de Velde neglected, however, to state the reason for this theological tolerance of female precoital and postcoital self-stimulation. The approving theologians believed that the female orgasm facilitated impregnation and was thus an acceptable part of the procreative act. Perhaps as a result of this failure to tell the whole story, *Ideal Marriage* was placed on the *Index Librorum Prohibitorum* of the Roman Catholic Church in 1931 — said to be the first such listing of a manual of sex technique in modern times.

copywriter's plug for a new product called After-play. But for others, today as in the 1920's, van de Velde successfully bridges the gap between romance and physiology in a way no other writer on sex has quite accomplished:

"*After-play* is an essential and most significant act in the love drama, but unfortunately the most neglected of all. Many men are in the habit of going to sleep immediately after coitus; yes, even men who *love* their wives do this sometimes, from ignorance or negligence. They turn round and presently lie torpid and snoring, while their wives feel the slow ebb of sexual longing, and thus they deprive themselves of the most exquisite psychic and emotional experiences, and they also destroy the illusions of the most loving wife, by showing that they have no idea of the woman's nature, of the aesthetic delicacy of her love, of the profound appreciation sexual pleasure arouses in her, of her need for caresses and sweet words, which lasts much longer than the orgasm. This is a closed book to them. In After-play the man proves whether he is (or is not) *an erotically civilized adult*." (The italics, as always, are van de Velde's.)

Nor is After-play a difficult art. "A word of love *will* do it, a kiss, a tender touch, an embrace! It will suffice for a loving wife to know that for him, too, all is not over at once, with the tempest of the orgasm, that his happiness endures and echoes through his whole nature, like hers."

Some husbands and wives, it is true, enjoy and are capable of kindling a new act of intercourse from the embers of the old; but "this means only that *the Epilogue is deferred*." And van de Velde concludes this section, as usual, with a collection of aphorisms:

"Joy is perfection." — Spinoza.

"Here is a perfect poem: to awaken a longing, to nourish it, to develop it, to increase it, to stimulate it — and to gratify it." — Balzac.

*"The chastest wife can also be the most voluptuous." — Van de Velde.**

So far we have been concerned with van de Velde's first main motif: how a married couple can learn to achieve ideal communion and simultaneous orgasm. But suppose that the erotic lessons are mastered and the rites successfully completed, time after time after time. Disaster still lies ahead "if those rites take place in the same invariably scheduled manner, with no variations of local stimulation or sensory adornment — sexual

* I am informed that the aphorisms in *Ideal Marriage* were selected by van de Velde's second wife, Martha.

satiety will in a few short years intrude itself into the consciousness of both, and equally imperil their marriage. For monotony can only be relieved by variation, and, to the uninstructed man, the only possible variation seems to be in the *object* of his efforts; and the rift in the lute is there, and widens."

The avoidance of monotony, van de Velde taught, is possible but not easy. "It is possible," he explained, "if the process of *courtship* is ever renewed afresh. If both partners 'meet each other half-way,' are attentive, and adaptable to one another's needs; display initiative and ingenuity in stimulating and satisfying one another's needs; and by *a culture of erotic technique* beyond all present marital usage."

Part of the responsibility for initiative and ingenuity van de Velde places on the husband. He quotes Balzac: "If a man cannot afford distinct and different pleasure to the woman he has made his wife, on two successive nights — he has married too soon."

But since it is the husband who is more likely to stray in search of fresh experience, van de Velde places a growing responsibility on the wife as the marriage matures. Once mutual orgasm is assured, he writes, "a certain feminine initiative and aggression brings a refreshing variety. Let her be the wooer sometimes, not always the wooed. She can be so while quite retaining her distinctive dignity and sweetness. This role of wooer can express her love in a very desirable way, and be intensely gratifying to the husband, who feels that he not only feels desire, but inspires it, too." It is at this stage that the wife may herself quite properly initiate the "genital kiss," bestowing as well as receiving it. Indeed, mutual genital kissing "may be enjoyed alternately or sometimes simultaneously." Thus, by a delicate turn of phrase, van de Velde awards his post-Victorian *nihil obstat* to the practice of *soixante-neuf*.

The wife can also enrich and vary the coital experience by learning to control her pelvic muscles. There are several sets of these muscles, and van de Velde believed that "a few women, specially adept and expert," have mastered the art of contracting and relaxing each set "either independently or together, at will — a faculty of enormous value in the technique of intercourse." Robert Latou Dickinson was amused by this theory that the pelvic muscles can be played on separately, like the keyboard of an organ. But the theory that use of the pelvic muscles is important both for heightening the pleasure of the male and for facilitating the orgasm of the female continues to be a concern of contemporary sex research.*

As his major proposal for introducing a refreshing variety between marital partners already familiar with and well adapted to one another, van de Velde relied on variations of *position* during coitus. "As the grade and locality of stimulation are different," he explained, "according to the relative position of the two partners to one another, so therefore the sensations arising from such stimulation vary also, and not only in degree but in kind — and this in a wide range of variation." Here, of course, van de Velde was following a very ancient tradition; scores of different coital postures, each with its advantages and disadvantages, had been described by sages a millennium before he wrote.

Van de Velde describes only ten postures — six in which male and female are face to face and four with the male behind the female. In a footnote he dismisses another possibility — "in which the face and abdomen of the man are brought into contact with the woman's side and flank" — as being "so little in harmony with both male and female physiology that it is only used as an occasional variation, with no charm." Others (myself among them) strongly dissent from this dogmatism; indeed, anthropologists report twelve cultures (out of 131 studied) in which the sideway position is the preferred, approved, or standard posture.

Van de Velde's Position Number One was, of course, the position most commonly adopted in our culture. "The woman lies on her back; her thighs are separated and her knees slightly bent. The man lies upon his partner's abdomen, supporting his knees and elbows as far as possible on the bed or couch, in order to relieve her of his weight; his legs and thighs are between hers." The other nine positions are described with equal directness.

* A relation between a woman's control of her pelvic muscles — especially the pubococcygeus muscle — and her ability to achieve orgasm has also been reported by Dr. Arnold Kegel of Los Angeles in a series of papers. Dr. Kegel believes that the muscle facilitating female orgasm is the same one which shuts off the urinary stream. Thus a woman who wishes to achieve control can practice quite readily, first by shutting off the urinary stream a few times, and later, after she has identified the muscle in this way, by practice in contracting and relaxing it repeatedly, day after day, perhaps for a period of weeks. Research on the pubococcygeus muscle is also under way at the Center for Marital and Sexual Studies, Long Beach, California, under Dr. William E. Hartman and Mrs. Marilyn Fithian.

This standard position — once known in some primitive parts of the world as "the missionary position" because natives were unfamiliar with it prior to the arrival of Christian missionaries and their wives — van de Velde believed to be "on the whole . . . both physiologically and psychologically appropriate." But, from the point of view of maximal genital stimulation, he praised several of the alternatives even more highly.

In one variation, "the attitude of extension," for example, the woman lies flat on her back with thighs closed and legs extended; the man's thighs enclose and clasp hers. "For the man, this has the double advantage of increased stimulation of the penile shaft . . . and of security that the phallos does not slip out of the vagina. . . . The woman has the advantage of increased stimulation of the vulva and exterior vaginal orifice. And, an even more important consideration for her, the clitoris in this attitude is offered more fully to the friction or stroking of the penile shaft." * The position with the man on his back and the woman astride also has several advantages, including the fact that the woman can move so as to cause the glans of the penis to stimulate her cervix directly. "This cervical friction can be performed in two ways: in a straight line (sideways or backwards and forwards), through rhythmic swaying of the woman's body; or with a circular 'corkscrew' motion of the pelvis. Both these methods give as it were a different color-tint and *timbre* of erotic pleasure; in the *circular* movement the pleasurable sensations, at least on the man's side, are the stronger" — and so on through all ten of the van de Velde positions. It was van de Velde's firm belief that by exploring and exploiting these postural variations the desire to achieve variety by a change in coital partners could be curbed and marital fidelity fostered.

Was he right? I know of no objective evidence either supporting or impugning his belief. In the absence of such evidence, his suggestions seem well worth a trial.

In addition to recommending the use of varying positions to avoid monotony, van de Velde recommended certain positions for use under specified conditions — and warned against others. Thus he recommended one position "in cases of small phallos or imperfect erection," another "when the vagina is slack and widely distended," and a third — the wife-astride position — "when the man is less vigorous." He warned against the usual or "missionary" position during the later months of pregnancy

* For Masters and Johnson's refutation of this belief, see pages 304–305.

because of the man's weight on the woman's abdomen. And he rated each of the ten positions in terms of whether it increased or decreased the likelihood of initiating pregnancy. (On this as on a wide range of other technical matters, van de Velde's views are outmoded by subsequent research — especially by the laboratory observations of Masters and Johnson.)

Van de Velde's significance in the *history* of sex research seems to me unchallengeable. He found a way, as noted earlier, to make at least some of the joys of human sexuality aesthetically and ethically acceptable to a severely inhibited generation in many parts of the world. Perhaps the most startling evidence of van de Velde's far-flung influence comes from the state of New South Wales, in Australia, where the state government in 1948 issued a fourteen-page pamphlet entitled *Marriage,* prepared under the direction of the Minister of Justice, to be handed out free by "church and district registrars" to young people about to be married. Surely the Minister of Justice or his subordinates had read and agreed with van de Velde when they officially informed engaged couples, at the state's expense:

> [The man] should realize that a woman is usually slower than a man in arriving at a state of complete sexual satisfaction, that, before every act of sexual union, a preliminary wooing is often necessary, and that he should endeavor to restrain his ardor so that his climax may synchronize with that of his wife.

But van de Velde's historical importance is quite separate from his current usefulness. Does he still make sense after a lapse of more than forty years?

My wife and I often faced this latter question in a practical context: should we continue to give *Ideal Marriage* to young friends of ours in love or recently married?

The arguments against such a choice are numerous. Many marriage counselors today, for example, believe that van de Velde's stress on simultaneous orgasm can have a harmful influence — not because simultaneous orgasm is not in fact a delight, but because it lies beyond the reach of many couples. Emphasis on the unattainable, it is alleged, may in such cases be disheartening; it may also discourage couples from learning about or discovering for themselves the countless approaches to orgasm which van de Velde overlooks altogether or castigates as perversions. Why should young couples who prefer some other pattern of satisfaction be forced into the Procrustes' bed of simultaneous orgasm? It has also been alleged that van de Velde's language and tone appeal today to only a minority of romantically minded young people, and that his many specific errors of fact may lead to some confusion.

The pages of *Ideal Marriage,* moreover, are strewn with all sorts of warnings — and some of the hazards warned against are quite imaginary. The warning that the vagina may be ruptured by excessively vigorous thrusting, for example, was dismissed by Robert Latou Dickinson with the statement that during his half a century of busy gynecological practice he had never seen an example. Van de Velde's concern that the human penis may become locked in the human vagina — a locking familiar enough in canines — is no doubt a further example of his zeal to admonish unnecessarily. Current readers of van de Velde should be assured that on these and other points, *Ideal Marriage* is unnecessarily restrictive.

Nevertheless, my wife's and my ultimate decision was to include van de Velde's volume as one of a *group* of books likely to prove enlightening to those just starting out on a heterosexual relationship. (We included Dr. Albert Ellis's *Sex Without Guilt* in the group as an antidote to van de Velde's primness, and relied on van de Velde to offset Albert Ellis's antiromanticism. *Partners in Love* by Dr. Eleanor Hamilton rounded out the group.)

No doubt one of our reasons for including *Ideal Marriage* was simple nostalgia. A third of a century ago, when very little was available on sex techniques at the ordinary bookstore, we both had found van de Velde highly rewarding personally. It was one of the books which profoundly influenced our own views on sexuality.

The main ground for our conclusion that van de Velde is still useful, however — especially if approached with a critical realization that his words are not to be accepted as gospel — is the power of *Ideal Marriage* to open up communication between spouses and lovers on precisely the topics of concern: the sensations, perceptions, and emotions arising before, during, and after coitus. I recall a dramatic example.

"I'm glad you gave me van de Velde," a young man told us a few years ago. "I was too bashful to read it with Ellen, so I gave it to her to read alone. After she returned it I thumbed through it again one evening — and found five sentences in it which she had underlined in red ink.

"Those five sentences told me all I needed to know. Wow! Life has been different since."

5

Who Does What, When, and with Whom

Alfred Charles Kinsey (1894–1956)

PRIOR to 1937, much had been learned about human sexuality — but very little had been firmly established. Even the most basic facts were still subject to debate.

Science had progressed centuries earlier in other areas from debate to solid accomplishment by introducing *quantitative* methods — chiefly counting and physical measurements. The achievements of Copernicus, Galileo, Newton, and Einstein all shared this quantitative mathematical foundation. During the nineteenth century, moreover, a special branch of mathematics — statistics — had proved of very great value, especially in the social and biological sciences. It was thus inevitable that, sooner or later, quantitative statistical methods would be harnessed to the scientific study of sex.

Dr. Alfred C. Kinsey (1894–1956) deserves the lion's share of the credit for belatedly placing studies of human sexuality on a firm quantitative foundation.

Three of Kinsey's predecessors — Krafft-Ebing, Freud, and van de Velde — knew nothing of statistics; I can recall not a single point on which any of these three brought statistical evidence to bear. Some of their most serious errors resulted directly from this failure to use even the crudest statistical measures. Krafft-Ebing's belief that masturbation leads to insanity, for example, arose out of his observations, and the observations of many of his predecessors, that insane people masturbated. Those observations remain unchallenged today. But even a primitive statistical approach would have revealed — and later did in fact reveal — that sane people also masturbate, and masturbate just about as often as those Krafft-Ebing labeled "insane." Similarly, Freud's early conclusion that coitus with a condom leads to anxiety neurosis was vitiated by his failure to present statistics showing that anxiety neurosis is more frequent among men who wear condoms, and their wives, than among other couples resembling the condom users in other relevant respects. Statisticians may err on occasion; but those who eschew statistics inevitably err very often.

Havelock Ellis, though he distrusted statistics in general, made effective use of them on many points. Consider his treatment, for example, of the popular belief that in the spring a young man's fancy lightly turns to thoughts of love. Is it true that the human species, like many other species, is sexually more often aroused or more readily arousable in the spring?

François Rabelais (c.1490–1553) was the earliest authority Ellis found who had approached this question from a statistical point of view. Rabelais nearly four centuries before Ellis had checked the monthly distribution of christenings in his part of France, and had found a peak incidence in October and November — leading him to the conclusion that the first thaws of January and February produced increased sexual activity. A later French investigator, Villermé, Ellis continued, had reported in 1831, on the basis of 17,000,000 births, that the maximum of French conceptions occur in April, May, and June. A nineteenth-century German reported that seasonal variations are more marked in illegitimate than in legitimate births. A nineteenth-century anthropologist reported that in the Northwest Provinces of India, the conception peak comes in December and January. In Canada, Ellis added, the peak in 1904 came in June, July and August. As for the United States, "Mr. John Douglass Brown, of Philadelphia, has kindly prepared and sent me . . . the statistics as to 4,066 births contained in the Biographical Catalogue of Matriculates of the College of the University of Pennsylvania," covering the 136 years from 1757 to 1893. August and September were the peak months for births, Brown informed Ellis, indicating maximum conceptions in November and December.

Conceptions, of course, are not necessarily a good index of *thoughts* of love. "It would certainly be interesting," Ellis stated, "if we can so simply show the connection between love and season by proving that when the birds begin to sing their notes, the young person's fancy naturally turns to brood over the pictures of mating in novels. I accordingly applied to Mr. Capel Shaw, Chief Librarian of the Birmingham Free Libraries." Mr. Shaw made available reports showing the number of novels drawn from the ten Birmingham free libraries, month by month for the year 1897, by 30,000 users, most of them aged fourteen to twenty-five. "It is clear at a glance," Ellis found after examining the reports, "that without exception the maximum number of readers of prose-fiction [at each of the ten libraries in the system] is found in the month of March."

But statistics can be misleading, and Ellis perceptively noted the flaw in what was "clear at a glance." There are thirty-one days in March, as compared with twenty-eight days in February in 1897. On a daily rather than monthly basis, Ellis concluded, "February is really the month during which most novels were read."

Ellis also sought and found rape statistics as evidence of seasonal sexuality. "In France, rapes and other offenses against modesty are most numerous in May, June, and July. . . . In Germany, Aschaffenberg [1903] finds that sexual offenses begin to increase in March and April, reach a maximum in June or July, and fall to a minimum in winter. . . . In Italy, Penta shows that sexual offenses reach a minor climax in May . . . and a more marked climax in August-September."

All of these examples made use of statistical data collected for other purposes; but Ellis was also familiar with statistics based on specially collected sexual data. One example out of many I have already quoted above: "A well-known physician in Chicago informs me that on making inquiry of twenty-five middle-class married men in succession he found that sixteen had first been seduced by a woman."

Though sexual surveys of this kind have been made in many countries, the bulk of the early examples of systematic sexual surveys based on questionnaires or interviews were American. Dr. Kinsey and his associates, in a review of the American literature, found nineteen such studies made in the United States between 1915 and 1947 — an average of one every twenty months for thirty-two years.

The earliest of these, interestingly enough, was made in 1915 for the Young Men's Christian Association by a YMCA physician, Dr. J. M. Exner. Dr. Exner prepared a questionnaire asking eight questions, and secured replies from 948 male college students. Six of the eight questions were not sexual; the other two concerned masturbation and nocturnal emissions. College students in 1915 were loath to admit masturbation; the incidence figures were low and nothing of much significance emerged.

Three years later a probation officer named Merrill interviewed 100 juvenile delinquent males aged eight to eighteen appearing before a Seattle juvenile court. "The study is notable," the Kinsey group later stated, "because it published the most definite record of pre-adolescent orgasm (for six boys in self-masturbation) and gave the highest recorded incidence figures (31 percent) for younger boys involved with oral techniques in homosexual contacts." On both points, Kinsey's later and far more voluminous data confirmed the 1918 Seattle findings.

A psychologist, Paul S. Achilles, made the first American study (1923) which included women in the sample surveyed. He secured questionnaire replies from 1,449 males and 483 females, all in the New York City area, for the American Social Hygiene Association — an organization engaged in combatting venereal disease, with primary emphasis on suppressing prostitution. The questions were mostly designed to determine the effectiveness of anti-venereal-disease propaganda publications.

A study published by the biologist Raymond Pearl in 1925 was concerned with the frequency of sexual intercourse among American males, and made a number of important points. Pearl noted, for example, that the 257 men in his sample engaged in sexual intercourse more frequently during their thirties than during their twenties; frequency declined thereafter. Pearl was not, however, misled by his own crude figures. Many of the men in his sample had not been married during most of their twenties, and therefore had less opportunity for frequent intercourse. "With approximate equality of opportunity," Pearl concluded, "the peak of activity is in the 20–29 decade, and thereafter there is a steady decline." Nor was this all. Few of the men in his sample had been married during their teens, but by studying the curve of frequencies actually reported, Pearl was able to deduce that in males "with unrestricted legitimate opportunity, the peak of sex activity is prior to age 20." A quarter of a century later, the Kinsey data confirmed Pearl's astonishing deduction. Males really do begin to suffer a gradual decline in sexual potency after the age of seventeen or eighteen.

The Pearl study, incidentally, was subject to a number of apparently crippling shortcomings. All 257 of the men in his sample were white, and all were over fifty-five years of age at the time Pearl's data were secured. All or most of them came from the Baltimore area — and all of them had had a prostate operation, which was how their records had come to Pearl's attention. These shortcomings in the sample did not prevent Pearl from correctly determining the shape of the curve relating age of husband with frequency of sexual intercourse.

Most of the pre-Kinsey sex surveys were characterized by a certain uneasiness, even prissiness, in approaching sexual material. No one except Merrill in Seattle asked, for example, about fellatio or cunnilingus. Questions were often worded so discreetly that respondents might miss their meaning — or might perceive and give the "proper" answer expected by the interviewers. A study of 1,029 North Carolina males aged fifteen to twenty, published in 1926 by a state health officer, included such questions as this one, which can surely be labeled as "loaded":

"Has anyone ever tried to give you the mistaken idea that sex intercourse is necessary for the health of the young man?"

Among the best known of these pre-Kinsey statistical studies were the following:

Katharine B. Davis, *Factors in the Sex Life of Twenty-two Hundred Women* (1929). Questionnaires were mailed to 20,000 women, of whom 2,200, aged twenty-five to fifty-five, responded. Many or most of the respondents were teachers, clubwomen, graduates of Eastern women's colleges.

G. V. Hamilton, *A Research in Marriage* (1929), based on records from 100 married males and 100 married females (including 55 married couples), most of them either patients of New York City psychiatrists or friends of such patients.

Robert Latou Dickinson and Lura Beam, *A Thousand Marriages* (1931) and *The Single Woman* (1934). These studies were limited to the patients of a single gynecologist.

Dorothy Dunbar Bromley and F. H. Britten, *Youth and Sex* (1938), based on questionnaire returns from 1,364 male and female students at forty-six colleges, plus personal interviews at fifteen colleges; among the best of the pre-Kinsey studies.

Lewis M. Terman and others, *Psychological Factors in Marital Happiness* (1938), based on questionnaire replies from 2,484 married men and women, mostly married couples, mostly Californians, and mostly college-educated.

The largest of these pre-Kinsey studies, and the one which immediately preceded the first Kinsey publication, was "The Sex Life of Unmarried Men," by L. B. Hohman and Bertram Schaffner (1947), based on interviews with 4,600 selective service selectees at military induction centers in New York State and Baltimore. This study was notable for its finding that only three or four inductees per thousand reported homosexual experience. But the unprecedentedly large size of the sample was surely no guarantee of the trustworthiness of the findings. As the Kinsey group later pointed out, "three-to-five-minute interviews . . . held in army induction centers were not conducive to winning admissions of socially taboo behavior." Moreover, most of the young men of the early 1940's were eager to help defeat Hitler, and "the men had been informed beforehand that they would be punished by being excluded from the Armed Forces if they did admit such behavior." Few of them admitted homosexual behavior.

Considering the nineteen pre-Kinsey studies as a whole, such shortcomings as these may be noted:

Twelve were limited to the New York City area or other points on or near the Eastern seaboard.

Ten were limited to college students or college graduates and six excluded or almost excluded the college groups. Since different questions were asked and different methods used, the two kinds of groups could not be compared. No studies covered the whole broad socio-economic spectrum, level by level.

The only three studies which approached nationwide coverage were limited to college students.

Not one of the pre-Kinsey studies covered more than a small fraction of the many kinds of sexual behavior known to exist, from solitary masturbation to large-scale orgies and from prepubertal activities to old age.

These criticisms should not be pressed too far. In the absence of more reliable data, the early statistical surveys cast fresh light on a variety of problems. But all of them became obsolete when Dr. Kinsey and his associates published, in 1948 and 1953, their first two epoch-making reports on the detailed sexual behavior of more than 12,000 Americans of both sexes and all ages, unmarried, married, and formerly married, drawn from every state and from every educational and socio-economic level, urban and rural, including Catholics, Protestants, and Jews, devout and not so devout, and varying as well in a number of other characteristics.

The man who revolutionized the scientific study of sex by bringing to the field the sophisticated statistical methods utilized decades earlier in other social and biological sciences was hardly a likely candidate for such a role. Alfred C. Kinsey was born in Hoboken, New Jersey, in 1894, of devoutly religious, middle-class, Victorian parents; and in youth he did not rebel against his repressive parental heritage.*

Alfred suffered as a child from rheumatic fever and rickets, but soon built up his strength through an active out-of-door life. He joined the Boy Scouts, became one of the country's first Eagle Scouts, and organized a troop for younger boys when he was seventeen. His first contribution to science was published during his Scouting days and was based on many hours of outdoor observation: "What Do Birds Do When It Rains?" Freudians might call this an early sign of voyeurism; if so, the science of sex research is even more deeply indebted to Kinsey's voyeurism than to Havelock Ellis's urolagnia.

Neither at the Stevens Institute of Technology nor at Bowdoin College, where he received his B.S. degree in psychology at the age of twenty-two, did Kinsey evince much interest in sex. He never dated. "At college he was the young man who played the piano at fraternity dances while the others danced," Dr. Pomeroy reports. A story which Dr. Kinsey once told Dr. Pomeroy illustrates the deep hold sexual Victorianism still had on young Alfred — as on many others of his generation.

One of his friends came to Alfred during his college days, deeply worried about the fact that he masturbated. Alfred was shocked when he heard his friend's confession — but he knew exactly what to do. At Kinsey's suggestion, he and his friend knelt down side by side in the college dormitory and prayed to God that his friend be given the strength to refrain from this sinful habit.

* What follows is based partly on my own meetings with Dr. Kinsey in 1953, but mostly on an intensive interview with Dr. Kinsey's closest associate, Dr. Wardell B. Pomeroy, which my wife and I enjoyed in 1966; and on Dr. Pomeroy's reminiscences of Dr. Kinsey published that year in my wife's and my volume, *An Analysis of Human Sexual Response.*

After graduation from Bowdoin, Kinsey received his Ph.D. in entomology from Harvard in 1920, and launched his studies of gall wasps, the insects which were to be his prime interest until 1937. A less likely preparation for sex research can hardly be imagined, for gall wasps are among the relatively few species in the animal world which can reproduce parthenogenetically — that is, without insemination of the female by the male. Yet in several respects, Kinsey's nearly two decades of gall wasp research constituted excellent preparation.

"Gall wasps are found primarily in oak trees," Dr. Pomeroy has explained, "and in the course of collecting specimens, Dr. Kinsey hiked through many parts of the country, camping out, carrying his pack on his back. To find the oak trees and gall wasps in a backwoods region, he would have to introduce himself to country folk, explain his mission, win their confidence, and persuade them to show him around the area. He was shy, almost intimidated by the country people at first, but soon learned to speak their language and developed a real liking for them. This became one of his major assets; later, he was able to secure from such people as well as from other strata of society full and frank accounts of their sexual behavior.

"Over a period of twenty years or so, Dr. Kinsey collected somewhere between two and four *million* gall wasps. He examined and classified 150,000 specimens while preparing a single paper on a single aspect of their structure."

Kinsey was appointed an instructor in biology at Indiana University in 1920, at the age of twenty-six, and continued on the faculty there until his death. At Indiana he met and married a young chemistry student, Clara McMillan — the first girl, Dr. Pomeroy reports, with whom Alfred ever "went steady." The Kinseys had four children, and the marriage was terminated only by Dr. Kinsey's death in 1956. He might thus have gone down in history as the world's foremost authority on gall wasps and as a typical Victorian surviving into a later generation, were it not for a seemingly minor happenstance at the age of forty-three.

In 1937, when universities under the prodding of Robert Latou Dickinson and others were beginning to introduce courses in sex education and marriage, Indiana University decided to launch such a course. Dr. Kinsey, as a respected biologist and as a husband and father of irreproachable personal conservatism, was selected to be the teacher. A sedate, stocky figure of a man, he might easily have been mistaken for the vice-president of a small-town bank — and Mrs. Kinsey was similarly the epitome of campus respectability. The late Albert Deutsch, who knew the Kinseys well, described Dr. Kinsey as a "medium-sized man with alert gray-green eyes and tawny, tousled hair" who combined "a quiet dignity and correctness with an outgoing, easy-to-get-along-with personality. . . . He is careless about clothes; I have never seen him in a pressed suit; even the tuxedo he wears for formal occasions is ill-pressed. The bow tie he has invariably worn since childhood makes him readily recognizable in most crowds." (Dr. William H. Masters has also adopted the bow tie as his distinguishing haberdashery detail.)

Dr. Kinsey's hobby was gardening. "The ideal married life of the Kinseys, and their wonderful relations with their children," Deutsch wrote, "stands as a living contradiction to those critics who have charged the scientist with manifesting an 'antifamily' bias in his project. None who has tasted the warm hospitality of the Kinsey home in Bloomington can fail to recall vividly the extraordinarily vital, mutually respectful and understanding relationship between man and wife and between parents and children."

No harm, the university authorities no doubt concluded, could come from exposing tender students to the facts of life as taught by so conventional an instructor. Fortunately, they failed to take into account Dr. Kinsey's scientific integrity.

"Knowing a good deal about gall wasps but little about human sexual behavior," Dr. Pomeroy notes, "Dr. Kinsey went to the library to learn more. He soon discovered that no one else knew very much either." The studies of such pioneers as Ellis, Krafft-Ebing, Freud, and Dickinson, however fruitful and revealing they had been in their time, were from Kinsey's point of view prescientific. They lacked the statistical validity Dr. Kinsey deemed essential. In order to teach the facts, he would first have to gather them himself, much as he had gathered gall wasps.

Making up a preliminary list of questions, Dr. Kinsey secured answers from 62 males and females during the latter half of 1938. Most of his initial respondents were associated with the university in one way or another; but even so, Dr. Kinsey was able to note what most of his predecessors had missed — an amazing variation of sexual behavior and attitudes from one socio-economic class to another. A campus policeman was a member of this early sample whom Dr. Kinsey often recalled in later years. This policeman, who had had no more than an eighth-grade education, complained to Dr. Kinsey that the Indiana students were mostly perverts. "They would lie under the trees in pairs and just pet and pet. Sexual intercourse the policeman could understand; but this interminable petting must be some form of perversion!"

The later Kinsey interviews explained the policeman's attitude. Based on subsequent records of sex histories collected from more than 17,000 men and women, Dr. Kinsey was able to show that petting is primarily an activity of middle-class or upper-level males who have attended high school or college. While some lower-level boys also occasionally pet, their petting "is often incidental, confined to a few minutes of hugging and kissing prior to actual coitus, and quite without the elaborations which are usual among college students. Petting at upper social levels may be indefinitely prolonged, even into hours of intensive erotic play, and usually never arrives at coitus." More precisely, "[male] orgasm as a product of petting occurs among 16 percent of the males of the grade school level, 32 percent of the males of the high school level, and over 61 percent of the college-bred males who are not married by the age of thirty." Among women, curiously enough, there is not a similar relationship of petting to social class.

During 1939, Kinsey added another 671 sex histories to his file, bringing the total to 733. In the course of these 733 interviews, he learned about kinds of sexual behavior he had never imagined existed, and added questions concerning these kinds of behavior to his rapidly growing questionnaire. Fortunately, Kinsey learned fast. More than 400 of the 521 items covered in the later Kinsey interviews were already present in the questionnaire by mid-1939.

The standard Kinsey interviews, unlike any of the earlier surveys, covered all six of the ways in which males and females achieve orgasm in our culture — through nocturnal sex dreams or seminal emissions, masturbation, heterosexual petting, heterosexual intercourse, homosexual intercourse, and contacts with animals of other species. The questions were gathered under nine major rubrics:

1. Social and Economic Data
2. Marital Histories (recorded separately for each marriage)
3. Sex Education
4. Physical and Physiological Data
5. Nocturnal Sex Dreams
6. Masturbation

7. Heterosexual History
8. Homosexual History
9. Animal Contacts

Within each of these nine areas, Kinsey introduced subdivisions and subsections. Thus the heading Masturbation covered data on twenty-nine points listed under seven subheads:

Masturbation

1. Ages involved, pre- and post-adolescent
2. Sources of learning
   - Conversation and reading
   - Observation
   - Participation, heterosexual or homosexual
   - Self-discovery
3. Frequencies
   - Maximum per week
   - Means at each age
4. Techniques
   - For male
     - Manual
     - Frictional
     - Oral
     - Special devices
     - Urethral insertions
   - For female
     - Breast
     - Clitoral
     - Vaginal insertion
     - Frictional
     - Thigh pressure
     - Urethral insertions
     - With devices
5. Time required for orgasm
6. Accompanying imagery
   - Self
   - Homosexual
   - Heterosexual
   - Zoo-erotic
   - Sado-masochistic
7. Subject's evaluation
   - Period involving fear or conflict
   - Sources of resolution of conflict
   - Rejection: period involved, reasons for
   - Estimate of moral, psychic, physical consequences

In some portions of the sex history even more detailed data were secured. Thus under Homosexual History, the items were first divided into pre-adolescent experience, post-adolescent experience, psychic reactions, sources of contacts, social conflicts, homosexual prostitution, and the subject's own sexual self-evaluation. The items on post-adolescent experience were then further divided into fourteen subsections such as age at first experience, frequency, partners, age preferences, and so on. One of these subsections was further concerned with the social position of the partners secured by the reporting homosexuals, and this subhead contained eleven further subclassifications listing homosexual activity with —

students in grade school
students in high school
students in college
clergy
teachers
art groups
professional persons
business groups
armed forces
laboring groups
law enforcement officers

Computer scientists today measure quantity of information in terms of units called "bits." One bit of information is the amount which is secured when a single question is answered "yes" or "no." By the end of 1949, Dr. Kinsey and his associates had secured and recorded many *millions* of bits of information from more than 16,000 respondents.

When the Kinsey reports were published, the most common criticism of them was that they failed to cover certain areas of interest, such as "falling in love," or "the psychic *meaning* of each experience." These criticisms, though literally true, were grossly unfair. They distracted attention from the overwhelming volume of data actually collected and presented. No prior survey of human behavior in history had even approached the Kinsey survey in completeness. As a doggerel poet commented at the time:

When that interview
Was through
What there was to know
Kinsey knew.

So grandiose an undertaking would ordinarily be parceled out, of course, among dozens or scores of interviewers. The brunt of this gigantic labor, however, was borne for the first ten years by Dr. Kinsey himself, for of the first 12,000 sex histories collected, he personally recorded more than 7,000 — an average of two a day, fourteen a week, for nearly ten years. Thereafter Pomeroy, Gebhard, and Martin picked up the interviewing burden, bringing the total to 17,500 at the time of Kinsey's death. To administer his vast project, Dr. Kinsey founded and headed Indiana University's Institute for Sex Research — then and now familiarly known as the Kinsey Institute.

Dr. Pomeroy has described how so much was accomplished by so few in eighteen years. "At the office [Dr. Kinsey] worked a twelve-to-fourteen-hour day, and pushed his staff almost as hard. On field trips we could not keep up with him; he was always after 'one more history' before knocking off for the day. He never took a vacation in his life.

"I remember one field trip to Chicago on which Dr. Kinsey and I interviewed ordinary people all day, and at night worked in a homosexual community. One night about midnight we came to a sailor who proceeded to give an unusually long and involved history which went on hour after hour. Kinsey asked the questions while we both recorded the replies independently, as we sometimes did to check the reliability of our code-recording techniques. About 4 A.M. there was a lull. I looked up from my code sheet and saw that Dr. Kinsey had fallen asleep. I picked up the thread and asked questions until he woke up again to continue the interview."

Dr. Kinsey's goal was 100,000 sex histories — but death intervened. Kinsey "literally and knowingly worked himself to death," Dr. Pomeroy reports. "In June 1956, when he was sixty-two years old, he had several heart attacks — particularly ominous because of his childhood bout of rheumatic fever. His physician told him he could still work two to four hours a day, and predicted that if he limited his work to this maximum he might last another four years. Dr. Kinsey utterly rejected the instructions. He said he would cut down to an eight-hour day, but no less than that, regardless of the consequences. When his physician came visiting the campus to urge him again to cut down on his work, Dr. Kinsey's response was to take him on a strenuous two-hour tour of the Institute." Two months later, he died.

Why were so many respondents willing to confess so much in such detail about their experiences with masturbation, extramarital intercourse, homosexuality, animal contacts, and other taboo behavior to Kinsey and the other Kinsey Institute interviewers? One of America's foremost authorities on the biology of sex, Dr. George W. Corner, has supplied the answer. Kinsey had raised interviewing to the level of a fine art.

> As a physician by training [Dr. Corner wrote] I have some appreciation of the difficulties of securing personal histories. I do not hesitate to say that the technique of history-taking employed by Kinsey is skillful beyond the imagination of those who have not experienced it. Every professional scientist with whom I have talked who has given his personal history to Dr. Kinsey has agreed with this statement. . . . The subject is aware from the first that he is being dispassionately studied by a sincere but shrewd and extremely well-informed scientific man — well-informed in the ways of the world and of the underworld as well.

My wife and I contributed our own sexual histories to the Kinsey project through Dr. Pomeroy — and came away with the same impression of superb craftsmanship. Comparing notes afterward, we agreed that Dr. Pomeroy's transparent honesty toward us had developed in us an almost compulsive need to be completely honest with him. Any omissions from the answers we supplied were attributable solely to the limitations of our memories.

Kinsey, Pomeroy, and the others established this rapport with their subjects in a number of carefully planned ways. Subjects were shown, for example, that their replies were being recorded in a code which only the interviewers themselves were able to decipher — and were assured that their names were even more artfully coded to prevent the association of names with responses by any unauthorized person.

As a further assurance to subjects, interviews were carried on in private rooms, behind closed doors, without interruptions.

Both Kinsey and Pomeroy were friendly men, genuinely interested in other human beings and accustomed to make that interest patent. "The interviewer should be as interested in the subject as in recording the subject's history," Kinsey wrote. "It is important to look the subject squarely in the eye, while giving only a minimum of attention to the record that is being made. People understand each other when they look directly at each other."

Each interview began with nonsexual questions (such as age and education) and continued through sexual but emotionally neutral topics (such as age at puberty and at first orgasm); the more threatening questions came near the end. Since different people feel threatened in different contexts, this meant that the order of questions sometimes had to be varied. "It is often easier to get the professional record from a female prostitute," Kinsey explained, "than it is to get the record of her personal sex life with her boy friend or with her husband. In dealing with an uneducated and timid older woman from a remote farm area or mountain country, the sequence has to become most desultory, including only the simplest questions about each type of sexual experience, with no details on any point until the whole of the history has been covered in a preliminary way. By then the subject should have become more confident, and it will be possible to ask her such details . . . as would have shocked her at the beginning of the interview. A good interviewer becomes very sensitive to the reactions of his subjects, immediately drops any line of inquiry which causes embarrassment, and stays with simpler matters until the subject is ready to talk in more detail. This technique, more than anything else, probably accounts for the fact that among the 12,000 persons who have been interviewed in the present study, all but three or four have completed their histories; and those few would not have been lost if we had known as much at the beginning of this study as we now know about a good sequence of questions in an interview."

Kinsey and his associates phrased their questions in a way which placed the burden of denial on the subject. "We always assume that everyone has engaged in every type of activity," Kinsey explained. "Consequently we always begin by asking *when* they first engaged in such activity. This places a heavier burden on the individual who is inclined to deny his experience; and since it becomes apparent from the form of our question that we would not be surprised if he had had such experience, there seems to be less reason for denying it."

Above all, the Kinsey interviewers asked their questions directly, "without hesitancy and without apology. If the interviewer shows any uncertainty or embarrassment, it is not to be expected that the subject will do better in his answers. Euphemisms should not be used as substitutes for franker terms." Previous studies, Kinsey recalled, used such circumlocutions as "touching yourself" for masturbation, "securing a thrill from touching yourself" for orgasm through masturbation, and "relations with other persons" or even "sex delinquency" for sexual intercourse. "With such questions, the subject cannot help but sense the fact that the interviewer is not sure that sex is an honorable thing, and a thing that can be frankly talked about. Evasive terms invite dishonest answers."

In addition to teaching his interviewers to phrase their questions frankly and directly, Kinsey taught them to tailor their vocabulary to match that of the respondents. Even a neophyte interviewer, of course, would hesitate to ask an Episcopalian dowager in Boston how old she was when she first got laid; Kinsey stressed the equally important lesson that you can't establish rapport with a longshoreman fresh out of a San Francisco brothel by asking him at what age he first had premarital heterosexual intercourse.

These simple examples hardly do justice to the many sensitive ways in which the Kinsey group developed the face-to-face interview into a precision instrument. Readers desiring more details should consult the 27-page chapter entitled "Interviewing" in the 1948 Kinsey report. Many later studies benefited from these interviewing techniques pioneered at the Kinsey Institute.

Much of the popular interest in the Kinsey studies was focused on broad generalizations. It was amazing and fascinating to learn, for example, that two-thirds of all the married women interviewed reported that they had achieved orgasm in one way or another before marriage. Of at least equal importance, however, were Kinsey's findings on the way sexual behavior differed among a wide variety of subgroups — the unmarried, the married, and the formerly married, the devout and the less devout, Protestant, Catholic, and Jewish, grade-school graduates, high-school graduates, and college graduates, unskilled laborers and professional people, young people in their teens and respondents in their seventies, those born before 1900 and those born after 1919.

Dr. Kinsey had planned to present his findings in a series of ten major reports, of which only the first four have to date been published:

Sexual Behavior in the Human Male (1948)
Sexual Behavior in the Human Female (1953)
Pregnancy, Birth, and Abortion (1958)
Sex Offenders (1965)

Sexual Factors in Marital Adjustment
The Heterosexual-Homosexual Balance
Sexual Adjustments in Institutional Populations
Prostitution
Sex Education
Other Special Problems

The first two of these reports are by far the most important. They are based on the histories of more than 5,000 white males and more than 5,000 white females. (Nonwhite respondents were excluded from the data summarized in the first two reports, and women interviewed in prison were excluded from the second report. Kinsey did not trust the size or the typicalness of his nonwhite sample, and deemed it unwise to distort the sample as a whole by averaging in the highly atypical female prison population.)

How reliable are the Kinsey statistics? Whole books have been written on that subject. At the time the Kinsey reports were first published, the issue was a matter of heated debate. Now that tempers have cooled, four generalizations seem warranted:

(1) Whatever their shortcomings, the Kinsey data remain today the fullest and most reliable sampling of human sexual behavior.

(2) Competent surveys made since 1953 in the U.S. and in other countries tend in most respects to confirm the key Kinsey findings. The better the methodology of the survey, the closer the agreement with Kinsey is likely to be.

(3) The comparative Kinsey findings are even more reliable than the individual figures. When Kinsey reports that 8 percent of his male respondents and 0.4 percent of his female respondents reached orgasm at least once in contacts with animals of other species, for example, the true figures for the American population as a whole may be either somewhat higher or somewhat lower. A larger and better-selected sample might somewhat alter the precise figures. When he reports, however, that such behavior is far more common among males than among females, it seems inconceivable that any improvements in sampling or in data-collecting and data-processing techniques would alter the comparative findings.

(4) To the extent that Kinsey's figures err, they almost certainly understate rather than overstate the facts concerning such taboo kinds of sexual behavior as orgasms with animals of other species.

While the Kinsey reports were based primarily on the data secured through interviews, they also tapped an exceedingly broad range of data assembled in other ways. The Kinsey Institute library is one of the world's foremost collections of materials on human sexuality; its contents were combed for relevant data, topic by topic, as the reports were being prepared, and the footnotes review in detail the ways in which the Kinsey interview findings agree or disagree with earlier views. Special studies were also commissioned by the Kinsey Institute. Gynecologists and others had long debated, for example, the degree of sensitivity of the female organs to tactile stimulation. Kinsey arranged to have the genitalia of 879 women tested by three male and two female gynecologists. The tests involved touching sixteen points on the clitoris, labia majora and labia minora, vestibule, vaginal lining, and cervix, plus gentle pressure at three points, to determine whether the women were aware of the contact or pressure and whether they could localize it. (Few women were conscious of a touch on the vaginal lining or cervix.)* The Kinsey group also secured and made use of detailed eyewitness observations of male and female orgasms during masturbation and during heterosexual and homosexual intercourse.

I can think of very few problems of human sexuality, except love, on which the Kinsey reports failed to cast a fresh, clear light. As examples, let us examine in some detail the Kinsey findings on three topics of major concern — female frigidity (and comparable conditions in the male), male homosexuality (with a note on lesbianism), and sexuality in children.

* The gynecological findings of absence of vaginal sensitivity might be challenged, however, on the ground of veterinary findings. Drs. R. L. Kitchell, B. Campbell, T. A. Quilliam, and L. L. Larson reported in the *Proceedings of the American Veterinary Medical Association* for 1955 that they had found free nerve endings emerging from "genital corpuscles" imbedded in the genital tissues of domestic animals. These genital corpuscles, they noted, might respond in one way under ordinary circumstances and in a quite different way when the surrounding tissues are engorged with blood during erotic arousal. This "curious morphological feature," they added, may lead to heightened sensitivity during sexual arousal. The nerve endings emerging from the genital corpuscles, moreover, were deeply enough imbedded so that they might be responsive during coitus but not responsive to a light touch or gentle pressure with the tissues in a nonengorged condition. The 879 women tested in the Kinsey project were presumably not sexually aroused, or not fully aroused, when the tests were made. The possibility thus remains open that the human vaginal lining, though insensitive on gynecological examination, develops a special sensitivity to coital stimulation during full sexual arousal.

Female frigidity

The crucial fact about female frigidity unearthed by the Kinsey study is its rarity. Nine out of ten of the women contributing their sex histories to the Kinsey project reported having experienced orgasm by the age of thirty-five. An additional eight percent reported having experienced sexual arousal, though without orgasm.

This leaves a *maximum* of two percent of women who could be characterized as "frigid" in the strictest sense — that is, incapable throughout their lives of experiencing either erotic arousal or orgasm.

Even this two percent figure, moreover, is almost certainly an overestimate. Some of the women who denied sexual arousal had no doubt forgotten earlier experiences. Some no doubt failed to identify arousing experiences as sexual, like Havelock Ellis's case of the woman who never identified the innocent little self-play she enjoyed with the evils of masturbation. Others among the "frigid" women, though never in fact aroused, might nevertheless have been arousable if suitably stimulated under appropriate circumstances. And, finally, some of the unaroused two percent might have been arousable as adults if their upbringing during childhood and adolescence had been less crippling.

The Kinsey group concluded:

"It is probable that all females are physiologically capable of responding [to sexual stimulation] and of responding to the point of orgasm."

Once that bold central generalization was established, however, the Kinsey study went on to stress the exceedingly wide variations which characterize female sexual behavior in almost all other respects.

Consider, for example, the age at which orgasm is first experienced. One girl baby was observed experiencing orgasm during masturbation at the age of four months. Four cases were observed before the age of one year, and 23 girls aged three or less were observed experiencing orgasm.

Among the women who contributed their histories to the Kinsey project, sixteen out of nearly 5,000 (0.3 percent) recalled having reached orgasm by the age of three. Thereafter the recollection became more common; 2 percent of the women respondents recalled orgasm by the age of five; 4 percent by seven, and 9 percent by eleven years of age. One respondent in seven (14 percent) reported having experienced orgasm before the onset of adolescence.

Thereafter the curve showing age at first orgasm becomes steeper.

Nearly a quarter of the women in the sample recalled experiencing orgasm by the age of fifteen, more than half by the age of twenty, and more than three-quarters by the age of twenty-five. More than two-thirds (64 percent) experienced their first orgasm before marriage. At the other extreme, three women in the sample reached their first orgasm between the ages of forty-eight and fifty.

Sexual arousal, of course, was more common than the experience of orgasm. Thus one girl in three had experienced erotic arousal prior to first menstruation, as compared with only one girl in seven who had experienced orgasm by then. By age twenty, 89 percent of the girls had experienced erotic arousal but only 53 percent had experienced orgasm.

The women also varied widely in the nature of the stimulation leading to first orgasm. For 40 percent the stimulus was masturbation, and about half of these discovered the possibility for themselves rather than reading about it or learning about it from others. For 24 percent the first orgasm was during heterosexual petting, for 10 percent it was during premarital coitus, for 5 percent it was during an erotic dream, for 3 percent it was during a homosexual experience, and for 1 percent it was purely psychical, without bodily stimulation. Of the 3,826 women reporting the nature of their first orgasm, only 17 percent reported that it occurred during marital coitus. These figures, however, include women unmarried at the time of the interview. Among married women, 30 percent reported that their first orgasm occurred during marital coitus.

Women also varied enormously in the *frequency* of their orgasmic responses. Some reported only one or two orgasms during their entire lives. "This was true even of some of the females who had been married for long periods of years. There were others who had responded in 1 or 2 percent of their marital coitus, but there were many more who had responded much more often, including some 40 to 50 percent who had responded in nearly all of their coitus." Some women had no orgasm with their first two or three husbands but experienced orgasm thereafter. Some women who never reached orgasm with their husbands experienced it during extramarital affairs — and some who regularly had orgasm with their husbands did not experience it during extramarital affairs.

Masturbation proved to be the surest route to climax; the women who masturbated reported achieving orgasm in 95 percent of all attempts.

Some women achieved orgasm in only one way — only through masturbation, or only through petting, or premarital coitus, or marital coitus, or homosexual contact. A few women experienced orgasm only during nocturnal dreams. At the other extreme, some women had experienced orgasms from all six types of stimulation. The Kinsey group found "every conceivable combination of the possible types of sexual outlet."

Havelock Ellis, van de Velde, and many others had reported that women take longer than men to reach orgasm. This observation, of course, was based primarily on marital coitus. The Kinsey group stressed, however, that tardiness is not an inherent limitation on female response.

> Actually there are some females who regularly reach orgasm within a matter of fifteen to thirty seconds in their petting and coital activities. Some regularly have multiple orgasms which may come in rapid succession, with lapses of only a minute or two, or in some instances of only a few seconds between orgasms. Such speed is found in only a small percentage of the females. . . . Of the 2,114 females in our sample who supplied data on the time usually taken to reach orgasm in masturbation, some 45 percent had regularly done so in something between one and three minutes, and another 24 percent had averaged four to five minutes. About 19 percent had averaged something between six and ten minutes, and only 12 percent regularly took longer than that to reach orgasm. In all of these groups there were, of course, females who had deliberately taken longer than necessary to reach orgasm in order to prolong the pleasure of the experience.

The most important and most obvious conclusion to be drawn from these and similar data is that the human female, like the human male, really is an orgasm-experiencing animal.

When we turn, however, from the number of women who experience orgasm to the number of *times* they experience it, and to the *proportion* of sexual encounters which terminate in orgasm, a very different picture emerges.

The average husband, to start with a simple Kinsey statistic, has experienced 1,523 orgasms* prior to marriage; the average wife has experienced only 223 premarital orgasms. Even allowing for the wife's younger age at marriage, this is a striking discrepancy.

After marriage, almost all husbands achieve orgasm in almost all of

* The number of orgasms experienced by the average male *before* marriage is thus roughly equivalent to the number he will experience in marital coitus during the first fifteen or twenty years of his marriage!

their marital coitus. For their wives, in contrast, only about 75 percent of coital acts end in orgasm.

The 25 percent of coital acts which do not lead to female orgasm, moreover, are very seriously maldistributed.

During the first year of marriage, for example, one wife in four fails to experience orgasm in coitus at all. Eleven percent experience it rarely, 25 percent experience it often, and 39 percent experience it always or almost always.

During the twentieth year of marriage, fewer women fail to experience orgasm at all, and nearly half experience it always or almost always. Nevertheless, 15 percent of coitus in the twentieth year of marriage still fails to culminate in orgasm.

A few women who had never once experienced orgasm in coitus during their first twenty-seven years of marriage learned to achieve it thereafter.

One final statistic. Almost all males, of course, experience orgasm during their first act of coitus. Among college girls, in contrast, only 8 percent in the Kinsey sample reported orgasm during their first coital experience.

How do the women who regularly experience orgasm in marital coitus differ from those who experience it only sometimes, or rarely, or never?

Formal education, the Kinsey group learned, has only a very slight effect. College graduates are only very slightly more orgasmic in marital coitus than eighth-grade graduates.

The daughters of men in white-collar occupations were a bit more likely to achieve orgasm in all or most of their marital coitus than the daughters of laborers, but the difference was small.

Women born in the 1920's were somewhat more likely to experience orgasm regularly in their marital coitus than women born in the Victorian 1890's; again the difference was small.

Women in their forties and fifties were somewhat more orgasmic in marital coitus than those in their teens and twenties.

But the major difference between wives who responded with orgasm always or almost always, as distinguished from wives who rarely or never achieved orgasm, was their premarital experience. Among girls who had experienced orgasm before marriage, for example, 45 percent experienced orgasm in all or almost all of their marital coitus during the first year of marriage. Of the girls who had not experienced orgasm prior to marriage, only 25 percent experienced it always or almost always during the first year of marriage. Among women who had experienced 25 or more orgasms before marriage, only 13 percent failed to reach orgasm during the first year of marriage; among those who had never experienced orgasm before marriage, 44 percent failed to respond to the point of orgasm during the first year.

"There was no factor which showed a higher correlation with the frequency of orgasm in marital coitus," the Kinsey group reported, "than the presence or absence of premarital experience in orgasm." The effect of this premarital experience was still visible after ten or fifteen years of marriage. "It is doubtful if any type of therapy has ever been as effective as early experience in orgasm, in reducing the incidences of unresponsiveness in marital coitus, and in increasing the frequencies of response to orgasm in that coitus."

Premarital orgasm during masturbation, premarital orgasm during petting, and premarital orgasm during coitus all proved to be correlated with greater orgasmic response to coitus in marriage. With respect to petting, for example, the Kinsey group reported:

> It is sometimes said that premarital petting may make it difficult for the female to be satisfied with coitus in marriage. The statement has never been supported by any accumulation of specific data, and we have not seen more than three or four such cases. On the other hand, we have the histories of nearly a thousand females who had done premarital petting and who had then responded excellently in their marital coitus.

They also pointed out:

> The techniques of masturbation and of petting are more specifically calculated to effect orgasm than the techniques of coitus itself, and for that reason it is sometimes possible for a female to learn to masturbate to orgasm even though she has difficulty in effecting the same end in coitus. Having learned what it means to suppress inhibitions, and to *abandon herself to the spontaneous physical reactions which represent orgasm** in masturbation, she may become more capable of responding in the same way in coitus. There are very few instances, among our several thousand histories, of females who are able to masturbate to orgasm without becoming capable of similar responses to coitus.

* The phrase which I have italicized is the Kinseyan equivalent of van de Velde's "conscious intention to enjoy all the stimuli received," and of the Masters-Johnson phrase, "sensate focus."

Against this background, the nature of the "frigidity problem" can be more clearly perceived.

The problem is *not* the inability of women to achieve orgasm. Ninety percent of all women (based on the Kinsey sample) can and do achieve orgasm at least occasionally. Among married women, 97 percent have experienced orgasm.

The problem is that a substantial minority of women fail to achieve orgasm *during coitus,* or achieve it only rarely or occasionally during coitus. Many or most of the women who achieve orgasm in only a proportion of their coital encounters achieve it promptly and regularly — always or almost always — in masturbation.

More bluntly stated, the problem of frigidity results in very large measure from the fact that coitus, for many women on many occasions, is a less effective route to orgasm than masturbation.

Note that Kinsey did *not* say that masturbation is more enjoyable than coitus, or that it is preferable in any other way. What Kinsey did report was a very simple fact which tens of millions of women know from their own experience: regardless of the joys of coitus, and regardless of its emotional rewards, it is less likely than masturbation to terminate in orgasm — and for some women it always or almost always terminates without orgasm.

I shall return to this problem of female frigidity in the chapter on Masters and Johnson. Even in the absence of the later Masters-Johnson findings, however, one point was abundantly clear by 1953:

The most probable cause of female frigidity in marriage is the repression of sexual responsiveness, and especially the repression of masturbation, in girls and young women before marriage.

Male inadequacies which more or less parallel female frigidity appear to be far rarer and to pose less of a problem — except, of course, for those individual males who happen to suffer from such a condition and who can draw little comfort from the fact that their problem is relatively rare. Three major types of male inadequacy have been described:

(1) Ejaculatory impotence. Males in this group are unable to ejaculate during coitus despite erotic arousal and durable erection. They generally achieve orgasm and ejaculation by masturbating after coitus. Masters and Johnson have described this rare condition in detail; Kinsey found only six cases among 4,108 respondents.

(2) Erectile impotence, that is, inability to achieve an erection or to maintain one until orgasm. This condition is slightly less rare (66 out of 4,108 respondents). It is exceedingly rare among young men; the Kinsey group found only six cases among 1,627 men aged twenty-five or less (0.4 percent). As men age, however, erectile impotence gradually sets in. Thus 6.7 percent of Kinsey's respondents were impotent by age fifty-five and 25 percent by age sixty-five. Most (but not all) men are impotent in their eighties. Kinsey concluded that the condition is less stressful than female frigidity, for an obvious reason. "In many older persons, erectile impotence is, fortunately, accompanied by a decline in and usually complete cessation of erotic response."

(3) Premature ejaculation, a condition in which the male ejaculates immediately following entry of the penis into the vagina, or even while entry is being attempted. Kinsey cited no statistics, except to report: "For perhaps three-quarters of all males, orgasm is reached within two minutes after the initiation of the sexual relation, and for a not inconsiderable number of males the climax may be reached within less than a minute or even within ten or twenty seconds after coital entrance. Occasionally a male may become so stimulated psychically or through physical petting that he ejaculates before he has affected genital union."

Kinsey conceded that premature ejaculation in the male is a serious problem for the female, but he refused to recognize premature ejaculation as a problem for the male. "The idea that the male who responds quickly in a sexual relation is neurotic or otherwise pathologically involved is, in most cases, not justified scientifically," he wrote. Rapid ejaculation is typical of male mammals generally; chimpanzees, for example, take from ten to twenty seconds. "Far from being abnormal, the human male who is quick in his sexual response is quite normal among the mammals, and usual in his own species. . . . It would be difficult to find another situation in which an individual who was quick and intense in his responses was labeled anything but superior, and that in most instances is exactly what the rapidly ejaculating male probably is, however inconvenient and unfortunate his qualities may be from the standpoint of the wife in the relationship."

It seems to me very clear that on this point Kinsey was quite wrong. The later Masters-Johnson studies of premature ejaculation reveal in precisely what respects he was wrong.

The history of epidemiology is replete with instances in which the conquest of a major disease brings to light minor diseases which have previously been overlooked. As typhoid fever disappeared, for example, a whole series of other kinds of fever previously mistaken for typhoid fever came into view. It is my personal belief that we are on the brink of such a development in the field of human sexuality. Many cases of *male* sexual inadequacy now mistakenly attributed to female frigidity are likely to come to diagnosis as preventive and therapeutic measures gradually whittle away the frigidity problem.

Male homosexuality

Havelock Ellis once estimated that from two to five percent of Englishmen were homosexual. Magnus Hirshfeld, the German authority on sexual studies (and himself a homosexual), estimated after many kinds of inquiry that about 2.3 percent of German males were homosexual. The Kinsey data are similar; about four percent of American males are homosexual — if you define a homosexual as a man whose sexual contacts and erotic arousals are exclusively with other males.

But the Kinsey group condemns this definition, or any other effort to classify men and women into rigorous categories such as "homosexual," "heterosexual," and "bisexual." The facts turn out to be much more complex, and can only be understood by focusing on *homosexual behavior* and *homosexual reactions* rather than on *homosexual people* or on homosexuality as a separate entity.

In addition to the four percent of respondents who informed Kinsey that they had *never* been aroused by a woman or had sexual relations with a woman, for example, there were an additional four percent who reported that during certain periods of their lives after adolescence — periods of three years or longer — both their sexual contacts and their sexual arousals were exclusively homosexual. Thus these two groups comprise eight percent of the population.

An additional five percent of the respondents reported a few heterosexual contacts or arousals — but with the homosexual very much predominating for a three-year period or longer. Thus thirteen percent of males reported being predominantly homosexual in behavior and responses for at least one period in their lives.

And five percent more (for a total of eighteen percent) reported that during at least a part of their lives, homosexual and heterosexual contacts and arousals were about equally balanced.

Next, seven percent of the males, though primarily heterosexual, reported occasional, more than incidental, homosexual contacts or arousals during a three-year period of their lives or longer. The five groups so far described add up to one male in every four.

Another five percent (for a total of thirty percent) had occasional homosexual experiences or arousals. And an additional thirteen percent of males or so, Kinsey estimated, react erotically to other males at least once in a while, even though they have never had an overt homosexual contact after adolescence.

In all, the Kinsey Institute figures indicate, thirty-seven percent of males have had or will have at least one homosexual experience to the point of orgasm at some time between adolescence and old age; only fifty percent of the male population will reach old age with neither a homosexual orgasm nor a homosexual arousal.*

We ourselves were totally unprepared to find such incidence data when this research was originally undertaken [the Kinsey group reported in 1948]. Over a period of several years we were repeatedly assailed with doubts as to whether we were getting a fair cross section of the total population or whether a selection of cases was biasing the results. It has been our experience, however, that each new group into which we have gone has provided substantially the same data. Whether the histories were taken in one large city or another, whether they were taken in large cities, in small towns, or in rural areas, whether they came from one college or from another, a church school or a state university or some private institution, whether they came from one part of the country or from another, the incidence data on the homosexual have been more or less the same.

* These male homosexual statistics aroused the most alarm and disbelief when first published in 1948. Yet the facts had been known in broad outline for decades. "As regards the prevalence of homosexuality in the United States," Havelock Ellis wrote in the 1890's, "I may quote from a well-informed American correspondent: 'The prevalence of sexual inversion in American cities is shown by the wide knowledge of its existence. Ninety-nine normal men out of a hundred have been accosted on the streets by inverts, or have among their acquaintances men whom they know to be sexually inverted. . . . The world of sexual inverts is, indeed, a large one in any American city, and it is a community distinctly organized — words, customs, traditions of its own; and every city has its numerous meeting-places: certain churches where inverts congregate; certain cafés well-known for the inverted character of their patrons; certain streets where, at night, every fifth man is an invert. . . . You will rightly infer that the police know of these places and endure their existence for a consideration; it is not unusual for the inquiring stranger to be directed there by a policeman.' "

As might be expected, orgasm through homosexual contact is less frequent among married men. About ten percent of married men reported one or more homosexual orgasms during marriage and prior to the age of twenty-five. Thereafter the incidence of homosexual orgasm among married men appears to go down; but the Kinsey group cites several reasons for believing that this drop is more apparent than real. "Many married males with homosexual experience currently in their histories have, undoubtedly, avoided us," they point out. "Younger, unmarried males have regularly given us some record of sexual contacts with older, married males." In this as in other respects, the Kinsey findings on the incidence of homosexuality, to the extent that they err at all, must err on the side of being too low.

In addition to the males who engage in homosexual behavior for a part of their lives and in heterosexual behavior for the remainder, many of the men in the Kinsey sample engaged in both types of activity during the same period of time. "For instance, there are some who engage in both heterosexual and homosexual activities in the same year, or in the same month or week, or even in the same day. There are not a few individuals who engage in group activities in which they make simultaneous contact with partners of both sexes." Hence, the Kinsey group concluded:

> Males do not represent two discrete populations, heterosexual and homosexual. The world is not to be divided into sheep and goats. Not all things are black nor all things white. It is a fundamental of taxonomy that nature rarely deals with discrete categories. Only the human mind invents categories and tries to force facts into separated pigeon-holes. The living world is a continuum in each and every one of its aspects. The sooner we learn this concerning human sexual behavior the sooner we shall reach a sound understanding of the realities of sex.

The Kinsey data also distinguish sharply between homosexual behavior on the one hand and such phenomena, often confused with homosexuality, as effeminate appearance or behavior. The effeminate type of male often identified as a "fairy," "fag," or "queen," for example, accounts for only about ten percent of men with homosexual acts in their histories. Similarly, homosexuality must be distinguished from submissiveness in sexual relationships; even exclusively homosexual males may be dominant or "masculine" in their sexual behavior. "The basic phenomenon to be explained is the individual's preference for a partner of one sex, or for a partner of the other sex, or his acceptance of a partner of either sex. This problem is, after all, part of the broader problem of choices in general: the choice of the road that one takes, of the clothes that one wears, of the food that one eats, of the place in which one sleeps, and of the endless other things that one is constantly choosing. A choice of a partner in a sexual relation becomes more significant only because society demands that there be a particular choice in this matter, and does not so often dictate one's choice of food or of clothing." While this can hardly be the whole truth, the Kinsey study's emphasis on homosexuality as a matter of *partner choice* rather than of inherent sexuality seems to me a profoundly clarifying step forward in our understanding of the human condition. The fact that one human being occasionally, frequently, or invariably has sex relations with persons of the same sex tells us as little about the rest of his character and behavior as does the fact that he occasionally, frequently, or invariably has sexual relations with persons of the opposite sex.

Dr. Kinsey drew several moral implications from his homosexual findings. One concerned the self-defeating nature of many of society's efforts to repress homosexuality. The high-school boy discovered in a single homosexual act, for example, "is likely to be expelled from school and, if it is in a small town, he is almost certain to be driven from the community. [This was written before 1948.] His chances for making heterosexual contacts are tremendously reduced after the public disclosure, and he is forced into the company of other homosexual individuals among whom he finally develops an exclusively homosexual pattern for himself. Every school teacher and principal who is faced with the problem of the individual boy should realize that something between a quarter and a third of all the other boys in the same high school have had at least some homosexual experience since they turned adolescent."

Community reaction to a boy or man caught in a homosexual act, Dr. Kinsey believed, "would probably be modified if it were kept in mind that the same individual may have a considerable heterosexual element in his history as well." Hence those in disciplinary positions "may profitably consider the balance between the heterosexual and homosexual in an individual's history, rather than the homosexual aspects alone."

Finally, Kinsey recommended, "the judge who is considering the case of the male who has been arrested for homosexual activity should keep in mind that nearly 40 percent of all the other males in the town could be arrested at some time in their lives for similar activity. . . . The court might also keep in mind that the penal or mental institution to which he may send the male has something between 30 and 85 percent of its inmates engaging in the sort of homosexual activity which may be involved in the case before him."

Let me add one final point. The Victorian era was by all odds the most restrictive in modern history with respect to homosexuality as well as heterosexuality. In particular, the trial and conviction of Oscar Wilde for homosexuality in 1895 triggered a rising concern with the problem throughout Europe and the United States. Thus we would expect little boys born during the 1890's — the final decade of Victoria's reign — to be the most firmly indoctrinated against homosexuality and the least likely to engage in homosexual behavior. Yet the figures for Kinsey's male respondents as a whole — 6.3 percent of all orgasms from homosexual contacts, 69.4 percent from heterosexual contacts, 24 percent from masturbation or nocturnal emissions, and 0.3 percent from contacts with animals of other species — apply with little change to men born in the 1890's as well as to those born two or three decades later. Victorianism could and did repress talk about sex, knowledge of sex, understanding of sex, and (in part at least) enjoyment of sex. It could and did surround sexual acts with feelings of guilt and shame. Yet sexual behavior — including homosexual behavior — was very much the same in Victoria's time as today.

Kinsey's findings concerning female homosexuality (lesbianism) parallel in most respects his findings on male homosexuality, except that almost all the actual figures are smaller.

Only 28 percent of his women respondents reported one or more recollections of homosexual arousal or orgasm by the age of forty-five, for example, as compared with nearly 50 percent of his male respondents.

Between the ages of sixteen and twenty, only 3 percent of his unmarried women actively engaged in homosexual relationships to the point of orgasm, as compared with 22 percent of his unmarried men. Between the ages of thirty-six and forty, this "active incidence" rose to 10 percent among his unmarried women but to 40 percent among his unmarried men. The proportion of exclusively homosexual women — that is, women who were never even once aroused by a male or reached orgasm with a male — was even smaller than the proportion of exclusively homosexual men. Women, like men, ranged all the way from this exclusively homosexual orientation to an exclusively heterosexual orientation, with about a third of all women, more or less, occupying the intermediate area.

One marked difference between male and female homosexuality did appear, however. Women were much less promiscuous than men in their homosexual contacts. Thus 71 percent of the women reporting homosexual contacts reported only one or two partners, as compared with 51 percent among men. At the other extreme, only 4 percent of the women having such contacts reported more than ten partners, as compared with 22 percent among men.

One problem which fascinated Dr. Kinsey was the greater harshness of social and legal attitudes toward male homosexuals. "Our search through the several hundred sodomy opinions which have been reported in this country between 1696 and 1952," the Kinsey group wrote, "has failed to reveal a single case sustaining the conviction of a female for homosexual activity." Only one woman was sentenced to Indiana Women's Prison for homosexual activity during a seventy-year period — "and that was for activity which had taken place within the walls of another institution." Male prisons, of course, hold large numbers of inmates imprisoned for homosexual acts. The Kinsey group made a special study of the enforcement of sex laws in New York City; they found tens of thousands of arrests and convictions for male homosexuality during a ten-year period but only three arrests of women — and all three of the women's cases were dismissed without conviction or punishment. To explain this differential vindictiveness on the part of the police, the courts and public opinion, the Kinsey group cited eleven possible factors:

1. In Hittite, Jewish and other ancient cultures, women were socially less important than males, and their private activities were more or less ignored.

2. Both the incidences and frequencies of homosexual activity among females are in actuality much lower than among males. Nevertheless, the number of male cases which are brought to court are, even proportionately, tremendously higher than the number of female cases that reach court.

3. Male homosexual activity more often comes to public attention in street solicitation, public prostitution, and still other ways.

4. Male homosexual activity is condemned not only because it is homosexual, but because it may involve mouth-genital or anal contacts. It is not so widely understood that female homosexual techniques may also involve mouth-genital contacts.

5. Homosexual activities more often interfere with the male's, less often interfere with the female's marrying or maintaining a marriage.

6. The Catholic Code emphasizes the sin involved in the wastage of semen in all male activities that are noncoital; it admits that female noncoital activities do not involve the same species of sin.

7. There is public objection to the effeminacy and some of the other personality traits of certain males who have homosexual histories; there is less often objection to the personalities of females who have homosexual histories.

8. The public at large has some sympathy for females, especially older females, who are not married and who would have difficulty in finding sexual contacts if they did not engage in homosexual relations.

9. Many heterosexual males are erotically aroused when they consider the possibilities of two females in sexual activities. In not a few instances they may even encourage sexual contacts between females. There are fewer cases in our records of females being aroused by the contemplation of activities between males.

10. There are probably more males and fewer females who fear their own capacities to respond homosexually. For this reason, many males condemn homosexual activities in their own sex more severely than they condemn them among females.

11. Our social organization is presently much concerned over sexual relationships between adults and young children. This is the basis for a considerable portion of the action which is taken against male homosexual contacts; but relationships between older women and very young girls do not so often occur.

Sexual Behavior from Birth to Adolescence

Here the Kinsey reports fully confirm the earlier findings of Havelock Ellis, Sigmund Freud, and others: human sexuality is not a phenomenon which makes its appearance at puberty or during adolescence. It is clearly visible during infancy and early childhood. Not only can infants and very small children experience sexual stimulation; they can and do experience orgasm as well. And their sexual experience takes many forms — homosexual, heterosexual, voyeuristic, exhibitionistic, oral, anal, and so on.

Part of the evidence, of course, comes directly from the Kinsey interview data. Among the more than 5,000 girls and women interviewed, as noted above, sixteen recalled having experienced orgasm by three years of age, more than a hundred recalled orgasm by the age of five, and some 600 respondents — 14 percent of the entire female sample — recalled experiencing orgasm by the age of thirteen.

How accurate were these adult recollections of orgasm in childhood? As one of several tests, Dr. G. V. Ramsey in a related project used the Kinsey interview schedule to question all 291 of the boys enrolled in the seventh and eighth grades of schools in a fairly large Illinois city. The Kinsey group also interviewed a limited number of children under the age of five years, and secured eyewitness accounts of sexual behavior in very young children from parents and scientific observers. These data led to the conclusion that "hugging, kissing . . . self-manipulation of genitalia, the exploration of the genitalia of other children, and some manual and occasionally oral manipulation of the genitalia of other children occur in the two- to five-year-olds more frequently than older persons ordinarily remember from their own histories."

The youngest infants in which orgasm was actually observed were a four-month-old girl baby and a five-month-old boy. In all, nine boy babies were observed having orgasm before their first birthday. These infant orgasms in boys, the Kinsey group reports, are, "except for the lack of an ejaculation, a striking duplicate of orgasm in an older male. . . . A fretful babe quiets down under the initial sexual stimulation, is distracted from other activities, begins rhythmic pelvic thrusts, becomes tense as climax approaches, is thrown into convulsive action, often with violent arm and leg movements, sometimes with weeping at the moment of climax. After climax the child loses erection quickly and subsides into the calm and peace that typically follows adult orgasm. It may be some time before orgasm can be induced again after such an experience."

Detailed observations in girls are quite similar. One intelligent young mother, for example, carefully recorded a masturbatory sequence of her three-year-old daughter in these terms:

> Lying face down on the bed, with her knees drawn up, she started rhythmic pelvic thrusts, about one second or less apart. The thrusts were primarily pelvic, with the legs tensed in a fixed position. The forward components of the thrusts were in a smooth and perfect rhythm which was unbroken except for momentary pauses during which the genitalia were readjusted against the doll on which they were pressed; the return from each thrust was convulsive, jerky. There were 44 thrusts in unbroken rhythm, a slight momentary pause, 87 thrusts followed by a slight momentary pause, then 10 thrusts, and then a cessation of all movement. There was marked concentration and intense breathing with abrupt jerks as orgasm approached. She was completely oblivious to everything during these later stages of activity. Her eyes were glassy and fixed in a vacant stare. There was noticeable relief

and relaxation after orgasm. A second series of reactions began two minutes later with series of 48, 18, and 57 thrusts, with slight momentary pauses between each series. With the mounting tensions, there were audible gasps, but immediately following the cessation of pelvic thrusts there was complete relaxation and only desultory movements thereafter.*

One of Havelock Ellis's informants, it will be recalled, reported that when he masturbated to orgasm at the age of three or four, "the curious thing was . . . that there seemed to be no limit to the number of times I could consecutively produce this sensation." The Kinsey Institute data fully confirm this ability of many young boys to achieve multiple orgasm. In a series of 182 cases actually observed, 81 of the prepubertal boys observed achieved orgasm only once, 17 achieved it twice, 42 achieved it three, four, or five times in succession, 30 achieved it from six to ten times in succession, and 12 achieved it more than ten times in succession. The record was twenty-one orgasms in a row. In sixty-four cases, the interval between orgasms was timed; it was a minute or less in eighteen cases and more than five minutes in twenty-one cases. One eleven-month-old baby boy had fourteen orgasms in thirty-eight minutes; one eleven-year-old had eleven orgasms in an hour; a fourteen-year-old had eleven orgasms in four hours; and so on. This multiorgasmic capacity appears to diminish in males at about the time at which orgasm begins to be accompanied by ejaculation of semen, though some adult males retain a multiorgasmic ability to an extent which astonishes other males.

Actual coitus — the introduction of the penis into the vagina — is also frequently reported before adolescence, though here there are marked differences depending on socio-economic level. For example, three-quarters of the boys who will never go beyond eighth grade report attempts at preadolescent coitus, as compared with only one-quarter of the boys who will subsequently go to college. The Kinsey report on males explains the difference in these ways:

* Havelock Ellis, incidentally, was quite familiar with this phenomenon. He described "masturbation in a child of six or nine months who practiced thigh-rubbing. . . . When sitting in her high chair she would grasp the handles, stiffen herself, and stare, rubbing her thighs quickly together several times, and then come to herself with a sigh, tired, relaxed, and sweating, these seizures, which lasted one or two minutes, being mistaken by the relations for epileptic fits." Ellis cited as his source a paper by J. P. West in the *Transactions of the Ohio Pediatric Society* for 1895.

The lower level boy has considerable information and help on these matters from older boys or from adult males, and in many cases his first heterosexual contacts are with older girls who have already had experience. Consequently, in this lower level, preadolescent contacts often involve actual penetration and the children have what amounts to real intercourse. The efforts of the upper level boys are less often successful, in many cases amounting to little more than the apposition of the genitalia. With the lower level boy, preadolescent coitus may occur with some frequency, and it may be had with a variety of partners. For the upper level boy, the experience often occurs only once or twice, and with a single partner or two.

Among the women in the Kinsey sample, about one in twenty recalled coitus or attempts at coitus before adolescence.

Sexual play as distinct from masturbation to orgasm and coitus, of course, is vastly more common. Some 48 percent of the women in the Kinsey sample reported sexual play before adolescence. Homosexual play was a trifle more common than heterosexual play, and about 18 percent of the women in the sample reported both kinds. Among males, 48 percent reported preadolescent homosexual play and 40 percent reported preadolescent heterosexual play.

I need hardly call attention to the significance of these findings for teachers, parents, and others concerned with sex education. I should point out, however, that these findings refer to a period in American history when the Victorian repression of childhood sexuality was still in full effect, and when the activities described were in many or most cases severely punishable. The conclusion is inescapable that parent and teacher attitudes toward sexual behavior in children have very little effect on the incidence of that behavior. The chief effects of adult efforts at repression are to drive the behavior underground and to surround it with an aura of guilt and shame.

One area of continuing social concern is sexual contact between children and adults. Krafft-Ebing's and Freud's approaches to this problem have been described above. Dr. Kinsey's approach was quite different.

First of all, he confirmed the frequency of such child-adult contacts. Among 4,441 women interviewed, for example, 1,075 or nearly one in four recalled sexual contacts before adolescence with males at least fifteen years of age and at least five years older than they were. In 609 cases in which the older males were identified, they were strangers in 52 percent, friends or acquaintances in 32 percent, uncles in 9 percent, fathers in 4 percent and brothers in 3 percent.

In more than half of the cases, the "contact" consisted in the exhibition of the male genitals to the child. In an additional 9 percent, the approaches were verbal only. In 32 percent there was fondling without genital contact, and in 27 percent there was either manipulation of the little girl's genitals or manipulation of the man's genitals by the little girl. Oral contacts with the male or female genitals was reported in about 20 cases (2 percent) and actual coitus in about 30 cases (3 percent).

Very little physical harm was reported from these contacts. "Among the 4,441 females on whom we have data," the Kinsey report notes, "we have only one clear-cut case of serious injury done to the child, and a very few instances of vaginal bleeding which, however, did not appear to do any appreciable damage." The Krafft-Ebing stereotype of the lust-crazed sadist appears to be a relatively minor risk to American little girls.

The little girls were erotically aroused, the Kinsey report adds, in five percent of the contacts, and experienced orgasm in one percent. "The contacts had often involved considerable affection, and some of the older females in the sample felt that their preadolescent experience had contributed favorably to their later socio-sexual development."

Eighty percent of the little girls, in contrast, reported that they had been emotionally upset or frightened. "A small portion had been seriously disturbed; but in most instances the reported fright was nearer the level that children will show when they see insects, spiders, or objects against which they have been adversely conditioned." And the Kinsey report concludes:

> When children are constantly warned by parents and teachers against contacts with adults, and when they receive no explanation of the exact nature of the forbidden contacts, they are ready to become hysterical as soon as any older person approaches, or stops and speaks to them on the street, or fondles them, or proposes to do something for them, even though the adult may have had no sexual objective in mind. Some of the more experienced students of juvenile problems have come to believe that the emotional reactions of the parents, police officers, and other adults who discover that the child has had such a contact, may disturb the child more seriously than the sexual contacts themselves. The current hysteria over sex offenders may very well have serious effects on the ability of many of these children to work out sexual adjustments some years later in their marriages.

Since Dr. Kinsey's death in 1956, his Institute for Sex Research at Indiana University has continued under the direction of Dr. Paul H.

Gebhard, and a number of publications have emerged. The most comprehensive are the two already cited — *Pregnancy, Birth, and Abortion* (1958), by Gebhard, Pomeroy, and Martin of the original Kinsey team, plus Cornelia V. Christenson, who joined the team under Dr. Kinsey but did not begin interviewing respondents until after his death; and *Sex Offenders,* by Gebhard, Pomeroy, Christenson, and John H. Gagnon, a sociologist who worked with the Kinsey Institute from 1959 to 1968.

Under Dr. Gebhard's direction, the Institute has moved in a number of new directions. Its doors have been opened to qualified outside scholars who are free to consult its materials. It is gradually becoming a training center for young scientists planning careers in sex research. A steady stream of journal articles and other publications flows from the Institute staff. Several of the volumes which Dr. Kinsey planned but never completed — such as the report on homosexuality — are currently in preparation.

One criticism of the initial Kinsey sample concerned the fact that the respondents were volunteers rather than a random sample. Kinsey countered this criticism in a number of ways which I find completely persuasive.* While agreeing that a random sample would be better, he pointed out that on a topic like sex behavior, a random sample was utterly impossible because too many members of the sample would refuse to answer questions.

Much has changed since Dr. Kinsey reached that conclusion, however. In 1967, the Kinsey Institute employed the National Opinion Research Center to conduct a Kinsey-type survey based on a random sample of college students — the first random sample in the history of American sex research. Dr. William Simon is in charge of this project. That such a sample can now be secured is the result in no small part of Dr. Kinsey's own earlier work — and is a tribute to the enormous popular impact of his 1948 and 1953 reports.

Publication of the results is scheduled for 1970 or 1971 and is being awaited with particular interest because it will reveal for the first time, at

* One brilliant Kinsey maneuver, for example, was to interview *all* of the members of many clubs, associations, and other local groups — even though days of effort might be required to secure the last few volunteers. The figures for these "100-percent samples" could hardly be challenged on the ground of inadequate or skewed sampling. When the figures for the 100-percent samples were compared with the figures for the Kinsey sample as a whole, moreover, few significant differences appeared.

least with respect to college students, whether the so-called "sexual revolution" of the 1940's, 1950's, and 1960's is a verbal revolution only, or is also a behavioral revolution.

Preliminary reports from the new college study suggest that there have been few startling changes; trends visible in the 1940's and 1950's have simply continued. Relatively few men in the original Kinsey study, for example, had their first coitus with prostitutes; even fewer reported first coitus with prostitutes in the 1967 sample. The usual time for first coitus reported by college girls in the original sample was during the last two years of high school and the first two years of college; this remains true of the 1967 sample. But one startling change in college sexuality has emerged from the current study:

A much larger proportion of the girls interviewed in 1967 reported that they *enjoyed* their first coital experience.

Here, surely, is a trend that augurs well for the future — a trend to be welcomed by those of us who believe that sexual fulfillment is better than sexual frustration. Certainly Dr. Alfred C. Kinsey would have welcomed it. And though he was hardly an arrogant man, he would no doubt have suspected and hoped that the greater sexual frankness and the clearer understanding of human sexuality which his two classic reports engendered were among the factors responsible for the greater capacity of today's college girls to enjoy sexual intercourse.

6

Women Rediscover Their Own Sexuality

Elizabeth Blackwell, Leah Schaefer, Niles Newton, Helena Wright, Mary Jane Sherfey

THE five towering figures whose work has been reviewed in prior chapters were all men — but this does not mean that women have remained silent through the decades. A comprehensive history of sex research would no doubt review the works of such women as the following, among others:

Josephine Ball
Dorothy W. Baruch
Marion Bassett
Lura Beam
Lauretta Bender
Therese Benedek
Phyllis Blanchard
Marie Bonaparte
Dorothy Dunbar Bromley
Mary Steichen Calderone
Cornelia V. Christenson
Katharine B. Davis
Maxine Davis
Simone de Beauvoir
Helene Deutsch
Evelyn Mills Duvall
Marynia F. Farnham
Jan Gay
Phyllis Greenacre
Gladys H. Groves
Eleanor Hamilton
E. W. Hardenberg
Ruth Herschberger
Marion Hilliard
Evelyn Hooker
Karen Horney
Isabel E. Hutton
Marie Jahoda
Judith S. Kestenberg
Sophia J. Kleegman
Melanie Klein
Viola Klein

Marie E. Kopp	Marie N. Robinson
Lena Levine	Margaret Sanger
Joan Malleson	Georgene H. Seward
Margaret Mead	Alice B. Stockham
Emily H. Mudd	Hannah M. Stone
Jane E. Oltman	Marie C. Stopes
Elizabeth Parker	Clara Thompson
Julia Rainer	Moya Woodside

No doubt many more might be added to this list.

Faced with the obvious impossibility of doing justice to so vast a literature, I have chosen instead to present here five women writers on sexuality. I have selected these five rather than others, in part because they span the major trends from Havelock Ellis's day to our own; and in part because their writings, when reviewed in sequence, have a synergistic effect. The combined impact is much greater than the sum of the impacts of the five considered individually. I should add, in all frankness, that these particular five women were also chosen in part because I found their ideas of personal interest to me.

I am well aware that some readers will find my segregation of female scientists from males objectionable. They may condemn my treatment of five men in five chapters, followed by a condensation of five women into a single chapter, as a typical example of arrogant male chauvinism. My defense is simple. Let women readers reconsider their objections when they come to the end of this chapter. I happen to believe that the five contributions reviewed in this chapter, considered as an integral developmental unit, present the most significant theme in the history of the scientific study of sex. I am unwilling to water down that significance by scattering the contributions through my book.

Four of the five women presented in this chapter are still living. I know them all personally and I am indebted to each of them for her helpfulness.

Elizabeth Blackwell (1821–1910)

Elizabeth Blackwell was a member of an amazing Anglo-American family dedicated to women's rights, the abolition of slavery, the suppression of prostitution, and other noble causes. Born in England, she was educated in the United States and graduated from the Geneva Medical

College in Geneva, New York, in 1849, at the age of twenty-eight — the first woman in either England or the United States to qualify fully as a regular physician. She also studied medicine in Philadelphia, Paris, and London.

Elizabeth was one of thirteen brothers and sisters, nine of whom survived to adult life and seven of whom became famous or at least recognized outside their personal circles.* Neither Elizabeth nor her four sisters — Anna, Marianne, Emily, and Sarah Ellen — ever married. Nor did her brother John Howard Blackwell. Elizabeth and Emily, however, each adopted a daughter, and Sarah Ellen adopted two daughters and a son.

Emily (1826–1910) secured her M.D. degree five years after Elizabeth. The prejudice against women physicians was strong in the 1850's; but these two remarkable sisters managed to found the New York Infirmary for Women and Children in 1853, when Elizabeth was thirty-two and Emily twenty-seven. Twelve years later they founded the Women's Medical College of the New York Infirmary as a doorway into medicine for other women.

In 1869, at the age of forty-eight, Dr. Elizabeth Blackwell returned to her native England and remained there until her death at the age of eighty-nine. Throughout her English years, she practiced medicine, campaigned against prostitution and against the hygienic regulation of prostitution, backed other legal reforms, and wrote about sex in Victorian England. Her published books and pamphlets include: *Counsel to Parents on the Moral Education of Their Children in Relation to Sex (Under Medical and Social Aspects)*, 1879; *Moral Education in Relation to Sex* (with Dr. Emily Blackwell), 1883; *Wrong and Right Methods of Dealing with Social Evil* (Prostitution), 1883.

In 1902, the year after Queen Victoria's death, Elizabeth Blackwell's writings were collected and published in a three-volume compendium entitled *Essays in Medical Sociology.* Because of her unorthodox and (for Victorian times) sensationally unconventional background, Dr. Blackwell's views on sex were of very great interest to her contemporaries, and her books went through many editions. I still find them interesting. Elizabeth Blackwell was not a researcher in the contemporary sense; her writings were based primarily on religious and philosophical principles

* For biographical details I have relied almost exclusively on Elinor Rice Hays's scholarly account of the family, *Those Extraordinary Blackwells.*

— spiced here and there with anecdotes from her medical experiences with patients. But contemporary research can be seen in clearer perspective, I believe, if projected against the relatively liberal views of Dr. Blackwell at the turn of the century.

Her most significant monograph, "The Human Element in Sex" (1894), with which *Essays in Medical Sociology* begins, opens with a statement of position:

> This work is written from the standpoint of the Christian physiologist.
>
> The essence of all religions is the recognition of an Authority higher, more comprehensive, more permanent than the human being. The characteristics of Christian teaching is the faith that the Supreme Authority is beneficent as well as powerful. The Christian believes that the Creative Force is a moral force, of more comprehensive morality than the human being that it creates. Under the symbol of a wise and loving parent — the most just, efficient, and attractive image that we know of — we are encouraged to regard this unseen Authority as being in direct relation with every atom of creation, and as desirous of drawing each atom into progressively higher forms of existence.
>
> The Christian physiologist, therefore, knowing that there is a wise and beneficent purpose in the human structure, seeks to find out the laws and methods of action by means of which human function may accomplish its highest use.

Having thus proclaimed her quintessentially Victorian point of view, Dr. Blackwell next proceeded to summarize her sexual doctrines under six major heads:

> The Distinctive Character of Human Sex
> Equivalent Functions in the Male and Female
> On the Abuses of Sex — I. Masturbation
> On the Abuses of Sex — II. Fornication
> The Development of the Idea of Chastity
> Medical Guidance in Legislation

The distinctive element in truly *human* sexuality, Dr. Blackwell explained, is its mental and moral character.

> The physical instinct is shared with the rest of the animal creation. . . . The brute, both male and female, is at certain times blindly dominated by the physical impulse of sex. This impulse in the lower animal is a simple imperative instinct, unhesitatingly yielded to, with no preparation or after-thought,

with no calculation, shame, triumph, or regret. But it is very different with the human race, as it grows from lower to higher states of society. Thoughts and feelings, social ties and conscience, religious training and the objects of life, all act upon the distinctive mental element in sex. . . . It will thus be seen that in the varieties of degradation of our sexual powers, as well as in their use and ennoblement, it is the predominance of the mental and spiritual element in our nature which is the characteristic fact in human sex. The inventions and abuses of lust, as well as the use and guidance of love, alike prove the striking and important distinction which exists between the sexual organization of man and that of the lower animals.

Dr. Blackwell stressed also the sense of *shame* as an important characteristic of human sexuality. "If an animal is not frightened by human beings it never hesitates to carry on sexual congress in their presence, and neither before nor after the special act does it exhibit the smallest approach to shame in relation to it. In man, however, from the earliest dawn of the approaching faculty, self-consciousness is intense. This is not only observed in well brought-up boys and girls, who shrink from indecency of word or action, but it is never entirely extinguished in the most corrupt man or woman; and even the poor little waifs of our streets, blighted from earliest infancy, exhibit marked consciousness of their infantile depravity."

Sexual education, Dr. Blackwell then went on to explain, consists in large part in enlarging and intensifying this innate sense of shame concerning sexual feelings and acts.

Dr. Blackwell conceded that sex is not entirely evil in itself. On the contrary, it is necessary for the propagation of the human race and is "capable of great development toward good or toward evil. . . . It may grow into a noble sympathy, self-sacrifice, reverence, and joy, which enlarge and intensify the nature through the gradual expansion of the inborn moral elements of sex." Alternatively, it may grow into "the perversion and extreme degradation of sex which is observable only in the human race. It is the degradation of this mental power when running riot in unchecked license that converts men and women into selfish and cruel devils — monsters, quite without parallel in the brute creation."

Dr. Blackwell described in guarded terms the joys of proper or licit sexuality: "The passing sight of the object beloved, a word, a look, a smile, will make sunshine on the gloomiest day. The consciousness of spiritual attraction will sustain and guard through long waiting for more complete union.

"The physical pleasure which attends the caresses of love is a rich endowment of humanity, granted by a beneficent Creative Power. There is nothing necessarily evil in physical pleasure. Though inferior in rank to mental pleasure, it is a legitimate part of our nature."

Nor did Dr. Blackwell limit her approval to "a word, a look, a smile," or to "the caresses of love." Even sexual intercourse is permissible under certain conditions:

> The sexual act itself, rightly understood in its compound [mental-moral-physical] character, so far from being a necessarily evil thing, is really a divinely created and altogether righteous fulfillment of the conditions of present life.

There are, however, limits to this permissiveness:

> This act, like all human acts, is subject to the inexorable rule of Moral Law. Righteous use brings renewed and increasing satisfaction to the two made one in harmonious union. Unrighteous use produces satiety, coldness, repulsion, and misery to the two remaining apart, through the abuse of a Divine gift.

This inherent dualism between licit and illicit sex, righteous and unrighteous sex, as we shall see later, remains a major characteristic of most sexual thinking today — even among those who have abandoned the religious grounds for the dualism, and among those who have abandoned the doctrine that the marriage ceremony provides an adequate dividing line between righteous and unrighteous.

Dr. Blackwell, like most parents today, thought it particularly important to *slow down* sexual development and to delay sexual awareness and satisfaction among children, adolescents, and young adults:

> Early chastity strengthens the physical nature, creates force of Will, and concentrates the intellectual powers on the nobler ends of human life. . . .
>
> Continence is indispensable to the physical welfare of a young man until the age of twenty-one;* it is advantageous until twenty-five; it is possible without physical injury throughout life. . . .
>
> In Moral Education, the first step is to secure the slow development of sex; the second, its legitimate satisfaction through honorable companionship, followed by marriage.

* By the age of twenty-one, however, as Kinsey noted, most males have already passed the peak of their sexual capabilities.

Charles Drysdale, it will be recalled, had considered nocturnal emissions of semen among boys and young men as a dreadful disease, *spermatorrhea,* which could be prevented only by sexual intercourse. This view remained influential even among proper Victorian ladies. Dr. Blackwell regarded it as the counsel of the devil; she herself taught that nocturnal emissions are a "natural form of relief," just like menstruation — "the parallel in the two sexes is exact."

"The measureless evil" caused by fear of nocturnal emissions, Dr. Blackwell wrote, "is illustrated by the inquiry made of a friend of mine, a clergyman, by an intelligent French mother about to move to Paris with her son. This lady, sensible and even pious, wrote to the clergyman to inquire 'if providing a mistress for her son would be very costly in Paris.' "

One mother of a twenty-year-old son, worried about spermatorrhea, consulted Dr. Blackwell directly about her son's nocturnal emissions.

> The joyful light of gratitude with which she learned the truth on this important subject — viz., that the occasional spontaneous action of the organs (not voluntarily forced by corrupt thought or actions) is natural and beneficial — will not easily be forgotten. It was like the gleam of transcendent joy which I have seen illuminate the face of a young mother at the shrill cry of her first-born infant.

Ignorance of the beneficial nature of nocturnal emissions, Dr. Blackwell added, has even led to "the cruel advice sometimes given to a young man to degrade a woman, and sin against his own higher nature, by taking a mistress or resorting to harlots."

Dr. Blackwell, in short, believed in "the single standard." Males as well as females should be held to the strictest moral standards in using their God-given powers of sexuality.

Though tolerant of *involuntary* seminal emissions, Dr. Blackwell echoed unhesitatingly the dire warnings against male masturbation which obsessed so many of her contemporary physicians. Indeed, she went further than many of them and added warnings against masturbation — which she termed "self-abuse or the Solitary Vice" — on the part of little girls. She defined this "dangerous practice" as "the voluntary purposed excitement of the genital organs, produced by pressure or friction of those parts, or by the indulgence of licentious thoughts." Like Freud, Dr. Blackwell observed that masturbation may begin "in little children from the age of two years old."

Dr. Blackwell did not recommend that these very young children be frightened or threatened if caught masturbating. "No punishment must ever be resorted to. The little innocent child, to whom the sentiment of sex is an unknown thing, will confide in its mother if encouraged to do so. If kindly but seriously told that it may make little children ill to do this thing, and the reply being given (as in cases I have known) that 'the little feeling comes by itself,' the child should be encouraged to come to its mother and she 'will help him drive the feeling away.' "

More stringent measures, of course, might be applied to older children who masturbate — for the risk of lifelong disaster hangs over them. "My attention was painfully drawn to the dangers of self-abuse more than forty years ago by an agonized letter received from an intelligent and pious lady, dying from the effects of this inveterate habit. She had been a teacher in a Sunday-school, and the delight of a refined and intelligent circle of friends. But this habit, begun in childhood in ignorance of any moral or physical wrong which might result to her nature, had become so rooted that her brain was giving way under the effects of nervous derangement thus produced, whilst her will had lost the power of self-control."

Fornication, the second abuse of sex against which Dr. Blackwell warned, she defined as "the promiscuous intercourse of the sexes. It is the yielding to the domination of the simple physical impulse of sex, with no regard to a fundamental aspect of this relation — viz., the well-being of offspring. Fornication is the attempt to divorce the moral and physical elements of human nature."

On this score, too, Dr. Blackwell was a feminist, insisting that men are no more sexually corrupt and no more licentious than women.

> The unbridled impulse of physical lust is as remarkable in the latter as in the former. The astounding lust and cruelty of women uncontrolled by principle is a historical fact.
>
> The most destructive phase of fornication is promiscuous intercourse. This riotous debauchery introduced the devastating scourge of syphilis into Western Europe in the fourteenth century. Promiscuous intercourse can never be made "safe." The resort of many men to one woman, with its results, is against nature.

In contrast to fornication, Dr. Blackwell set "chastity and continence." These, she remarked, "are not primitive instincts in either sex;

they are the higher growth of reason, and of the religious and legal guidance by which in every age it has been found indispensable to direct the impulse of sex."

Parents, of course, are the chief agents for instilling the ideals of chastity and continence into children; but Dr. Blackwell also believed that the state had an important role — through the legal repression of prostitution. She wrote many essays on this subject, and devoted much of her energy throughout her long life to secure repressive action in Parliament. In this, she and her fellow Victorians were only partially successful; prostitution (as distinct from street soliciting) is still not a crime in England. In 1885, however, the Victorian reformers did succeed in securing the repeal of the law designed to curb venereal disease by providing periodic medical inspection for prostitutes.

Dr. Blackwell stressed the value of modesty; indeed, she thought that physicians were physically examining too many patients, and in particular making too many vaginal examinations with the speculum:

"The personal modesty of patients — that elementary virtue in Christian civilization — must be carefully cherished by the physician, who, more than any other, is acquainted with its influence on the sexual nature. The common resort to sexual examination is an evil grown up in medical practice of comparatively modern date. The use of the speculum should be strictly limited by absolute necessity." Dr. Blackwell apparently assumed that no physician would unnecessarily examine the vagina of a well-to-do patient — but what about the poor? "Reckless use [of the vaginal speculum] among the poor is a serious national injury. I know from fifty years' medical experience amongst the poor, as well as the rich, that this custom is a real and growing evil." Indeed, "the natural sentiment of personal modesty is seriously injured amongst respectable people," poor as well as rich, by too many physical examinations.

Above all else Dr. Blackwell urged parental sexual vigilance:

> The earliest duty of the parent is to watch over the infant child. Few parents are aware how very early evil habits may be formed.

And again:

> The mother's eye, full of tenderness and respect, must always watch over her children. Self-respect cannot be too early inculcated. The keynote of moral education is respect for the human body. The mother should caution

the child plainly not to touch or meddle with himself more than is necessary; that his body is a wonderful and sacred thing, intended for important and noble ends; that it must not be played with or trifled with, or in any way injured. Even thoughtless breach of delicacy should be checked with a gentle gravity which will not repel or abash, but impress the child.

This watchfulness over the young child, by day and night, is the first duty to be universally inculcated.

Having devoted so much attention to masturbation, fornication, prostitution, and other sexual evils, what has Dr. Blackwell to say about the joys of proper sexuality — sex in marriage?

On a rapid first reading of her work, I thought she had omitted marital relations altogether — but on more careful rereading, I found two paragraphs on marital coitus hidden away in the chapter on fornication.

Although physical sexual pleasure is not attached exclusively, or in women chiefly, to the act of coition, [she stated], it is a well-established fact that in healthy, loving women, uninjured by the too frequent lesions which result from childbirth, increasing physical satisfaction attaches to the ultimate physical expression of love. A repose and general well-being results from this natural occasional intercourse, whilst the total deprivation of it produces irritability.

Dr. Blackwell, unlike many of her contemporaries, conceded that women as well as men have orgasms. She called them "sexual spasms."

Coitus, however, remained for Dr. Blackwell "the special act of the male":

The affectionate husbands of refined women often remark that their wives do not regard the distinctively sexual act with the same intoxicating physical enjoyment that they themselves feel, and they draw the conclusion that the wife possesses no sexual passion. A delicate wife will often confide to her medical adviser (who may be treating her for some special suffering) that at the very time when marriage love seems to unite them most closely, when her husband's welcome kisses and caresses seem to bring them into profound union, comes an act which mentally separates them, and which must be indifferent or repugnant to her. But it must be understood that it is not the special act necessary for parentage which is the measure of the compound physical and moral power of sexual passion; it is the profound attraction of one nature to the other which marks passion, and delight in kisses and caresses — the love touch — is physical sexual expression as much as the special act of the male.

If I understand this correctly — and I'm not sure that I do — Dr. Blackwell is saying — in modern terminology — that "refined women" enjoy mild necking ("kisses and caresses"), but find coitus "indifferent or repugnant"; other women may enjoy coitus occasionally after they have been married awhile but before they have had too many children.

I have not selected Dr. Blackwell as an extreme example of Victorian sexual repression. Far more horrendous examples can be found on the shelves of almost any library. Indeed, it is Dr. Blackwell's sweet reasonableness which marks her off from the thundering denunciations of sex voiced by so many of her contemporaries.

This sweet reasonableness, I believe, brings Dr. Blackwell remarkably close to the attitudes many young parents today seek to achieve in the sexual education of their young children, and to the attitudes of most schools today. As Dr. Blackwell recommended, parents and schools do not actually punish young children for masturbating or for other childhood sexual activities — but the sense that sex is shameful and disgusting is nevertheless effectively communicated. The taboo against *nudity* persists, and the parental *watchfulness* recommended by Dr. Blackwell persists, along with the parental compulsion to *slow down* or delay the onset of sexual feelings and behavior. Indeed, the proper time for the onset of sexual activity might be defined, today as in Dr. Blackwell's day, as "several years later than it actually does arise."

As I shall show in the next section of this chapter, the effects of this Blackwellian approach — today as in Dr. Blackwell's day — are sexually disastrous.

Knowing Dr. Blackwell's strong views on the sexual upbringing of children, I was naturally curious to know what happened to her adopted daughter, Kitty. Elinor Rice Hays's *Those Extraordinary Blackwells* supplies the details. Dr. Blackwell had adopted Kitty in 1854, when, as she herself wrote, "the utter loneliness of life became unbearable." She had gone for the purpose to the immigration center at Randalls Island (predecessor of Ellis Island), and had "deliberately selected the most pathetic child she saw." Dr. Blackwell was then thirty-three and Kitty seven-and-a-half. Kitty thereafter attended various girls' boarding schools, often unhappy and always miserably dressed; when a pitying relative bought her new clothes, another relative took them away from the girl and burned them. When Kitty was thirteen she and a girl cousin fell in love; the two girls began their letters to each other, "Dear Betrothed"; some of Kitty's were signed "Captain Kidd" or "Robert Kidd." The rest of the family was amused and pleased.

Mrs. Hays describes Kitty at twenty-three as "an attractive, gay, energetic girl, a good pianist, an excellent cook, excellent in French and Italian, an omnivorous reader, and 'a perfect encyclopaedia on a variety of subjects.' " Kitty was inordinately fond of children. Dr. Blackwell approved of this and promised Kitty that when money became available Kitty would be permitted to adopt "first one and then another tiny urchin, so that you shall have a little family always with you." The idea that Kitty might want children of her own apparently never occurred to Dr. Blackwell.

Dr. Blackwell in her fifties took under her wing a young man of twenty-four who (by Blackwellian standards) had lived a profligate life and had turned to Dr. Blackwell for moral succor; the two remained close for several years. Kitty, then thirty, fell in love with the young man — but Dr. Blackwell remained blind to her feelings, and nothing came of the relationship. Indeed, Kitty never did marry. To Dr. Blackwell's delight Kitty remained at her side as companion, housekeeper, and nurse until her death when Kitty was sixty-three.*

Leah Cahan Schaefer

Much of the sexual misery and sexual inadequacy in Western culture today stems directly from the methods of child rearing urged on parents by Dr. Blackwell and other Victorians, and still followed to a considerable extent by many parents.

The best large-scale documentation of this cause-and-effect relationship between a Victorian upbringing and sexual frustration in adult life — for women especially — was assembled by Dr. Robert Latou Dickinson. Dr. Dickinson practiced gynecology in Brooklyn and Manhattan

* Cornelia, the adopted daughter of Elizabeth Blackwell's unmarried sister Sarah Ellen, fell in love at twenty with a young man of whom the Blackwells did not approve. One of Cornelia's unmarried aunts talked to the young man sternly, and the affair was apparently ended. But Cornelia continued to see him secretly and soon became pregnant. The family objections to the affair were thereupon withdrawn and Cornelia married. Susan, also adopted by Sarah Ellen, died at eleven. Paul, Sarah Ellen's third adopted child, was neglected by Sarah Ellen and mistreated by the rest of the Blackwells; he was often told that he would come to no good end, and eventually disappeared. Anna, Emily's adopted daughter, married conventionally and had children.

from 1882 to 1924; during this period he accumulated 5,200 meticulously recorded case histories of his women patients — and from 1,200 of these women he secured in addition detailed sexual histories. Nowhere else in the history of sex research are the bitter fruits of sexual Victorianism more tragically documented than in Dickinson's *A Thousand Marriages* (1932) and *The Single Woman* (1934), both based on his patients' histories, and both of which he wrote with Dr. Lura Beam. A typical Dickinson case history:

No. 617. A bride of eight months comes to Dr. Dickinson for obstetrical care. She says that sexual intercourse is painful, and reports lack of any sexual arousal. The baby is born; a second baby follows. On her next visit, "after five years of marriage she is actively considering separation and divorce. She 'adores' her husband, he is intellectual and fine; she 'admires' him immensely. Sexually she has only indifference and repulsion toward him."

What is wrong? Why has sex been divorced from love in this and so many other cases?

"The facts in the background," Dr. Dickinson answers, "are that she was brought up by an aunt [who] had a fear complex and a disgust of sex. She in turn was the oldest daughter of a mother who had many children and hated to have them." Thus the basic pattern emerges: the dual heritage of Victorian idealism and Victorian frigidity, passed like an empty hope chest from generation to generation. And the male sexual heritage is no richer.

"The characteristic coitus of these couples," Dr. Dickinson summed up, "is brief and physiologically male, the female remaining passive and isolated. Once or twice a week there takes place, without preliminaries, an intromission lasting up to five minutes, at the end of which the husband has an orgasm and the wife does not. Both man and woman know that the woman has no animating desire. She submits without welcome to the embrace; it may occur without excitement and she expects it to terminate without orgasm."

Dr. Dickinson's patients, however, belonged to a generation now dead and gone. To document in detail the reasons for *their* sexual problems would serve little useful purpose today. Instead, let us consider the generation of women now in their twenties and thirties and forties. For many of them, I regret to report, Victorianism on the Blackwellian pattern remains a debilitating sexual disease today. The most recent documentation of this sad fact is an unpublished thesis entitled "Sexual Experiences and Reactions of a Group of Thirty Women as Told to a Female Psychiatrist" — submitted in 1964 to Teachers College, Columbia University, by Dr. Leah Cahan Schaefer.

Dr. Schaefer is a former jazz and folk singer who after a dozen years in show business and an unhappy marriage felt the need for psychoanalysis. In the course of therapy she decided, at the suggestion of her analyst, to become a therapist herself. She is now in her forties, remarried, practicing in New York City, and has a small daughter. I first heard about her thesis via the sex-research grapevine, secured a copy from Dr. Schaefer, and began to thumb it through with very little interest. Its shortcomings were immediately obvious. Dr. Schaefer had simply interviewed thirty women at length — in several sessions totaling eight hours per respondent on the average — about their sexual experiences and feelings. All of her respondents were white, all middle-class, all married, all living in or near New York City. Almost all had attended college, and almost all had careers outside the home. Fifteen had had psychotherapy with Dr. Schaefer herself before being interviewed; the other fifteen had had therapy with other psychotherapists. As I scanned these methodological preliminaries, the likelihood that I would learn anything of value from Dr. Schaefer's thesis seemed to dwindle further.

Then, suddenly, my hopes soared. What Dr. Schaefer in all modesty had succeeded in doing was to bring Robert Latou Dickinson up to date. She had shown that the sexual tragedies of the 1890's were still occurring in the 1950's and 1960's — and for the same underlying reason: Victorianism.

The thirty women Dr. Schaefer selected for her sample were peculiarly qualified both by their education and by their prior experience during psychotherapeutic sessions to talk frankly, precisely, and feelingly about their own sexuality. They had had substantial numbers of sexual encounters, and partners. They knew the right words, and were not afraid to speak them.

To summarize Dr. Schaefer's findings succinctly, these women born in the nineteen thirties and forties had been reared very much as Dr. Blackwell had recommended in 1894 that children should be reared. They were taught that all sex, including masturbation, was taboo except within the bounds of marriage. The feeling that sex is shameful, as Dr. Blackwell had urged, was inculcated in them from an early age. Though the thirty women differed in many respects from one another, "a degree of similarity pervaded the individual cases. This similarity was in the manifested expressions of guilt, the need for secrecy, the feelings of wrongness, and the fear of discovery and punishment which colored most of [their sexual] recollections."

Dr. Schaefer asked her thirty respondents, for example, about their very first sexual memories. A few could remember back to the time before they learned to talk and to understand spoken words; these few dredged up warm, accepting feelings toward sex. One woman recalled "a sensation of warm water, and my little brother being in the tub with me, a lovely feeling." * The earliest sexual recollection of another woman was of "playing a delightful game with my little brother and a neighbor girl. I was about three years old then." The three children were able to explore one another sexually with "no fear at all of being caught . . . like any other game."

Memories dating from *after* the age of three, however — after the acquisition of spoken language — were almost invariably surrounded by feelings of fear, shame, and guilt.

One woman recalled "great difficulty in sleeping" as a child "because I was so afraid I might pee in bed and then my mother would beat me. That too-early toilet training sure made me afraid I'd lose control." This fear of losing control runs like a refrain through Dr. Schaefer's entire study.

Another woman recalled putting her finger in her own feces and a feeling that she was "doing something terribly wrong. I led such a sneaky life, it seemed to me, and everything that had to do with *me* was always done in secret."

A third woman recalled at age four seeing "a friend's father lying naked on his bed." The memory was still surrounded by a strong and persistent feeling that it was *wrong* for her to have seen this. She explained that the feeling of wrongness stemmed "from the fact that I don't ever remember seeing my own parents naked." Doors were always shut in her own home, "so somehow I knew I wasn't supposed to see a man naked." Dr. Blackwell would have applauded.

Two further reports:

* The interviews were tape-recorded. This and the quotations which follow are verbatim transcripts from the tapes.

(Age 4) I was so shaken by being discovered, and I am still left with such a feeling of guilt, for being under the bed with my brother — as though we were having sex.

(Age 5) I remember bewildering feelings of attraction for boys when I was in kindergarten . . . and even though I knew this was wrong, my fantasy desire for sex excitement was very strong.

But while feelings of shame and guilt surrounded sex generally during the childhood of these girls, it was with respect to masturbation that Dr. Blackwell's doctrine was most intensively inculcated. Even homosexuality was less anxiety-provoking than masturbation in these women. Says Dr. Schaefer, "The words used . . . to describe the feelings attached to these [masturbatory] experiences seem to be mainly guilt, anxiety, and shame." And these, we must remember, were not little Victorian girls; they are women now in their thirties and forties — the mothers of today's children and adolescents.

One of Dr. Schaefer's respondents recalled discovering at the age of four "the pleasure involved in exposing my genital area to the forceful stream of water in the bathtub. My mother seemed to be very angry when she caught me doing this." The mother, it is true, did not punish her four-year-old daughter; in this as in other respects, she followed Dr. Blackwell's prescription. But the message got through all the same. "There was something very repressive about her when she reprimanded me — as though she were holding in something . . . but it was coming out in anger from her frozen face." Needless to add, maternal anger did not curb the masturbatory activity. "I just found a different way — a private way, so that she wouldn't catch me at it anymore . . . under the covers while I was taking a nap every day. I knew I shouldn't do this, but used to feel that I just couldn't help myself."

Other little girls, instead of defying the taboo, "internalized" it and did their best to obey it — but they emerged with the same overpowering sense of guilt as the defiers. Thus one woman reported that as a child she felt "a powerful need to control myself from any kind of desires for self-stimulation. I thought it was just wrong, terrible — I still do — and I remember that as a child I used to go to sleep at night wearing many, many layers of underclothes" in order to protect herself from "those hateful feelings."

Several of the girls reported masturbating by rubbing against the bedclothes or some other object in order to escape the taboo against *handling* or *touching* themselves. (This evasion of the literally interpreted taboo is also common among boys.)

One respondent cogently remarked, "Masturbation was a good idea in the sense that it was a pleasure . . . but the guilt robbed it of all those good feelings."

Even sophisticated older girls continued to feel shame and guilt after they learned that the taboo was unfounded. One woman recalled: "I certainly knew [masturbation] was something that could not be acceptable to my mother, because sex in general wasn't acceptable to her. I had read enough parents' magazines to know that you should allow your children to masturbate, so I felt legally justified, but I think I felt morally corrupt."

Another respondent, who had practiced masturbation to orgasm from the age of six, recalled during her interview with Dr. Schaefer a puzzling nightmare which she had repeatedly experienced during her adolescence:

"The dream began with me and my mother going up in an elevator. Suddenly my mother looked like a witch, and said to me, 'You know what you have, don't you? You have the hands of a devil!' "

The meaning of the nightmare seemed to hit this woman for the first time as she retold it to Dr. Schaefer, and she immediately blurted out — "I just realized what that dream meant . . . what my mother was referring to — that I had *masturbating* hands!"

The shame-guilt-"dirty" feelings attached to masturbation survived in one woman following her marriage, separation from her husband, and a series of subsequent affairs. "Since I wasn't having an affair with anybody," she reported, "I just decided to try [masturbation]. But I felt so darned guilty that I very soon stopped. . . . I just feel it is wrong — it's perverted. I don't think it is something we were meant to do."

Then, in a direct though unwitting echo of Dr. Blackwell, she added: "Masturbating is animal-like. There's no love, so what's the purpose?"

Another, also unhappily married and divorced, reported: "I tried it a few times during my adult married life, but I can't have an orgasm and I don't enjoy it. I have the feeling that it's wrong to touch my own genitals and that it's wrong to masturbate, so I don't try any more."

The horror of masturbation inculcated in these women during their childhood, it is very important to note, spread out to contaminate their feelings toward other sexual activities as well. Three of the women in Dr. Schaefer's sample reported difficulty in learning how to use a vaginal diaphragm, or an inability to use one at all, because it involved the forbidden childhood act of "touching themselves." And *all thirty* reported a feeling of repulsion and disgust when they first realized that their parents must have performed sexual intercourse in order to have children. Masturbation is bad; hence sex is bad — yet their own parents were guilty of that filthy practice!

The clearest example of the way in which the childhood masturbation taboo contaminated the entire sexual lives of these women, decade after decade, came from a woman who quite consciously recognized that her adult inability to have orgasm in sexual intercourse with her husband grew directly out of the taboo.

"I know that if we lie on our sides, face to face, and I hold my thighs together in a particular way, I can have an orgasm in just a few moments. But I'm always ashamed to let him see me do this — because this is the way I used to masturbate, and I'm so afraid he might recognize it as such — and then I'd feel mortified."

One woman reported that, as a result of the childhood taboo, it was still "absolutely impossible" for her to touch her own genitals. She, significantly enough, was the only woman in the group who had developed the capacity to achieve orgasm by fantasy alone, without any genital stimulation. Yet, she reports, "even *that* was just filled with guilt. I feel that it is a terribly sick thing to do. It's not so much wrong, it's sick." Dr. Blackwell, it will be recalled, had included sexual arousal through "the indulgence of licentious thoughts" in her definition of masturbation, along with actual genital friction.

Only three of these women, interestingly enough, had been brought up in piously religious families. The religious foundation for the masturbation taboo and for other forms of sexual repression had faded since Dr. Blackwell's time — but the taboos and repressions had survived. The psychiatrists had replaced the bishops. "It's not so much wrong, it's sick."

As they approached adolescence, a few of the girls in Dr. Schaefer's sample looked forward to their first menstruation with eager anticipation as a welcome sign of approaching womanhood. But several others had no advance warning whatever of menstrual bleeding — and not one of the thirty received *adequate* advance briefing.

"I thought I was bleeding to death," one recalled.

"It was just terrible — I thought I was having an appendicitis attack," said another.

"I felt guilt and embarrassment about it happening because I thought it was connected somehow with masturbating," said a third. And a fourth added, "Somehow I got the feeling that this, too, was my *fault.*"

Nor did communication between mothers and daughters improve after the menstrual flow appeared. One woman reported:

"It was a tremendous shock to me. . . . I ran home from school that day and there was a big flurry and scurry" to find a sanitary pad and belt. "Mother finally explained to me that 'this would happen every month,' but no other information at all — not why, not what for, nothing."

Other mothers used their daughters' first menstruation as the occasion for instilling further negative attitudes toward sex. The dangers of pregnancy, for example, were strongly stressed at this sensitive turning point in the girl's life. "Stressed but not explained. Even those who received warnings that they must be 'careful' about boys 'from now on' were not given any clear physiological explanation of the menstrual-ovulatory cycle. The consequent misapprehensions, such as 'if you went to bed with a man you got a baby,' or the assumption that one could get pregnant 'even from sitting on a boy's lap' were common among them. The result of these 'warnings,' as well as accompanying misinformation, seemed to have the general effect of associating pregnancy with 'danger,' 'threat,' 'trouble,' and some kind of 'mysterious uncontrollable phenomena.' "

Necking and petting generally followed menstruation. These girls, of course, had been repeatedly warned against petting:

"I learned that some girls would let fellows feel them up and they were the bad girls. It was possible to get real close and have somebody rub up against you but heaven knows what would happen if any of that stuff got up your pants — that would be terrible, and it was possible to get a baby that way. I used to think that even if somebody happened to have an orgasm on your leg you could get pregnant."

Despite these warnings and fears, nine of the thirty girls experienced their first orgasms during petting.*

* Other girls among the thirty also experienced orgasms during petting — but not their first orgasms.

One of the girls whose first orgasm came during petting expressed unalloyed delight:

"I was engaged, I was nineteen. I will never forget it — it was such a shock. We were standing up and he was rubbing against me and all of a sudden my knees kind of buckled — and I experienced an orgasm and that was my first time. It was different and Wow! — I loved it."

Another was delighted in retrospect — though her enjoyment at the time was ruined by her fear of losing control:

"We were in the back seat of a car, necking and petting, and I don't even remember exactly what we were doing, but suddenly everything stopped! I was so stunned, and I thought 'oh my gosh — I mustn't let this get out of hand!' — and I tried to stop that feeling, but I couldn't."

Three of the nine girls who had their first orgasms during petting had had sexual intercourse earlier, without orgasm. One of these three reported: "It was only *after* I had experienced that [petting] orgasm that I knew how much I had missed before and the crazy thing about it was that I thought all along I *had* been having it. . . . Up until then I didn't even know what the devil it *was!*"

These enjoyable petting experiences were exceptions, however. Petting, like masturbation and coitus, was in general surrounded by feelings of anxiety, guilt, shame, filthiness.

As might be expected, these girls who had had so inadequate a preparation for menstruation and for petting also faced their first act of coitus almost wholly unprepared.

"I remember when we were in school they gave us pamphlets about menstruation," one respondent remarked, "but nobody ever handed out any pamphlets about having intercourse." *

Other comments:

"My mother told me that a man plants a seed in the woman so I thought that a man picks up a spade and puts a little dirt on — I don't know where — and put in a little seed, like a geranium seed."

"My mother told me there wasn't much more to it than going to the

* Ignorance is sometimes extreme. Eighteen of Dr. Dickinson's thousand patients remained virgins for one or more years after marriage — the average was four years — because neither wife nor husband knew how to perform sexual intercourse. Gynecologists I have interviewed tell me that virgins still continue to appear at infertility clinics, wondering why they have not become pregnant.

bathroom — and that after you got married, that was the end of lovemaking."

"When one of my girl friends told me about intercourse I told my mother about it. She turned to me with a look of horror on her face and yelled, 'Who told you about that!' and didn't add any further information. . . . All she did was confirm the horror by the way she handled it."

One mother handed her daughter a book on childbirth, but managed to transmit with it the feeling that "it was all absolutely repulsive. And mother didn't explain how [the sperm and ovum] got together in the first place. She wasn't explaining *that* part of it. Finally I did ask her, but boy, I sure felt lousy about it. I might even have started to cry. I thought the whole thing was dirty and filthy and I thought to myself that nobody was ever going to catch me dead doing this — taking off my clothes and fooling around with all of this."

Thus was Dr. Blackwell's message handed on to future generations.

Note that these were not the daughters of Victorian parents, or of ignorant parents. The experiences reported occurred during the nineteen forties and fifties. And the parents were in general middle-class and educated. One mother was a nurse, one father a physician, another an instructor in physical education — all presumably better trained than the average parent to educate their daughters. The physician's daughter "was never given adequate sexual information, was never told that sex might be pleasurable." She "felt dominated by the need to retain her virginity so as 'not to lose respect.' [She] was married for fifteen years before ever experiencing orgasm — from any source whatever."

The central purpose of the home-and-school indoctrination described above, of course, was to keep these thirty girls chaste and virginal until marriage. The effort failed utterly. Twenty-three of the thirty engaged in premarital intercourse. The indoctrination didn't keep these girls chaste; it simply robbed them of the enjoyment which coitus might otherwise have provided.

Why did the twenty-three "sinners" engage in so "filthy" and "shameful" an act?

Five reported that their primary reason was simply a desire to get rid of their virginity.

"I was a 'virgin on the verge,' and felt I just wanted to get it over with."

"I had thought about it for years, it seemed, and I just wanted to get it over with."

Mere curiosity was another explanation given:

"I had so much curiosity by then that I just wanted to experience this so I could know what everybody was talking about."

"I was curious to try it with him. I thought perhaps if I slept with him I would fall in love with him." She slept with him, but she didn't fall in love with him.

For several, the first act of coitus was in considerable part, consciously or unconsciously, a deliberate defiance of parental authority. Thus one woman stated: "I knew that if my mother found out that I was no longer a virgin . . . that I was sleeping with this fellow, and right in his own parents' home . . . she'd have a fit. Then, when he went back to college, we kept in touch through letters. . . . Well, don't you know, my mother discovered those letters one day? I thought I'd kept them well-hidden from her, but she was very snoopy." A pause. Then — "Now that I think of it — knowing how nosey and suspicious she always was anyhow — it seems strange to me that I'd have left those letters around the house at all. Must have *wanted* her to find out, I guess."

Nine of the girls engaged in their first coitus because they wanted to marry the boys in question, and six more "gave in" for fear of losing the boy. A typical comment:

"He told me that if I didn't have sex with him that meant that I didn't care for him. Actually I didn't really love him — but I was afraid that if I *didn't* have this affair with him, he would leave me . . . and I couldn't stand the thought of being abandoned."

Another, who had her first coitus at seventeen with a man to whom she was not particularly attracted, told Dr. Schaefer:

"Holding on to him, not feeling abandoned or separated, was more important to me than the marriage or the sex or anything. It was my first experience of realizing that there was something *I* could do to *keep* a man, and have *some* control over the situation."

While the antisexual milieu in which these girls were brought up did not succeed in keeping them chaste until marriage, it did in some cases prevent them from having sex with men they loved and wanted. One girl, for example, chose her first coital partner "strangely enough, because I *wasn't* attracted to him. I have a feeling that when I experienced passion there was so much guilt involved with what I felt that I couldn't *allow* myself the relationship. . . . It seems I could justify what I was doing sexually only if I didn't really want it."

Another of Dr. Schaefer's respondents reminisced:

"The boys I dated and petted were boys chosen from the wrong side of the tracks. They were more acceptable to the base and sex side of my nature." Her initial coitus with such a boy was at the age of fifteen. "He never tried to force anything on me. I just decided to do it." She reported a sense of defilement when it was over, and decided to marry the boy because she was now no longer a virgin and "no one else would have me."

Coming to their first coital acts with so much ignorance and with such passionless, seemingly trivial motivations, it would seem most unlikely that any of these thirty women would enjoy the experience. Only a few of them did. One woman who had her first premarital intercourse at nineteen, for example, reported:

"To me, this man represented all the qualities I admired and respected . . . and he was also sensitive, good-looking, powerful . . . and a nice person, such a very nice person." He had also, though this was not mentioned, escaped the general view that sex is dirty and shameful. "I remember thinking that he felt like a locomotive . . . on top of me. That all the force of nature was hitting me. All the force of nature. It was just as poetic as it could be. . . . It was fabulous, marvelous."

Thirteen of the twenty-three girls who engaged in premarital intercourse had expected to have an orgasm the first time; this girl was the only one of the thirteen who actually did have an orgasm. "This subject was unique in another respect as well," Dr. Schaefer adds. "She reported masturbation to orgasm at four years of age, the youngest of any of the women in the group."

Another girl, who had looked forward to her first coitus as an ordeal and had expected neither enjoyment nor orgasm, was astonished to experience both. No doubt the qualities of her lover had a lot to do with it. "Despite all the violent things I had been told about sex up to this point," she recalled, "I am bewildered that I was able to have such a delightful and even rewarding experience from the very first time. He . . . apparently knew a lot about sex and all that could make it pleasurable and rewarding."

But these pleasant experiences were the exception rather than the rule.

The group as a whole, Dr. Schaefer reports, did not expect to experience orgasm the first time round and in fact did not. They half expected pleasure — but did not experience it. They expected coitus to be painful — and it was.

A typical comment: "I didn't expect anything like the stars turning purple and music in the background, but I felt terrible that we never really enjoyed it."

Even one of the three girls who experienced orgasm at first coitus had the experience spoiled by her sense of shame. In her own words:

"I felt terribly frightened. . . . Sexually it was very exciting and I recall feeling a lot of pleasure from it, but after a few times I did not want to see the fellow anymore. I was so dreadfully ashamed that I had had these feelings, and ashamed of being faced with the person who saw them — and finally, so ashamed that I couldn't face this person, and then I couldn't face the *feelings*."

Equally sad was the case of a girl who at sixteen had been brought to orgasm for the first time by cunnilingus. "It was such a fantastic experience," she told Dr. Schaefer, "that I went home with a raging fever and stayed in bed three days, just sick with guilt." Her feelings of guilt did not, however, prevent her from continuing to engage in the same practice for the next three years. Then, at nineteen, she had her first experience of coitus. "The male organ was very repulsive to me," she reported. "I didn't like intercourse." Yet she continued to engage in it, as she had continued to engage in cunnilingus.

Dr. Blackwell would not have been surprised, of course, at these miseries of premarital sex. This was precisely what she had frequently predicted: "Unrighteous use [of our sexual capacities] produces satiety, coldness, repulsion, and misery." It is only "righteous use" which "brings renewed and increasing satisfaction to the two made one in harmonious union."

But on this latter point, Dr. Blackwell proved to be mistaken. The seven girls in Dr. Schaefer's sample who retained their virginity until marriage fared no better than the twenty-three who did not. All seven, Dr. Schaefer reports, had "held out" because of fear:

"If I had intercourse, he would lose respect for me."

"I'd be *ruined* if I allowed sex to happen."

"The kind of fellow I wanted to marry — who was looked up to by the society in which I lived — would certainly not marry a girl who wasn't a virgin." *

Only three of the girls who engaged in premarital intercourse, it will be recalled, experienced orgasm on first coitus. *None* of the girls who were virgins at marriage did.

One respondent described her defloration on her honeymoon at the age of twenty-two: "I remember it being terribly painful. . . . I didn't like it at all. I bled a great deal and I didn't like the first experience — and I didn't like the second one, either. I didn't like intercourse for a very long time, as a matter of fact."

Another girl who was a virgin at marriage and who had never had an orgasm from any source had come perilously close to orgasm during premarital petting with the man she later married — but held back. "I would always say to myself," she explained, "that I simply must control my sexual emotions or I'll ruin this relationship just like I ruined every other one. So I learned how to control and stop with him."

Alas, she overlearned. She continued to have no orgasms, coital or otherwise, until the sixteenth year of her marriage.

Of the seven women who were virgins at marriage, three expressed regrets. "It would have been a good idea to have known more men," one of them mused. "I'd have something to compare my experiences with, and be a better partner for my husband."

Despite the generally unsatisfactory nature of their premarital affairs, the girls who "gave in" before marriage expressed very little regret. Three regretted their choice of their initial partner. Only four of the twenty-three regretted having "given in." The other sixteen expressed no regrets whatever.

The usual expectation is that a girl who remains virginal until marriage, even though she may have a little trouble at first, will soon learn to enjoy sexual relations, and then to experience her first orgasm. This expectation was fulfilled only rarely in Dr. Schaefer's sample.

Ten of the girls, it will be recalled, experienced their first orgasm through masturbation and nine during premarital petting. Two more ex-

* In sharp contrast, another respondent stated: "I was ashamed to let my fiancée discover on our wedding night that I was completely inexperienced sexually, so I had sex with another boy first because I felt I just *had* to get my virginity over with. He was the best one to do it with because both of us wanted only one thing out of the relationship."

perienced it during nocturnal dreams. This left only nine who first experienced orgasm during coitus. Of these nine, five experienced their first orgasm during premarital coitus, one during an extramarital affair while she was living with her husband, and one during her second marriage. Thus the astonishing result is reached that only two of these thirty women experienced their first orgasms during coitus with their first husbands!

One of these two, moreover, was married at twenty-two and failed to experience orgasm from coitus or any other source for the first fifteen years of her marriage. She entered psychotherapy at the age of thirty-four, and it was only after three years of therapy that she ultimately experienced her first orgasm. It was in marital coitus — but the fifteen-year wait was hardly a recommendation for premarital chastity.

Most of the other women in Dr. Schaefer's sample, as might be expected on the basis of their repressed childhoods and traumatic adolescences, also had difficulty in experiencing orgasm during coitus with their husbands. The relationship between the childhood masturbation taboo and subsequent frustration in marital coitus is strikingly illustrated by one respondent, aged forty when she was interviewed. This woman had first had intercourse when she was fifteen, had had a wide variety of subsequent sexual encounters, a disastrous marriage, and various post-marital affairs. At the age of thirty-eight she still did not know what an orgasm was. Then she remarried — and again, for three months, failed to experience orgasm. Then —

"He masturbated me and that's when I had my first orgasm. It was about three months after we were married. I felt shook up and also very much out of control at the same time. I knew that I'd had an orgasm and I enjoyed it, but I didn't permit myself to have this again . . . even though my husband tried very hard for me."

When Dr. Schaefer asked her *why* she never permitted herself to have another orgasm, either with her second husband, or with lovers, or from masturbation, she replied:

"I couldn't ask a man to do anything. It had to come from him and if it didn't then I felt I just had to suffer.* I did make some efforts at masturbating thereafter, and I guess it's significant that the fantasy that

* Robert Latou Dickinson reported six similar cases of wives who "knew of some method which would give orgasm if the husband used it, but they have never told him."

would usually accompany this was of being attacked by a male — and me being the helpless female. Gosh — I was so masochistic, it's really sickening."

By fantasying the act as involuntary, and herself as the "innocent victim," this woman — like many others — sought to escape her Blackwellian sense of guilt and shame.

The failures of many of these women to experience orgasm in marital coitus was particularly threatening to their marriages because they lived in a culture in which husbands generally expect their wives to have orgasm. It is hardly surprising, accordingly, that some of the wives met the problem by pretending to have orgasms. What is surprising, however, is that *most* of the wives in Dr. Schaefer's sample — seventeen out of the thirty — pretended to have orgasms which they did not in fact experience.*

One woman pretended to have orgasm to avoid hurting her husband's feelings:

"I thought he would have a feeling of failure . . . and that he would feel that he had disappointed me. I did it to protect his feelings."

This same woman, however, confessed that she also thought having an orgasm was essential to her feminine status:

"I was afraid he would think I wasn't very feminine or sexy if I didn't have an orgasm each and every time."

Another woman reported:

"Sometimes I pretend to have an orgasm because my husband gets upset if I don't. I've often told him that I can enjoy giving *him* pleasure and being close to him and that it isn't *always* necessary for me to have a climax. But you can't ever make a man believe that!"

A woman who fails to experience orgasm sometimes finds herself paired with a man capable of and willing to continue coitus indefinitely in the hope that she will eventually "come." Some women pretended to have orgasm to escape from this seemingly endless process:

"Sometimes I pretended to have an orgasm just to get it over with, when I knew nothing was going to happen to me."

* In addition, an eighteenth pretended *not* to have orgasm because her husband "thought it was disgusting and horrifying, so I learned to cover up those feelings from him. I don't know why . . . I believe now that it must have had to do with his strong moralistic attitudes." Shades of Dr. Blackwell!

Whether the husbands were actually fooled by the pretending or not, and just what effect the pretending, successful or otherwise, had on marital rapport, does not emerge from Dr. Schaefer's study.

Not all women brought up in the Victorian tradition, of course, are frigid in adult life; but, as Robert Latou Dickinson demonstrated in *A Thousand Marriages,* the women who escape are likely to suffer from the Victorian upbringing of their husbands. Dr. Dickinson's sexually responsive women patients described their husbands in such terms as these:

"He thinks coitus is carnal."

"I have never seen him naked."

"He will not touch my vulva."

"He locks himself in the bathroom."

"He thinks it would be wrong to make clitoris friction."

"He thinks procreation is the only basis for intercourse."

"He ought to be glad to have a passionate woman. I'm true to him, but he don't make it easy."

"He thinks it is bad for him." (Throughout Dickinson's case histories, both women and men use the ambiguous and emotionally rejecting word "it" to refer indiscriminately to the penis, the vulva, the vagina, coitus, and orgasm.)

In short, as Dr. Dickinson often remarked, "It takes two people to make one frigid wife."

Despite the guilt-ridden and generally unsatisfactory nature of most of their sexual experiences, the women in Dr. Schaefer's sample never stopped trying. Twenty-three of them (as noted above) had premarital coitus. Ten engaged in extramarital coitus while living with their husbands.* Several engaged in postmarital or intermarital coitus. The thirty women had chalked up forty-eight marriages at the time of interviewing, with many more marriages no doubt in store for them.

The moral for parents of the next generation of little girls seems to me crystal clear. The repression of masturbation and of other forms of childhood sexuality is not going to lead your daughters to maintain their chastity until marriage, or to remain faithful and monogamous thereafter. But if your intention is to spoil your sons' and daughters' *enjoyment* of

* The extramarital affairs were rarely successful. As Dr. Dickinson pointed out, the same factors which impair marital fulfillment — in men as well as in women — often impair extramarital fulfillment as well.

their future sexual experiences, including marital coitus, then the castigation of childhood masturbation and other forms of sexuality as shameful and filthy is almost guaranteed to succeed beyond your expectations.

Only one small ray of light emerges from Dr. Schaefer's generally dismal review of the sexual feelings of these thirty women. To her own amazement she discovered, when she totaled up the findings, that every one of the thirty — often after years of sexual frustration — learned eventually to experience orgasm at least occasionally during sexual intercourse. Even the woman who at thirty-eight experienced her first orgasm when her second husband masturbated her, and who never "let herself" have another, did learn to enjoy orgasm in coitus with her third husband after prolonged psychotherapy.

Dr. Schaefer sums up:

> Despite guilt-ridden object lessons and other negative forces, the human spirit does not easily permit itself to be cowed. Regardless of how tragic were the experiences that these women encountered in childhood, or how unfortunate were their ensuing experiences in later adolescence, each of them exhibited constantly an intense drive for sexual survival and undefeatable wishes to find life fulfillment.

This ray of light, however, is more than overshadowed by another of Dr. Schaefer's unexpected findings. These women had suffered throughout their lives from their own sexually repressed childhoods. Many of them had suffered the terrors of the damned. They had also achieved considerable insight into the relationship between the way in which they were brought up and their subsequent sexual frustrations. Intellectually, every one of them had rejected sexual Victorianism. Yet there is reason to believe that many or most of them are bringing up their own daughters today in much the same way that they themselves were brought up — along the lines laid down by Elizabeth Blackwell in 1894.

One woman of thirty, for example, expressed her own lack of confidence in her ability to instruct her ten-year-old daughter about sex. She would *like* to convey the idea that "sex is something great," she told Dr. Schaefer, but she was afraid — afraid that this might encourage her daughter "to be promiscuous."

This woman reported that she herself had begun masturbating to orgasm at the age of twelve. When asked if her daughter masturbated, she replied: "You know, I've been wondering about this lately. It's so hard for me to look at this lovely little creature who — you would think — is so pure, and to think of her doing things like that. . . . Yes, I guess I do mean 'dirty things like that,' even though I hate to admit that I'm still thinking in those ways."

Thus the wheel comes once again full circle. The ten-year-old girl of today, the great-great-granddaughter of Dr. Blackwell's readers, is doomed — it would appear — to relive the same sorry cycle of masturbatory shame, disappointment in premarital coitus, frustration in marital sex, frustration in extramarital and postmarital sex, and, in general, a feeling of being guilty, nasty, and filthy.

Unless parents change their ways.

Niles Newton

Dr. Elizabeth Blackwell had stressed in her writings the fact that sex means much more for a woman than merely genital response; all of the functions related to pregnancy and childbirth are also inherently sexual — and in this, she was certainly right. Indeed, as we shall see, the gently repressive upbringing of a little girl which Dr. Blackwell recommended can foul up these reproductive aspects of her subsequent biological role much as it fouls up her enjoyment of coitus and other heterosexual relationships.

Credit for stressing, and for exploring in a scientific context, the intimate relationships among the varied aspects of female sexuality belongs to a psychologist, Niles Newton, Ph.D., Associate Professor in the Department of Psychiatry and Neurology, Northwestern University Medical School. Dr. Newton's first major contribution on this topic, published in 1955, was a monograph entitled *Maternal Emotions: A Study of Women's Feelings Toward Menstruation, Pregnancy, Childbirth, Breast Feeding, Infant Care, and Other Aspects of Their Femininity*. Like Dr. Schaefer, Dr. Newton secured the bulk of her data for this study by questioning women face-to-face — and by questioning them particularly about their feelings and emotions rather than merely about their behavior and responses. The "Other Aspects of Their Femininity" referred to in the title of her monograph included their feelings toward sexual intercourse.

Dr. Niles Newton is married to Dr. Michael Newton, Clinical Professor of Obstetrics and Gynecology in the Pritzker School of Medicine, University of Chicago. Each of the Newtons has contributed individually to sex research, and the two have collaborated on a number of research projects, especially in the area of breast-feeding. My wife Ruth and I first learned of their work back in the late forties, interviewed them, liked them, followed with great satisfaction the steady deepening of their insights through the years, and reported on their findings in magazine articles for lay readers. Of the greatest immediate interest is a study which the Newtons jointly published in the *New England Journal of Medicine* (1967) entitled "Psychological Aspects of Lactation." This paper begins:

> The rapidity with which lactation failure spreads through human groups suggests that it is triggered by psychologic factors. For example, national surveys indicate that the neonatal breast-feeding rate in the United States fell by almost half during just ten years.

The Newtons then proceed to review many possible reasons for this increasing unwillingness of women to breast-feed, and their concomitant increasing inability to breast-feed enjoyably and successfully. Against the background of Dr. Blackwell's doctrines and Dr. Schaefer's findings, one of these reasons stands out with startling clarity.

"Feelings of aversion for the breast-feeding act," the Newtons report, "appear to be related to dislike of nudity and sexuality."

As evidence for this relationship, the Newtons cite four prior studies:

An English husband-and-wife team of researchers, Drs. John and Elizabeth Newson, after interviewing more than 700 English mothers, reported: "For many mothers, modesty and feeling of distaste form a major factor in their preference for [bottle feeding]."

Dr. Eva Salber and her associates at the Harvard School of Public Health and Children's Medical Center, Boston, working with mothers who had never even attempted to nurse their babies, reported: "The idea of nursing repelled them. They were excessively embarrassed at the idea or 'too modest' to nurse."

Another American researcher, A. B. Adams, found that women who wanted to bottle-feed their first babies showed significantly more psychosexual disturbance than those who wanted to breast-feed.

Finally, R. R. Sears and his associates in Boston found that mothers who breast-feed are also significantly more *tolerant* in such sexual matters as masturbation and social sex play.

So we are back where we started — with Dr. Blackwell. We teach little girls that sex is wicked and filthy. Years later they are inhibited not only from the pleasure of coitus but also from the closely related pleasure of breast-feeding their own babies. They suffer not only from coital frigidity but also, in Niles Newton's marvelously telling phrase, from "breast-feeding frigidity."

This phrase, let me emphasize, is not just a literary device; it is also, as the Newtons and others have demonstrated in great detail, the quite literal truth. The parallel between breast-feeding responses and female coital responses is startlingly close.

Contrary to a widespread belief among even educated women, the baby does not suck the milk from his mother's breast as he will later suck it out of a glass through a straw. Rather, a marvelously complex and integrated sequence of nervous and hormonal events intervenes between the sucking and the securing of milk — a series of events known as the "let-down reflex."

The female nipple is richly supplied with sensitive nerve endings. The let-down reflex is initiated when the infant's suckling stimulates these nerve endings — the same ones stimulated during necking or petting. Messages promptly ascend along special nerves from the nipple to a portion of the brain called the hypothalamus, which is a relay center for many or most emotional responses. It is also a center of nervous inhibition. If inhibition does not prevent it, the hypothalamus relays the message to the nearby pituitary gland. The pituitary thereupon releases a hormone, oxytocin, which has the special property of causing certain kinds of muscle fibers to contract. The oxytocin released into the bloodstream by the pituitary flows with the blood and reaches the breast within a few seconds.

In the lactating breast, the milk is stored in tiny chambers called alveoli, which are surrounded by muscle fibers of the kind sensitive to oxytocin. The oxytocin from the pituitary causes these muscle fibers to contract; and the milk is thereupon expelled into the channels leading to the nipple. The baby who has initiated the whole reflex by suckling his mother's nipples receives, within a few seconds, his tasty and nutritive reward.

Though the physiological details have not yet been worked out, there is no doubt a similar chain of neural and hormonal events leading from the female genitals through the hypothalamus and pituitary to orgasm. Oxytocin is in all probability involved in the orgasmic reflex as well as the let-down reflex. Both reflexes, as we shall see, are readily inhibited by the same psychological factors such as anxiety.

The let-down reflex was discovered by veterinary researchers concerned with milk production in the domestic cow — a production valued at billions of dollars per year. Until the Newtons came along, no similar research had been performed on humans, an interesting sidelight on the relative value our culture places on cow's milk vs. human milk. The Newtons in 1948 performed a series of experiments indicating the existence of precisely the same reflex in a human female — namely, Niles Newton.

Their research was undertaken while Niles Newton was nursing the second of her four children, Lees, and was designed to show the role of oxytocin in human breast-feeding. Under ordinary circumstances, the let-down reflex occurred quite readily in Niles's case, and little Lees Newton thrived. On occasion, however, a distraction would be introduced early in the breast-feeding act — sometimes an electric shock, sometimes the plunging of Niles's bare foot into a bucket of ice water, and sometimes an effort on her part to perform a task in mental arithmetic, with an electric shock as a punishment if she made a mistake. Under these circumstances, her let-down reflex was inhibited — and little Lees was temporarily deprived of her milk.

On such occasions, Michael Newton gave Niles a small injection — sometimes of ordinary saltwater, sometimes of oxytocin. The water injection had no effect. But following an oxytocin injection, little Lees secured her milk despite the distraction and inhibition. These and other data left no room for doubt that oxytocin mediates the let-down reflex. (It was this experiment, incidentally, which first attracted my wife's and my attention to the many-faceted research of the Newtons.)

The Newtons' oxytocin experiment, however, has turned out to have a significance extending far beyond breast-feeding. For the research of others has shown other oxytocin effects. It causes the muscle fibers of the uterus to contract, for example — and, as Masters and Johnson have shown, rhythmic contractions of the uterus are a major feature of the female orgasm during both masturbation and coitus.

The close relation between the let-down reflex and female sexual response is demonstrable in several ways. Some uninhibited women are able to achieve orgasm by means of breast stimulation alone. Some women find breast-feeding sexually arousing. Indeed, Masters and Johnson report that some women refuse to breast-feed their babies after discovering that it is pleasurable. (If sex is wicked, breast-feeding must be wicked.) Breast-feeding problems, in short, are at least in part traceable — like coital problems — to the antisexual feelings we continue to instill in our little girls.

The broad implications of these findings for human survival were reviewed by the Newtons in their 1967 paper.

> The survival of the human race, long before the concept of "duty" was evolved, depended on the satisfactions gained from two voluntary acts of reproduction — coitus and breast feeding. These had to be sufficiently pleasurable to ensure their frequent occurrence.
>
> The physiological responses in coitus and lactation are closely allied. Uterine contractions occur both during suckling and during sexual excitement. Nipple erection occurs during both. Milk ejection has been observed to occur during sexual excitement in women. Moreover, the degree of ejection appears to be related to the degree of sexual response.
>
> Extensive breast-stimulation occurs during breast-feeding. Breast stimulation alone can induce orgasm in some women. Emotions aroused by sexual contact and breast-feeding contact both involve skin changes.

This recognition of the sexual nature of breast-feeding, let me add, is deeply troubling and anxiety-arousing for many women — as my wife and I discovered when we published an article on the Newtons' work in a women's magazine. The reaction of a number of women who read the article was intense.

"How dare you say that there is anything sexual about so warm and loving an act as nursing a baby!" one of our readers wrote us indignantly.

Nor is the childbirth experience divorced from the coital and breast-feeding experience. Oxytocin is believed to trigger both the rhythmic contractions of the uterus during labor prior to birth, and the shrinking of the uterus back to normal size after the baby is born. Many physicians, indeed, give an oxytocin injection to the mother immediately after her baby is born in order to contract the uterus and thus avoid excess bleeding. Old-fashioned doctors used to secure the same effect simply by placing the baby at the mother's breast immediately after its birth.

Niles Newton's most impressive evidence on the close parallel between a woman's reactions during coitus and her reactions during labor and childbirth is presented in her table below (from *Maternal Emotions,* 1955), showing the similarities stage by stage. The data on childbirth in the lefthand column are based on Dr. Grantly Dick-Read's observations of 516 consecutive women giving birth in an undrugged, uninhibited condition. The data on coitus in the right-hand column are based on the Kinsey observations.

Uninhibited, Undrugged Childbirth	*Sexual Excitement*
Breathing	
In the first stage of labor, breathing becomes deeper during contractions	During early stages breathing becomes faster and deeper.
Second stage brings on very deep breaths with breath holding	As orgasm approaches breathing becomes interrupted.
Tendency to make noises, grunts, etc.	Tendency to make gasping, sucking noises.
Facial Expression	
As delivery approaches face gets intense, strained look which makes observers often assume woman is suffering great pain.	As orgasm approaches face gets what Kinsey, *et al.* call a "tortured expression." Mouth open, glassy eyes, tense muscles.
Face looks like that of an athlete undergoing great physical strain.	Face looks like that of an athlete under great physical strain.
Uterus	
The upper segment of the uterus contracts rhythmically.	The upper segment of the uterus contracts rhythmically.
Loosening of mucus plug from os of cervix is one of the standard signs of labor.	Cervical secretion may loosen mucus plug which ordinarily lies at os of cervix thus opening it for spermatozoa.
Abdominal Muscles	
Contract periodically. A strong, instinctive urge to bear down by using abdominal muscles as delivery approaches.	Abdominal muscles contract periodically with considerable force. Movement builds up as orgasm approaches.
Legs wide apart and bent.	This position is used by women in intercourse.

Central Nervous System	
Woman becomes uninhibited particularly during second stage of labor. All veneer of "refinement" disappears.	Inhibitions and psychic blockages are relieved and often eliminated.
Delivery of the baby through the narrow passage calls for unusual strength and body expansion.	Unusual muscular strength. Many persons become capable of bending and distorting body in ways they could not otherwise do.
Sensory Perception	
The vulva becomes anesthetic with full dilatation, so that woman often must be told of birth of baby's head.	Whole body of person who becomes sexually aroused becomes increasingly insensitive even to sharp blows and severe injury.
Amnesia, tendency to become insensitive to surroundings as delivery approaches.	As orgasm approaches loss of sensory perception is nearly complete—sometimes leading to moments of unconsciousness.
Suddenly, delivery completed, woman becomes wide awake.	After orgasm, sudden return of sensory acuity.
After the birth of the baby there is a flood of joyful emotion. Read describes it as "complete and careless ecstasy."	There is a strong feeling of well being in most persons. Many psychologists believe that this relief from tension is the chief source of satisfaction gained from intercourse.

Niles Newton's 1955 monograph also presented data on the intimate relationships among all of a woman's biological functions—her responses to menstruation, coitus, childbirth, and breast-feeding alike. These data were drawn from Dr. Newton's interviews with women who had just given birth to babies at Jefferson Hospital in Philadelphia. Three examples:

Women who do not feel that menstruation was "the curse" were less likely to have difficulties during childbirth and more likely to exhibit maternal feelings toward their newborn infants.

Women who complained that childbirth was hard were more likely to dislike breast-feeding and personal care of their babies.

Women who were negative toward breast-feeding were also more likely to be resentful of and less efficient in certain other aspects of their female role. Women who were positive toward breast-feeding were more likely to continue to breast-feed successfully, to feel childbirth was easy, and to feel that women had at least as satisfying a time in life as men.

Eleven years later, several quite similar relationships were reported by Masters and Johnson. As the Newtons pointed out in their 1967 paper:

> Masters and Johnson found that nursing [i.e., breast-feeding] women had a higher level of sexual interest than non-nursing post-partum women. Nursing mothers not only reported sexual stimulation from suckling but also, as a group, were interested in as rapid a return to active intercourse with their husbands as possible.

Dr. Niles Newton's most recent work has been devoted in considerable part to exploring further the relationship between emotional experiences in childbirth and the normal physiology of childbirth — using mice as her experimental subjects. Anything which interrupts or distresses the female mouse during labor, she has found, lengthens labor and lessens the likelihood of a normal outcome. Her findings at least suggest that, in addition to coital frigidity and breast-feeding frigidity, there may also be a "childbirth frigidity."

Let us return for a moment to the young mother in Dr. Schaefer's sample who *wanted* to tell her daughter that "sex is something great," but was afraid the news might "make her promiscuous." The Newtons' findings suggest that *failure* to tell the truth to "that lovely little creature" — and failure to convey the message in nonverbal ways as well —may impair that lovely little creature's ability to fulfill her biological role as an adult woman, and perhaps impair also her ability to teach *her* daughters a generation hence.

Helena Wright

The position we have reached in this chapter so far is hardly an optimistic one. Countless women are unable to perform their biological role with joy, or to enjoy sexual relations, because of sexual repression in childhood. Feelings of anxiety, guilt, and shame get in their way. And these same feelings cause these women to bring up their daughters the same way.

Is this vicious cycle unbreakable?

Most of the efforts to break it have in recent years been focused on improved sex education for children. No doubt these efforts are worth making — but they face at least two major obstacles. If parents are to be expected to educate their own children, their deeply rooted guilt-shame-anxiety feelings toward sex are almost sure to get in the way — and if the schools, churches, or other public institutions are to take over the task, where will they find teachers who are not similarly obsessed with sexual anxiety, guilt, and shame?

It is against this background that the work of an English gynecologist, Dr. Helena Wright, takes on special significance. She has been engaged since the 1920's in seeking to break the vicious cycle at a later phase — at the point where the young wife, deeply aware of sexual frustration but not yet so overwhelmed by it as to surrender all hope, is ripe for a change in attitude. Both in her medical practice and in a series of books for lay readers, Dr. Wright has sought to effect such a change among her patients and her readers.

I visited Dr. Wright — now a woman in her seventies, still in active gynecological practice — in London in 1968. I found her forthright, opinionated, dominating, as well as agreeable and gracious. She was enormously sure of herself and of the rightness of her views — and she had an almost hypnotic ability to transmit this feeling of certainty to others. She didn't argue or persuade or cite evidence; she simply told me what was what. Even on points where I disagreed with her, I was amazed to find myself changing my mind. It is this remarkable power — not persuasiveness, but *contagiousness* of opinion — which may explain Dr. Wright's ability to alter even the deepest-rooted prejudices of some of her patients.

After qualifying as a gynecologist, Dr. Wright told me, she went to work in a newly opened birth control clinic serving working-class London women. In the course of fitting diaphragms or recommending other forms of contraception, she found it natural to ask her patients questions about their marital adjustment.

"Do you enjoy having connection with your husband?"

In a high proportion of cases, Dr. Wright discovered, the patient looked quite blank and said nothing at all. So Dr. Wright would repeat the question:

"Do you enjoy having connection with your husband, as you should do?"

The women in the 1920's often answered in surprise:

"Why, Doctor — *what is there to enjoy?"*

These women saw sex as one of their matrimonial duties, like washing their husband's dirty socks.

A decade or two later, this ignorance even of the possibility of female sexual enjoyment was rarer. Most women had learned that sex *can* be enjoyable. (Dr. Wright's own low-priced and enormously popular books contributed to this knowledge.) But many women still hadn't learned *how.*

It was to both of these groups that Dr. Wright's books were addressed. The first of them, published in 1930, was a primer entitled *The Sex Factor in Marriage.* It was a frank book, which instructed women on how to masturbate as well as how to secure orgasm in coitus.

"The publisher and I expected the whole edition to be seized, banned, and destroyed," Dr. Wright told me, "so we grabbed the first copies off the press and buried three of them in secret places — two in England and one in France."

The book opened with a quotation from the Archbishop of Canterbury and one from Havelock Ellis, an introduction by a Protestant clergyman, an acknowledgment to van de Velde's *Ideal Marriage,* and a blunt denial of almost everything Englishwomen had been learning from their mothers or from Dr. Blackwell:

> Sex desire is a natural characteristic of every normal adult woman and man, in itself as beautiful and blameless as moving or breathing. The idea that there is anything wrong or "nasty" in sex itself is a man-made notion entirely untrue, and evil in its effects.

And again:

> The false idea that intercourse undertaken for a reproductive purpose is more meritorious than intercourse performed purely as an expression of love, is dying. It never had any foundation in reason and science.

When Dr. Wright made such statements to her patients personally, she carried conviction against the weight of all their childhood taboos. Even in cold ink on the printed page, her words had some effect. And hopes were raised when she promised her readers:

> A successful and satisfactory sex relation is within the reach of every married couple who are willing to take enough trouble about it. Knowledge,

sympathy, courage and persistence are the necessary weapons. With them success is certain.

Thus were the familiar household virtues — knowledge, sympathy, courage, persistence — enlisted in favor of sex instead of against it. Dr. Wright was the antidote against Blackwellism.

Dr. Wright stated the purpose of her book in blunt, dogmatic terms:

> The writer wants to give such definite and practical information that no one reading it can any longer be ignorant of the nature of the sex-act, or fail to know exactly how it should be performed.

The first step toward coital orgasm and marital fulfillment, Dr. Wright taught, is to sweep away the accumulated cobwebs of guilt and shame.

> The wife who means to have a happy sex life must . . . decide with all her strength that she *wants* her body to feel all the sensations of sex with the greatest possible vividness. A wife who allows her mind to keep any unworthy ideas about sex lurking in its corners, is her own worst enemy. Her body will only yield its fullest joy, will only allow her to know the experience of physical ecstasy, if her mind and her soul are in active sympathy with it.

But physical as well as mental preparation, Dr. Wright taught, is necessary. A woman must first become familiar with her own body, and particularly with her clitoris — "a small round body, about the size of a pea, movable to a slight extent, and coated with delicate membrane, which is always more or less moist. . . . This little organ is capable of giving the most acute sensations; the tissue of which it is made is similar to that of the penis, and during sex stimulation it has the same power of filling with blood, and thereby becoming larger and harder than it is in an inactive state. The only purpose of the clitoris is to provide sensation; a full understanding of its capabilities and place in the sex-act is therefore of supreme importance."

This printed description, however, proved to be inadequate in orienting women who had long been taught that touching themselves was wicked. Accordingly, in her later book entitled *More About the Sex Factor in Marriage* (1947), Dr. Wright waxed much more explicit.

"In the author's opinion," she wrote, "it is important that every woman who is about to be married should not only know that her clitoris exists and why, but that she should find out exactly where it is and what it looks like. Women in general take an endless interest in their faces, study them in the mirror and know all their details by heart; but their usual attitude toward their far more important sexual equipment is one of fear and ludicrously complete ignorance."

Dr. Wright's instructions for overcoming this fear and ignorance were precise, detailed, and authoritative:

Arrange a good light and take a mirror and identify all the parts described. To find the clitoris, the thighs must be separated widely enough for comfortable vision, then if two fingers hold apart the larger lips, the mucous membrane-covered hood will be seen immediately inside the front end of the space between the larger lips. The hood can be gently drawn backward by the finger tips and inside will be seen a small, smooth, rounded body (sometimes it is very small and only just visible), which glistens in a good light. This is the clitoris. Its root runs upward under the hood and the junction of the outer lips and extends for about an inch. The two inner lips begin in the mid line close together just under the clitoris, and extend downward and backward on each side of the smooth space in the middle, and come to an end by fading away at about the middle of the ring-shaped opening which is the entrance to the vagina.

In addition to instructing her readers on how to *observe* the clitoris, moreover, Dr. Wright instructed them on how to test it for sexual responsiveness — in violation of those "don't touch" taboos — by actually touching and stroking it with a smooth object in front of a mirror

When all external parts of the sexual equipment have been carefully and thoroughly identified, it is next necessary to prove at first hand the truth of the statement that the clitoris does possess a unique kind of sensitiveness. It is best to do this with something other than the owner's finger, because the finger-tip is, naturally, itself sensitive to touch, and if it is used, there may be confusion of effect between the feeling finger and the part felt. Any small, smooth object will do, such as an uncut pencil, or a tooth-brush handle. The procedure is one of comparison of response by a very light touch. One hand separates the outer labia without touching the inner ones, and the other hand, holding the chosen object, touches first one inner lip and then the other, and then the clitoris, through or under its hood. If the hand movements are watched in the mirror, it is easy to get the touches accurately in the right places, but without a mirror and a good light, it is not easy, because an inexperienced woman has practically no sense of accurate position if she tries to use a finger unguided by her eyes. The effect observed is that the instant the clitoris is touched, a peculiar and characteristic

> sensation is experienced which is different in essence from touches on the labia or anywhere else.
>
> This difference has to be experienced; it cannot be described in words.

In thus instructing women readers to perform an experiment akin to those familiar in high-school science classes, Dr. Wright is of course accomplishing far more than just teaching them where the clitoris is and how it feels. She is providing them with an altogether new approach to their own anatomy and sexual sensations — an approach which, precisely because it is so cold and "scientific," is relieved of the sense of guilt and shame.

Dr. Wright's exploratory procedure, it seems to me, should be an intrinsic part of the education of every female teacher of sex education.

Merely finding and touching her clitoris, however, does not cure a woman of frigidity. "The next step," Dr. Wright explains, is "to discover what happens when it is given the right kind of stimulus necessary to produce its full functioning."

At this point, of course, all of a woman's childhood repressions and guilt feelings become mobilized. Actually *rub* the thing! Dr. Wright answers in terms which even Dr. Blackwell would understand. The sole purpose of the clitoris is to respond to frictional stimulation; surely there is nothing wrong about using an organ in the way for which it is specifically constructed to be used.

Just as our eyes respond only to light waves of a certain kind and our ears only to sound-waves of certain pitches, Dr. Wright continues, so the clitoris "needs *rhythmic friction.*"

> Those two words are the heart of the matter. Without rhythmic friction no sexual sensations are possible either to man or to woman. . . . It is no exaggeration to say that since the clitoris is the essential organ of sexual sensation in women, and that rhythmic friction is the only stimulus to which it can react, orgasm failure at the outset of sexual experience is unavoidable if the clitoris is not discovered and correctly stimulated.

The husband, of course, quickly learns his own preferred rhythm in the course of his experiences in masturbation or first coitus. The wife, "following his example . . . must discover her own pattern of rhythmic friction" — and must teach it to her husband.

The best way to accomplish this, Dr. Wright directs, is for the husband to place his hand over his wife's clitoral region and keep it relaxed and flexible. "The wife can then put her hand over his and move his fingers in any way she likes. It is not necessary for her to think, or plan; her clitoris and the sensitive area around it respond instantly to touch; all she has to do is to move her husband's fingers instinctively and freely and to go on with the movements for as long as she feels pleasurable sensations. The object, of course, is that she shall receive an orgasm . . . and this is, as a rule, easily attained." Sometimes the climax does not occur quite so readily; in such cases it may be necessary to take a short rest or to try again the next night. But with reasonable promptness, "a method as simple as this is bound to succeed if the wife wishes it to."

Think back for a moment to the thirty women in Dr. Schaefer's New York City sample — women whose aversion to masturbation was warping their whole sexual outlook. Dr. Wright's approach, it seems to me, is aimed with exquisite precision at their problems. Her instructions can accomplish far more for such a woman than merely showing her how she can teach her husband her preferred clitoral rhythm.

Many women with orgasm problems, as Dr. Schaefer's respondents so frankly reported, are afraid to lose control, to "let the thing get out of hand." Dr. Wright is here describing a procedure which the woman herself *does* control. It is *her* hand which guides and sets the rhythm.

Even more important, perhaps, Dr. Wright with all of her moral and medical authority is assuring her patients and readers that sexual response to clitoral stimulation is *licit* — even in the presence of a man, and at his touch. These indirect psychic effects of the procedures Dr. Wright prescribes, I strongly suspect, are as important as the direct physical effect, rhythmic stimulation of the clitoris — though the importance of the latter should certainly not be underestimated.

So far, however, Dr. Wright's patients and readers have learned only how to have an orgasm in masturbation with their husbands. The final step, of course, is to learn how to have orgasm similarly in coitus.

Success in the masturbatory orgasm, Dr. Wright teaches, is itself a long step towards coital orgasm. It is "the essential feminine experience which demonstrates sexual capacity, and . . . automatically removes the haunting sense of inferiority and failure which is otherwise inevitable. Every wife who has learnt that the behavior of her clitoris is reliable finds it easier to believe that one day her vagina might also come alive."

But the wife need not wait until this occurs automatically, as if by a miracle. She can teach herself to enjoy vaginal as well as clitoral stimulation.

> The rhythmic caressing finger-movements of the clitoris region can be designed to include adjacent areas of the vagina, and so express the idea that the two regions can function as a unit. There is probably an indefinite number of ways in which this can be done. It will be enough to suggest three.
>
> First, a downward stroke beginning just above and beyond the root of the clitoris, passing over the clitoris and on down the midline, into the vaginal entrance following the front wall of the passage and ending a little way inside.
>
> Second, the reverse of the first, a movement beginning inside the front vaginal wall and coming up and out along the midline, over the clitoris back to where the first movement started. A rhythm of these two alternating movements carries a strong suggestion that the clitoris and the vaginal entrance are being treated as one and not two places of sensitive response. The effect is as if the vividly sensitive nerve-endings in the clitoris were saying to the sleeping capacities of the vagina, "come, do as we do, wake up and feel."
>
> The third movement is based on a frequent observation that the first area of the vagina to become sensitively alive is a band just inside the front wall in the middle, an inch or so from side to side, and extending about three quarters of an inch inside. Gentle stretching movements of this front part of the ring of the vaginal entrance seem to give the strongest stimulation. Two finger-tips can easily be slid into place and gently and rhythmically moved to stretch the front edges of the vaginal ring.

On most points Dr. Wright is dogmatic — but with respect to vaginal stimulation she encourages independent explorations. "It must be emphasized that there is nothing absolute about these suggestions. The ways that different individuals begin to respond is sure to vary enormously, and every husband and wife must be prepared to find out for themselves, adventurously and imaginatively, those rhythmic movements which awake the keenest pleasurable response."

I hope these excerpts do not suggest that Dr. Wright is solely concerned with direct genital stimulation. Like van de Velde, she also stresses the importance of emotional rapport, of foreplay, and of other factors. But her instructions for genital stimulation are her unique contribution to sex research, and have therefore been singled out here.

I shall return to this matter of sexual instruction in my chapter on Masters and Johnson.

Dr. Wright has published no statistics concerning the percentage of her patients who are "cured." Nor is there any way of estimating the proportion of readers who benefit from reading her books. But I would venture to make two guesses concerning the efficacy of the Wright approach:

The cure rate, I have no doubt, is much higher among those women who are able and willing to follow her instructions, as compared with the ones whose masturbation taboo is so deeply rooted that, even under Dr. Wright's guidance, they balk.

The women who do succeed in following Dr. Wright's instructions with a clear conscience and a joyful outcome will be far less likely thereafter to repress their daughters' sexuality, or to hand along the masturbation taboo to yet another generation.

Mary Jane Sherfey

Many Victorian authorities on sex believed that respectable women don't enjoy coitus at all and that women are not capable of having an orgasm. Dr. Elizabeth Blackwell, as we have seen, took a somewhat more enlightened view. It is Dr. Mary Jane Sherfey, however, who has carried the doctrine of female sexual responsiveness and orgasmic capacity to its ultimate and extreme conclusion.

Dr. Sherfey was an undergraduate at Indiana University while Dr. Alfred C. Kinsey's researches were under way there; and a course which she took under Dr. Kinsey set the pattern for her subsequent career. She resolved to enter sex research, secured her M.D. degree in 1943 as a step in that direction, then qualified as a psychiatrist and entered the practice of psychiatry in New York. Despite the demands of her practice, her interest in sex research was maintained; the first fruit of this interest, a startling hundred-page monograph entitled "The Evolution and Nature of Female Sexuality in Relation to Psychoanalytic Theory" was submitted to the *Journal of the American Psychoanalytic Association* in December 1963 and published in its January 1966 issue. Dr. Sherfey visited us to discuss her work the summer after her monograph was published, and my wife and I found her shy and self-effacing but very sensitive and knowledgeable.

Dr. Sherfey describes her monograph as "the initial product of a fairly global approach to the study of man, requiring familiarity with physiology, anatomy, comparative embryology, endocrinology, gynecology, paleontology, evolutionary biology, population genetics, primatology, and ethology — not to mention anthropology and psychiatry, the central foci upon which the rest converge." In the course of her hundred pages she considers the historical reasons for the introduction of circumcision, the nature of the female orgasm, the conversion from matriarchal to patriarchal forms of social organization, and many other fascinating topics. I shall here review only a small segment of Dr. Sherfey's views — the segment directly relevant to the works of Elizabeth Blackwell, Leah Schaefer, Niles Newton, and Helena Wright reviewed above.

Dr. Sherfey sees the sexuality of women today in an evolutionary perspective. We humans, she points out, are primates — closely akin to the chimpanzees, gorillas, baboons, and other higher primates. What can be said of female sexuality among these related species?

"Having no cultural restrictions," Dr. Sherfey replies, "these primate females will perform coitus from twenty to fifty times a day during the peak week of estrus, usually with several series of copulations in rapid succession. If necessary, they flirt, solicit, present [their genitals], and stimulate the male in order to obtain successive coitions. They will 'consort' with one male for several days until he is exhausted, then take up with another. They emerge from estrus totally exhausted, often with wounds from spent males who have repulsed them."*

The evolutionary advantage of this behavior, of course, is self-evident. Though wounded and exhausted, the nymphomaniac female primate is almost certain to emerge pregnant. If not, she repeats the behavior during her next monthly cycle. "The breeding advantage would thus go to the females with the most insatiable sexual capacity."

The mystery of female sexuality in the *human* species is thus squarely posed: Why are human females so different, so sexually inadequate, as compared with the other higher primate females?

Dr. Sherfey reviews at length the customary explanations of human female sexual inferiority, and especially the Freudian explanations. Dr. Sherfey herself is a committed Freudian — but on this point she, like a number of other psychoanalytically trained women, parts company with the founder of her discipline. She concentrates her particular fire on Freud's view that women have sexual problems because the clitoris is vestigial, rudimentary, inadequate, and inferior to the penis — in Freud's own phrase, a "stunted penis."

The truth is, Dr. Sherfey points out, that the glans and shaft of the

* While this is true of some primate females, it is far from true of others.

human clitoris are merely the superficially visible or palpable manifestations of an underlying *clitoral system* which is at least as large, as impressive, and as functionally responsive as the penis — and which responds as a unit to sexual stimulation in much the same way that the penis does.

The penis, for example, has two roots known as *crura* which play an essential role in its functioning. During sexual excitation these crura become engorged with blood and contribute to erection of the penis. The clitoris, too, has two broad roots, of approximately the same size as in the male. The clitoral crura, too, become engorged with blood early in the woman's sexual excitation.

Again, the penis contains within its shaft two caverns or spaces known as *corpora cavernosa,* which fill with blood during sexual excitation, and contribute to the expanded size of the erect penis. The female clitoral system has a precisely analogous pair of bulbous *corpora cavernosa,* which similarly fill with blood during sexual excitation. They are not inside the shaft of the clitoris, it is true. Rather, they are located where they can be the most useful — surrounding the vestibule and outer third of the vagina. (They are therefore known as the vestibular bulbs.) The spongelike body (*corpus spongiosum*) inside the penis is paralleled by a similar spongelike structure in the clitoral system which functions in the same way.

The penis, Dr. Sherfey continues, is associated with sets of muscles which help to erect it during sexual excitation. The clitoris is associated with precisely homologous sets of muscles which serve to retract it, too — though, as Masters and Johnson have shown, at a somewhat later stage in the sex act. Other male muscles contract during orgasm, forcing the ejaculation of semen. Precisely homologous muscles function during the female orgasm, causing a rhythmic contraction of the outer third of the vagina. Indeed, as Masters and Johnson have also shown, the male and female sets of muscles respond in the *same* rhythm — one contraction every four-fifths of a second.

There are also differences, Dr. Sherfey concedes, between the penis and the clitoral system — but the differences, astonishing as it may seem to readers brought up in a male-dominated society, are in favor of the clitoral system. That system, for example, includes at least three (and possibly four or five) networks of veins called *venous plexi,* which extend diffusely throughout the female pelvic area — but especially through the regions immediately to the left and right of the vagina. These networks are also, Dr. Sherfey reports, a part of the clitoral system; and in addition they merge with the venous networks of the vaginal system. Together the clitoral and vaginal networks become engorged with blood during female sexual excitation. Thus the clitoris itself, far from being a vestigial or rudimentary organ, is merely the visible tip and harbinger of a vast anatomical array of sexually responsive female tissue. When fully engorged, the clitoral system as a whole overshadows the clitoral glans and shaft in the ratio of almost thirty to one. The total blood-vessel engorgement of the clitoral system during sexual excitation may actually exceed the more obvious engorgement of the male. Clearly the anatomical inadequacy of the clitoris is *not* the explanation of female sexual inadequacies.

I, for one, would like these facts to be known to every high-school girl *before* her first coitus, and preferably before her first orgasm. Boys, after all, know about *their* erections.

In an interesting aside to her readers, Dr. Sherfey points out that assembling these data was not easy. Almost all of the anatomy books are written by men — and they almost wholly ignore the clitoral system as distinguished from the tiny clitoris itself. This male prejudice, she adds, is one of the clues to the problem of female sexual inadequacy.*

Dr. Sherfey also rejects another Freudian explanation of female sexual inadequacy — the view that the female has two kinds of orgasm, a clitoral and a vaginal kind. The young girl who masturbates, according to this theory, experiences only a minor, malelike, clitoral orgasm. As the girl matures, she must learn to transfer her responsiveness from her clitoris to her vagina — and many women, it is alleged, fail to make this transfer successfully. I shall treat this theory at greater length in my

* Dr. Sherfey was not, however, the first to call attention to the importance of the clitoral system as distinct from the clitoris. One predecessor, amazingly enough, was Elizabeth Blackwell herself.

"The chief structures of the male," Dr. Blackwell pointed out, "are external, but they are internal in the female. This difference of structure first suggests to the boy the meaning of actions of the lower animals, whilst the girl may grow up to full womanhood in complete unconsciousness of their significance.

"This failure to recognize the equivalent value of internal with external structure has led to such crude fallacy as a comparison of the penis with such a vestige as the clitoris, *whilst failing to recognize that vast amount of erectile tissue, mostly internal, which is the direct seat of special sexual spasm* [orgasm]." (The italics are mine.)

chapter on Masters and Johnson. Here I need only say that Dr. Sherfey, like Masters and Johnson, wholly rejects the notion that there are two kinds of female orgasm.

By disposing of these and other technical explanations of female sexual inferiority, Dr. Sherfey clears the way for her major positive finding: *The human female is in fact not sexually inadequate or inferior*. If freed of *cultural* restrictions, she is capable of behaving like the other primate females — copulating all day long, day after day, with one male after another, until physical exhaustion puts an end to it. "The 'wide' gap between women's sexuality and the animals' is nonexistent."

In support of this unorthodox view, Dr. Sherfey cites first of all this finding of Masters and Johnson:

> If a female who is capable of having regular orgasms is properly stimulated within a short period after her first climax, she will in most instances be capable of having a second, third, fourth, and even a fifth and sixth orgasm before she is fully satiated. As contrasted with the male's usual inability to have more than one orgasm in a short period, many females, especially when clitorally stimulated, can regularly have five or six full orgasms within a matter of minutes.*

Dr. Sherfey fully agrees with this view.

"The popular idea," she writes, "that a woman should have one intense orgasm which should bring 'full satisfaction,' act as a strong sedative, and alleviate sexual tension for several days to come is simply falla-

* This Masters-Johnson finding astonished many readers and dismayed some; it was alleged that the women participating in the Masters-Johnson laboratory research must have been "sex freaks" of some kind, or that Masters and Johnson had invented multiple orgasm rather than discovered it. Yet precisely the same phenomenon had been described a generation earlier in England by Havelock Ellis, in Austria by Sigmund Freud, in Germany by Wilhelm Stekel, in the Netherlands by Theodoor van de Velde, and in the United States by Robert Latou Dickinson. The existence of multiple orgasm had thereafter been confirmed in studies by Paul Popenoe, G. V. Hamilton, W. R. Stokes, Robert Street, and no doubt others. Lewis M. Terman had reported in 1938 that among 792 married American women, thirteen percent experienced multiple orgasm; Kinsey reported in 1953 that fourteen percent of sexually experienced American women, married and unmarried, had enjoyed multiple orgasm on one or more occasions. Ernst P. Boas and Ernst F. Goldschmidt at Mt. Sinai Hospital in New York City in 1932 had even recorded with cardiotachometers a coital sequence in which a wife experienced four distinct orgasms to her husband's one. Far from being a recent St. Louis discovery, in short, multiple orgasm in women is among the well-attested facts of human physiology.

cious. It should be stressed that the intensities of the multiple orgasms do not abate until fatigue of the responding muscles has set in. Each orgasm is followed promptly by refilling of the venous erectile chambers; distention creates engorgement and edema, which creates more tissue tension, etc. The supply of blood and edema fluid to the pelvis is inexhaustible.

"Consequently, the more orgasms a woman has, the stronger they become; the more orgasms she has, the more she *can* have. To all intents and purposes, *the human female is sexually insatiable in the presence of the highest degrees of sexual satiation.*" The italics are Dr. Sherfey's.

Just two-thirds of a century separates Dr. Sherfey's "Evolution and Nature of Female Sexuality" from Elizabeth Blackwell's "Human Element in Sex." But in content, surely, they are millennia apart.

Much of the Masters-Johnson data on multiple orgasm in women had been secured during masturbation rather than coitus — and especially through the use of the electric vibrator or massager as a device for stimulating the clitoris.

"The average female with optimal arousal," Masters and Johnson reported, and Dr. Sherfey quotes, "will usually be satisfied with 3–5 manually induced orgasms; whereas mechanical stimulation, as with the electric vibrator, is less tiring and induces her to go on to long stimulative sessions of an hour or more during which she may have from 20 to 50 consecutive orgasms. She will stop only when totally exhausted. Such sessions [occur] as often as 2–3 times a week."

Dr. Sherfey confirms these findings.

"In clinical practice," she writes, "a number of married and single women using the electric vibrator to achieve up to fifty orgasms in a single session have come to my attention in the past few years. To have the comfort of a label, I had considered them to be cases of nymphomania without promiscuity. From the standpoint of our cultural norm, this may be an accurate enough phrase. From the standpoint of normal physiological functioning, these women exhibit a healthy, uninhibited sexuality — and *the number of orgasms attained, a measure of the human female's orgasmic potentiality.*" Once again, the italics are Dr. Sherfey's.

Dr. Sherfey concedes that these multiorgasmic sequences are more commonly met with in female masturbation than in coitus — but she attributes this, no doubt quite properly, to the sexual shortcomings of the human male:

"The reason is obvious, I think, in that few males can maintain an erection long enough for more than three or four orgasms in the woman."

There are recorded cases of a dozen or more men having intercourse with one woman in rapid succession. Since the writers on this subject are invariably men, they tend to interpret such events as either prostitution or mass rape — the "gang bang" so familiar in pornographic writing and adolescent folklore. Dr. Sherfey, however, suggests an alternative explanation.

"Throughout historic time — and even today," she writes, "it could well be that women have indulged in the so-called 'orgastic parties,' having relations with one man after another, for precisely the purpose of gratifying this capacity for numerous, successive orgasms with intravaginal coition."

Most men who write about nymphomania consider it a form of frigidity — a frantic and inevitably unsuccessful effort to achieve satisfaction among women who are somehow blocked from orgasmic response. Indeed, one male psychoanalyst, Dr. Edmund Bergler, goes so far as to apply the label "frigid" to all multiorgasmic women. Dr. Sherfey indignantly dissents: "I urge the re-examination of the vague and controversial concepts of nymphomania and promiscuity without frigidity. Until now, it has not been realized that regular multiple orgasms, with either clitoral or vaginal stimulation, to the point of physical exhaustion could be the biological norm for women's sexual performance. . . . It could well be that the 'oversexed' woman is actually exhibiting a normal sexuality — although because of it, her integration into her society may leave much to be desired."

Dr. Sherfey gives this process of orgasms-repeated-until-exhaustion a new label: "Satiation-in-Insatiation," which she explains in these terms:

> No doubt the most far-reaching hypothesis extrapolated from these biological data is the existence of the universal and physically normal condition of women's inability ever to reach complete sexual satiation [even] in the presence of the most intense, repetitive orgasmic experiences, no matter how produced. Theoretically, a woman could go on having orgasms indefinitely if physical exhaustion did not intervene. . . .

> I must stress that this condition does not mean that a woman is always consciously unsatisfied. There is a great difference between satisfaction and satiation. A woman may be emotionally satisfied to the full in the absence of *any* orgasmic expression (although such a state would rarely persist through years of frequent arousal and coitus without some kind of physical

or emotional reaction formation). Satiation-in-insatiation is well illustrated by Masters' statement, "A woman will usually be satisfied by 3-5 orgasms. . . ." I believe it would rarely be said, "A man will usually be satisfied with three to five ejaculations." The man *is* satisfied. The woman *usually wills* herself to be satisfied because she is simply unaware of the extent of her orgasmic capacity. However, I predict that this hypothesis will come as no great shock to many women who consciously realize, or intuitively sense, their lack of satiation.

And Dr. Sherfey, despite her psychoanalytic orientation, draws a very nonanalytic conclusion:

On the basis of these observations, it seems that the vast majority of cases of coital frigidity are due simply to the absence of frequent, prolonged coitus.

If it is true that women today, like their primate cousins, retain the capacity for enjoying an unlimited series of orgasms during unlimited coitus, why do so few of them make full use of this capacity?

Dr. Sherfey's reply to this key question is based largely on a theory of human prehistory first announced in 1861 by the German historian, J. J. Bachofen — and generally discounted today. In his classic work, *Das Mutterrecht,* Bachofen deduced from an analysis of Near Eastern myths and art objects that human societies were ruled by women until about 8,000 B.C., and that these early women freely displayed the extreme kind of eroticism still found in the other higher primates — a pattern of arousal which might be called "the Sherfey syndrome." Dr. Sherfey concedes that the Bachofen thesis has been "summarily rejected by twentieth-century anthropologists," partly for lack of objective evidence — but also, she adds, because of "cultural bias." In a word, most anthropologists are males.

Dr. Sherfey goes on to explain the transition from the erotically unleashed human female of matriarchal society to the profoundly inhibited female of civilized societies in these terms:

If the conclusions reached here are true, it is conceivable that the *forceful* suppression of women's inordinate sexual demands was a prerequisite to the dawn of every modern civilization and almost every living culture. Primitive woman's sexual drive was too strong, too susceptible to the fluctuating extremes of an impelling, aggressive eroticism to withstand the disciplined requirements of a settled family life — where many living children were necessary to a family's well-being and where paternity had become as important as maternity in maintaining family and property cohesion. . . .

There are many indications from the prehistory studies in the Near East that it took perhaps 5,000 years or longer for the subjugation of women to take place. All relevant data from the 12,000 to 8,000 B.C. period indicate that precivilized woman enjoyed full sexual freedom and was often totally incapable of controlling her sexual drive. Therefore, I propose that one of the reasons for the long delay between the earliest development of agriculture (c. 12,000 B.C.) and the rise of urban life and the beginning of recorded knowledge (c. 8,000–5,000 B.C.) was the ungovernable cyclic sexual drive of women. Not until these drives were gradually brought under control by rigidly enforced social codes could family life become the stabilizing and creative crucible from which modern civilized man could emerge.

Let me here indulge in a parenthetical aside. Throughout this volume I have used the term Victorian to describe the repression of human sexuality and especially of female sexuality. Many contemporary writers on sex talk instead of Puritanism or "the Judeo-Christian ethic." I use Victorian instead of Judeo-Christian in part because it was the term in common use during most of the period with which this book is concerned. In the perspective of Dr. Sherfey's theory, however, both terms are woefully inadequate. Sexual repression, it would appear, is not only older than Victorianism and Puritanism but older than Christianity and Judaism.

Dr. Sherfey is not resentful of these thousands of years of repression of her sex, or even of the ruthless manner in which, she believes, it was at times imposed.

"Although then (and now) couched in superstitious, religious, and rationalized terms," she explains, "behind the subjugation of women's sexuality lay the inexorable economics of cultural evolution which finally forced men to impose it and women to endure it. If that suppression has been, at times, unduly oppressive or cruel, I suggest the reason has been neither man's sadistic, selfish infliction of servitude upon helpless women nor women's weakness or inborn masochism. *The strength of the drive determines the force required to suppress it.*" (This time the italics are mine.)

Thus Dr. Sherfey comes in the end to the immediately practical question:

"Assuming this analysis of the nature of women's sexuality is valid, we must ask ourselves if the basic intensity of women's sexual drive has abated appreciably as the result of the past 7,000 years of suppression (which has been, of course, only a partial suppression for most of that time)."

Dr. Sherfey answers her own question in the negative: each baby girl born into the world today still has that insatiable capacity for sexual response, a capacity waiting to be unleashed. And there are signs that in an increasing number of women, the capacity is in fact being unleashed.

"Just within the very recent past, a decided lifting of the ancient social injunctions against the free expression of female sexuality has occurred," Dr. Sherfey declares. "This unprecedented development is born of the scientific revolution, the product of both efficient contraceptives and the new social equality and emotional honesty sweeping across the world (an equality and honesty which owe more to the genius of Sigmund Freud than to any other single individual)."

Dr. Sherfey hesitates to predict the results of this unleashing of female sexuality. She has promised a second monograph in which this and other issues raised in her first publication will be more fully explored. But she does provide a word of caution:

> One thing is certain: if women's sexual drive has not abated, and they prove incapable of controlling it, thereby jeopardizing family life and child care, a return to the rigid, enforced suppression will be inevitable and mandatory. Otherwise the biological family will disappear and what other patterns of infant care and adult relationships could adequately substitute cannot now be imagined.

Some additional evidence for Dr. Sherfey's view of female sexuality is provided in recent studies of the Sexual Freedom Movement in California and elsewhere (see Chapter 9). Some (not all) women participating in this movement do in fact exhibit "the Sherfey syndrome" — unlimited multiorgasmic response in coitus with an uninterrupted series of males. But this mode of behavior does not, interestingly enough, appear to "jeopardize family life and child care," as Dr. Sherfey fears. Many of the women who participate in the sexual freedom "parties" attend in company with their husbands — and leave their telephone numbers with their baby-sitters so that they can be summoned in case of need, just as would be the case if they were at the movies or a bridge party. The most impressive testimony to the compatibility of the "Sherfey syndrome" with sensitive maternal behavior comes from a male participant in the Sexual Freedom Movement who writes:

I was one of two males who on this occasion spent the night with R—— in her own home. R—— is one of the two most multiorgasmic women I have ever met. Sexual activity occupied approximately the first four hours of the night, and was renewed in the morning. During the four-hour session, we two men took turns with R——, and at times when we were both unerect, we stimulated her orally and manually. While no one kept count, I would estimate that she experienced between 100 and 200 orgasms during the four-hour period. Her orgasms were quite obviously physiological; there was no possibility of "pretending." At no point between orgasms did she relax or fall below the level of sexual arousal which Masters and Johnson call "the plateau level" — with one exception:

About an hour and a half after the evening session began, R—— suddenly catapulted herself out of bed, bolted out of the room, and disappeared without warning or explanation. The other male and I were utterly baffled. I surmised that she had had a sudden cramp, or an attack of diarrhea. After a discreet interval, I followed her out of the room. To my amazement, I found her three bedrooms away, comforting her three-year-old son who had awakened and cried out in the night.

Neither the other male nor I had heard anything at all. I doubt whether I, who was R——'s active partner at the moment of interruption, would have heard a sonic boom in the same room. But R——, at the height of a period of sexual arousal as extreme as any I have ever seen in a woman, heard the cry three bedrooms away through two closed doors, and responded to it instantaneously in the orthodox maternal way.

Let me say very frankly that I do not accept Mary Jane Sherfey's Bachofenian theory of prehistory. Readers, of course, are free to reject her other theories as well. We are here on highly speculative ground. Nevertheless, I regard Dr. Sherfey's theories as very important, well worth the space I have devoted to them in this history of sex research — *merely because they exist.*

Let me explain. The major sex-research reports such as the Kinsey and Masters-Johnson studies do much more than describe the existing nature of human sexuality. They also help to mold the future development of that sexuality. We men and women of the 1960's are a little different sexually, and we behave and respond in somewhat different ways, because of the impact of the Kinsey reports on us and on our culture. As Dr. Sherfey's theories become better known — and I have no doubt they *will* become widely known and debated — the nature of female sexuality will to that extent be affected.

Indeed, it may even happen that the Sherfey syndrome will prove to be a "self-fulfilling prophecy." Whether or not Dr. Sherfey is right about female sexuality in the past, more and more women familiar with Dr. Sherfey's theories may *hereafter* respond in the way she describes.

7

Males, Females, and Others

Hermaphrodites, Tomboys, Sissies, Transvestites, Transsexuals, Homosexuals, Bisexuals, and Heterosexuals — What John Money and Others Have Been Learning about Us All

WHY are some human beings male and others female?

Why are some human beings hermaphrodites — possessing sexual organs which are partially male and partially female?

Why are some girls "tomboys" and some boys "sissies"?

Why are some human beings transvestites — imbued with a compulsive urge to dress in the clothing of the opposite sex and to be accepted as members of the opposite sex?

Why are some human beings transsexuals — imbued with a similarly compulsive urge to be physically transformed into members of the opposite sex through surgery and other means? (Christine Jorgensen and Myra Breckenridge are, of course, the best-known real-life and fictional examples.)

Finally, why are some human beings heterosexual, others bisexual, and still others homosexual in their selection of sexual partners?

In this chapter I shall review a broad range of current scientific findings on these fascinating questions. I shall rely heavily on the research findings and opinions of Dr. John Money of the Johns Hopkins School of Medicine, who has devoted the past twenty years to research on these and related topics. Following Dr. Money's lead, I shall describe nine levels of maleness and femaleness, ranging from the chromosomal level to the level of sex partner choice.

The Chromosomes

During the nineteenth century, various microscopists examining human and animal cells noted that they invariably contained sets of tiny rod-shaped particles which came to be called chromosomes. The number of chromosomes in a cell appeared to depend upon the species from which the cell came. In 1891, however, a German scientist named Henking noted a complicating detail when he examined the spermatozoa of an obscure species of insect, *Pyrrhocoris apterus* — an insect of the kind known to entomologists as "true bugs." About half of these insect sperm cells contained eleven chromosomes; the others contained a twelfth, "accessory" chromosome.

Let me add parenthetically that there is a widespread tendency among nonscientists, and also among some psychiatrists, to discount the findings of animal research on the ground that "mice are not men." And it is true that in the past, the indiscriminate introduction of animal findings into theories of human sexuality has sometimes proved misleading. But the quality of research into animal sexual behavior has greatly improved in recent years. Today, we ignore or discount animal findings at our peril. Some of the most significant clues to human sexuality came originally from animal experiments — even from such insignificant animals as the "true bug," *Pyrrhocoris apterus*.

During the decade after Henking's 1891 discovery, chomosome counts were made of the sperm cells of other species, including some mammals; and in 1902, in a paper entitled "The Accessory Chromosome — Sex Determinant?" an American investigator, C. E. McClung, announced a solution to the central mystery. The accessory chromosome carried by half of the sperm cells but not by the other half, he stated, is "the bearer of those qualities which belong to the male organism."

Among mammals, including humans, the story turned out to be a little more complicated than that. Normal human sperm cells, we now know, contain twenty-two ordinary chromosomes plus either an X or a Y chromosome. Normal human ova contain the same twenty-two ordinary chromosomes plus an X chromosome. If an ovum is fertilized by a Y-bearing sperm, the resulting baby has forty-four ordinary chromosomes plus one X and one Y chromosome (XY) in each of its bodily cells and it is chromosomally a boy. If the ovum is fertilized by an X-bearing chromosome, the resulting baby has forty-four ordinary chromosomes plus two X chromosomes (XX) in each bodily cell and is chromosomally a girl. Thus the first of the questions above appears to be decisively answered: the presence or absence of a Y chromosome determines maleness or femaleness.

Since 1956, however, scientists at many medical research centers, using subtle new chromosome-visualization techniques, have discovered additional complications. Indeed, a whole new science of chromosome study known as cytogenetics has arisen and has notably enriched our understanding of human sexuality.

It has been learned since 1956, for example, that some girl babies are born with three X chromosomes (XXX) instead of the usual two. Other girls are born with one X chromosome missing (XO). Some boy babies are born with an extra X chromosome (XXY) or two extras (XXXY), or with an extra Y chromosome (XYY). Rare cases of XXXXY and XXYY have also been reported, and there are other variants. Some individuals are "mosaics," so that some cells in their body are, for example, XY, while other cells are XXXY. I shall postpone discussion of the effects of these variations except to say that they confirm the basic 1902 finding of McClung: at the first level of maleness or femaleness, namely the chromosome level, maleness depends (with a few rare exceptions) on the presence of a Y chromosome. Femaleness develops in its absence.

The Gonads

For the first six weeks or so of human pregnancy, embryologists report, the Y chromosome seems to have no noticeable effect. All human embryos look alike at six weeks, and all look female. Even the sex glands — the gonads — look alike; you can't tell whether a gonad is going to become a testis or an ovary, even under the microscope.

Beginning at about the seventh week, however, the Y chromosome begins to have a decisive effect. If it is present, the core of the gonad begins to develop, and the gonad matures as a testis. In the absence of a Y chromosome, the rind develops instead and the gonad matures as an ovary.

But just as errors may occur at the chromosomal level, so errors occasionally occur at this second, gonadal level. Some babies are born with one ovary and one testis. Some are born with two ovaries and two testes. Some are born with two "ovotestes" — gonads in which both the cores and the rinds have developed. Some are born with no gonads at all (the

Turner syndrome); these are the babies with one X and no Y chromosome (XO). Lacking a Y chromosome, they are girls.

Fetal Hormones

The ovaries and testes, as everyone knows, awaken at puberty and begin to secrete effective amounts of female hormones (estrogens) and male hormones (androgens). What few laymen appreciate is the fact that for the testes, puberty is a *reawakening*. During the second or third month of gestation, too, the testes of the male fetus secrete substantial amounts of androgens — and it is these androgens from the fetus's own testes which masculinize the rest of the fetal body. If androgens are not secreted in sufficient amount at the right time, the fetus develops as a girl.

The principle here illustrated appears to be true not only for humans but throughout the world of mammals. In the absence of hormones, the developmental pattern is female. A specific female hormone is not necessary to achieve femaleness. Maleness, however, does depend on the right amount of male hormone at the right time.

At this third level, the fetal hormone level, several kinds of error can occur. The testes of a male fetus may fail to secrete enough androgens at the right time. Sometimes they secrete the androgens, but the fetus is for some reason insensitive to them and therefore fails to masculinize. Sometimes androgen gets into the bloodstream of a female fetus — through the umbilical cord or in some other way — and masculinizes it. If the fetus has both ovaries and testes, or if it has ovotestes, the balance of hormones may be affected and the condition traditionally known as "true hermaphroditism" may arise. It can in very rare cases take bizarre forms. The left side of the body may be female, for example, with an ovary and large breast, while the right side is male.

Internal Sex Organs

Every human fetus is partially hermaphroditic during one stage in its development. It possesses the rudiments of two separate systems of internal sex organs — the male or Wolffian system and the female or Müllerian system. If the fetal testes are functioning properly, the Wolffian system develops and the Müllerian system withers away, so that the baby is born with a prostate gland, seminal vesicles, and other male internal sex accessories. In the absence of fetal androgens, the

Müllerian system develops and the Wolffian system withers away; the baby is born with a uterus, cervix, Fallopian tubes, and other female internal sex accessories.

External Sex Organs

Just as the normal human fetus starts off with gonads which may become either testes or ovaries, depending upon the presence or absence of the Y chromosome, so it starts off with a "genital tubercle" which — depending upon the presence or absence of androgens — develops into either a penis or a clitoris. Similarly, the fetus in the absence of androgens develops two external labia at the entrance to the vagina; if androgens are present, the two labia fuse together to form a sac or scrotum into which the testes descend. In the absence of androgens, the fetus develops internal labia and a hood for the clitoris; androgens convert the same embryonic tissues into the skin which sheathes the penis.

Several kinds of errors can occur at this fifth level. A male fetus with a Y chromosome and testes, for example, may develop female external sex organs if the testes fail to secrete androgens during the critical period when the external organs are taking shape. Similarly a fetus which is female in all other visible respects may develop masculinized external sex organs if androgens are introduced during the critical period. The external labia may be fused to form a scrotum — though there are no testes to fill the scrotum. More commonly the external sex organs in pathological cases reveal an ambiguous, in-between condition. The baby may be born with a clitoris, but the clitoris may be much larger than usual. The external labia may be only partly fused, like a half-finished scrotum. In some cases external organ development may be so ambiguous that even the most experienced pediatrician cannot decide, after careful scrutiny, whether to assign the baby as a girl or a boy on the basis of external appearance alone.

In such cases today, the assignment is properly postponed for a few days while chromosome studies and gonadal studies are performed; it may also prove necessary to search for Wolffian and Müllerian organs by means of an exploratory operation. Before these diagnostic techniques became available, parents decided for themselves, or physicians decided for them — in extreme cases by flipping a coin.

Hormones at Puberty

Shortly before or after birth, the testes stop secreting androgens in significant amounts. They are rearoused at puberty, however, and flood the boy's body with androgens which lower his voice, trigger the growth of his beard, and produce the many other changes signaling male adolescence and maturity. At puberty, too, the ovaries are aroused for the first time to secrete estrogens which trigger the swelling of the breasts, the growth of pubic hair, the onset of the menstrual cycle, and the other signs of female maturity.

Errors? Of course. The boy at puberty may be feminized by estrogens; the girl may be masculinized by androgens; puberty may set in prematurely, or it may be long delayed, or it may fail altogether to make its appearance unless androgens or estrogens are prescribed as medication.

Several of the patterns I have described above are "hermaphroditic"; that is, the babies are born partly masculine and partly feminine. But to which cases should this vague term be applied?

A baby born with the XXY chromosome pattern is no doubt *chromosomally* hermaphroditic; he has both the XX chromosome combination characteristic of the normal female and the XY combination diagnostic of maleness. Yet his gonads, hormones, internal sex organs, and external sex organs are all essentially male. Why label him a hermaphrodite? Some authorities in the past distinguished "true hermaphroditism" — cases with both ovarian and testicular gonadal tissue — from "pseudohermaphroditism," but this distinction is seldom drawn today. In the rest of this chapter, I shall use the term hermaphroditism to mean any ambiguity of *visible* development — the kind of ambiguity which would lead the child himself, his parents, or his friends, to be in doubt.

So far I have answered the first two of the questions with which this chapter began — why most of us are either firmly male or firmly female, and why a few of us reveal an ambiguity of physical sexual development at one or more of the six developmental levels: chromosome, gonad, fetal hormone, internal sex-organ, external sex-organ, and adolescent hormone level. The remaining questions concerning tomboys, sissies, transvestites, transsexuals, heterosexuals, bisexuals, and homosexuals are even more complex — and it is here that I rely most heavily on Dr. Money.

Born and educated in New Zealand, John Money came to the United

States for graduate work in education and psychology as a young man in 1947. After a year in the Middle West, he won a scholarship to the Psychological Clinic of the Harvard Graduate School. Though he had formerly planned to be a teacher, sex research had always been among his interests. Harvard opened up for him the opportunity to engage in research — and he grasped it.

Hermaphroditism during the 1940's was one of the least-understood aspects of sex research, even from the physical point of view; many of the facts reviewed above had not yet been established. The *psychological* study of hermaphroditism lagged even further. John Money saw here an opportunity to make, while still in graduate school, a significant contribution to the scientific study of sex. He selected the psychology of hermaphroditism as the topic of his Harvard Ph.D. thesis — not merely because of its inherent interest, but also because he hoped a study of these pathological phenomena might throw light on *normal* human sexuality. His hopes, as we shall see, were very abundantly realized.

For his thesis, young Money needed both the hospital case records of hermaphrodites and contacts with hermaphrodites whom he could interview and test psychologically. The Department of Pediatrics at the Johns Hopkins Medical School was a promising source of both records and contacts. Dr. Lawson Wilkins (1894–1963), who headed the Johns Hopkins pediatric endocrine clinic and later its Department of Pediatrics, was a clinician trained in both pediatrics and endocrinology, with a special interest in unraveling the *physical* mysteries of hermaphrodism. Dr. Wilkins was pleased to cooperate — and as John Money's research progressed, Dr. Wilkins recognized its importance. In addition to hormone therapy and surgery, many of the hermaphrodites who came to the Hopkins for help needed psychological counseling and guidance. To fill this role, Dr. Wilkins brought Money to Baltimore in 1951. The following year, Money's thesis, entitled "Hermaphroditism: An Inquiry into the Nature of a Human Paradox," was accepted by Harvard, and he became Dr. Money.

At the Hopkins, Dr. Money enlisted the assistance of a young woman psychiatrist, Dr. Joan G. Hampson. Three years later her husband, Dr. John L. Hampson, also a psychiatrist, joined the team. Beginning about 1955, a steady stream of papers began to emerge from the Hopkins, on hermaphroditism and related problems, by Money, or by Money, Hampson and Hampson, or by the Hampsons, or by Money and other collaborators and students — all under the aegis of Dr. Wilkins. The Hampsons moved to Seattle in 1960, and Dr. Wilkins died in 1963; but Dr. Money carries on at the Hopkins as Associate Professor of Medical Psychology and Pediatrics in the medical school and as director of its office of psychohormonal research.

Dr. Money's major contribution to sex research has been to delineate three separate levels of *psychological* development, parallel to the six levels of anatomic and physiological development described above, in the etiology of maleness and femaleness. Let me describe these psychological levels briefly.

Sex of Assignment and Rearing

Common sense, as did Freud, tells us that if a physician calls a baby a boy and if his parents rear him as a boy, this will have a profound effect on his subsequent sexual development. The idea is so simple it hardly seems worth stating — yet, as we shall see, it is an essential preliminary to an understanding of psychological maleness and femaleness.

Gender Role and Identity

Most children, of course, accept the gender to which they are assigned at birth, and grow up in accordance with it — in manner, gestures, choice of toys, choice of sports, choice of clothes, and so on. Males play the role of males and females play a female role. Males think of themselves as male — accept a male identity; females think of themselves as female — accept a female identity. This, too, is so obvious it hardly seems worth stating until we consider the exceptions:

Tomboys and sissies reject in some small measure their gender role and identity.

Transvestites reject in much larger measure their gender role and identity.

Transsexuals entirely reject their gender role and identity. Male transsexuals think of themselves as women locked by some awful quirk of fate into a man's body. They plead or demand to have their bodies altered to match their "true" or "inner" identities. Many of them want not only to marry as women but to have children and mother them. Much the same, in reverse, is true of female transsexuals.

Choice of Sexual Partner

Most of us are heterosexual; this means that we choose sexual partners of the opposite sex. Some of us, however, are homosexual; this means that we choose sexual partners of our own sex. Still others of us are bisexual; this means that we choose sexual partners of both sexes.

This concept, too, is so absurdly simple — once it has been formulated and understood — that it seems hardly credible that even many specialists in homosexuality have failed to recognize its full significance.* Instead, many experts through the decades have tried to equate homosexuality with femininity in the male and with masculinity in the female, or with passivity in the male and aggressiveness in the female, or they have tried to characterize homosexuality as some kind of disease, or have applied the term "latent homosexual" to men and women whose behavior and fantasies are exclusively and insistently heterosexual, or have muddied the waters with other kinds of nonsense. Only when we recognize heterosexuality, homosexuality, and bisexuality for what they are — alternative approaches to the choice of sexual partners — can we begin to make progress in understanding them.

A male homosexual may be as masculine as Gary Cooper or Rock Hudson. A female homosexual may be as feminine as Marilyn Monroe or Brigitte Bardot. Failure to recognize this simple fact — to distinguish male and female homosexuality from male effeminacy and female masculinity — has impeded sex research into these conditions for generations.†

Merely delineating these nine levels of sexual differentiation — six physical and three psychological — sweeps away a lot of confusion. But the Money analysis accomplishes much more than that. It leads toward an explanation of the mystery that fascinates everybody: *why* are some of us sissies, tomboys, transsexuals, transvestites, homosexuals, and bisexuals? (A related mystery, though few people seem to be interested in it, is why so many of us are heterosexuals.)

The *why* question is usually phrased in fruitless ways. People ask with respect to tomboyism, transvestism, or homosexuality, for example:

* Kinsey, of course, understood, and made the same point.

† A man *may* be both homosexual and effeminate, of course. A woman *may* be both homosexual and masculine or "butchy." But this hardly warrants confusing the two characteristics. The Kinsey group reported that only about ten percent of males with histories of homosexual contact fitted the usual concept of effeminacy.

Is it inherited or acquired?

Is it the result of nature or nurture?

Are people born that way, or is their deviation the result of environmental factors?

The Money analysis enables us to put the question in a more useful form:

Are the deviations which here concern us determined at the chromosomal level, the gonadal level, the fetal hormone level, the adolescent hormone level — or at one of the psychological levels?

Through the study of hermaphroditism and many other forms of sexual variation, Dr. Money has assembled vast amounts of fresh data on this key question.

These data were collected in two phases. During the first phase (roughly the 1950's), a broad flow of evidence assembled by Dr. Money and others supported the conclusion that the psychological deviations with which we are here concerned — tomboyism, sissyism, transvestism, transsexuality, homosexuality, and bisexuality — arise at level 7, sex of assignment and rearing. Chromosomes, gonads, and hormones appeared to be almost irrelevant. As Freud had taught, it is the *child* which is father to the man — not the ovum, the sperm, or the fetus.

During the second phase (beginning about 1959), however, a trickle of fascinating data has begun to suggest that in quite subtle ways, chromosomes and hormones are also relevant. I shall first review the broad flow of evidence, and then the more recent counterflow.

Among 76 hermaphrodites and other mixed-sex cases of various kinds, Drs. Money, Hampson, and Hampson reported in a pioneering 1955 paper, adult psychological gender role and identity agreed with sex of assignment and rearing in all except four cases.

Babies assigned as male at birth, and brought up as boys by their parents, thereafter thought of themselves as male, played with male toys, enjoyed male sports, preferred male clothing, developed male sexual fantasies, and in due course fell in love with girls. Similarly, babies assigned and reared as girls accepted the assignment, followed the feminine pattern of development, and in due course fell in love with boys.

The four exceptions to the rule among their 76 cases, Dr. Money and the Hampsons found, confirmed the general principle that it is primarily sex of assignment and rearing (level 7) which determines male or female gender role and orientation (level 8) and choice of sex partner (level 9). In these four cases, and in other similar cases identified and studied since 1955, something had gone wrong at level 7 which could explain the subsequent psychosexual deviations.

There was never an ambiguity in adult *psychological* maleness or femaleness, for example, in cases where the external genitals *looked* completely male or completely female. Problems arose only in a few of the many cases where "the external genitals looked ambiguous, thereby permitting the child from infancy onward to make comparisons and conjecture about being a boy or a girl."

In some cases, too, "personal ambiguity was reinforced by ambiguity in the social environment. The parents remained basically unconvinced that they had a son — or a daughter."

Failure to develop firm psychological maleness or femaleness also occurred in a few of the many cases where there was neighborhood gossip. "Neighbors remembered and talked about the boy who had turned into a girl, and playmates made verbal ammunition of the accusation of being half-girl, half-boy, or a freak."

In the absence of such psychological disturbances, the babies assigned and reared as boys grew up to be male in gender role and identity, and heterosexual in partner choice; those assigned and reared as girls similarly grew up to be female heterosexuals. "Chromosomes, gonads, hormones — they all played second fiddle to rearing."

The evidence from those first 76 cases (confirmed in many more since 1955) is even more impressive when the details are considered. In 19 cases, for example, babies with a male chromosome pattern were assigned and reared as girls, while babies with a female chromosome pattern were assigned and reared as boys. In every one of these 19 cases, Dr. Money and the Hampsons reported, "the person established a gender role and orientation consistent with assigned sex and rearing and inconsistent with chromosomal sex. Thus, it is convincingly clear that gender role and orientation as male or female evidenced itself independently of chromosomal sex, but in close conformity with assigned sex of rearing."

Again, in 20 cases, babies with testes were assigned and reared as girls while babies with ovaries were assigned and reared as boys. In all but three of these cases, the children grew up psychologically in accordance with their assigned sex rather than their gonadal sex; the exceptions have been explained above. "Gonadal structure *per se* proved a most unreliable prognosticator of a person's gender role and orientation as a man or woman, boy or girl," Dr. Money and the Hampsons noted. "By contrast, assigned sex and rearing proved a most reliable one."

Evidence concerning hormonal sex proved even more convincing. In twenty-seven patients, hormonal sex differed from sex of assignment and rearing. In some cases this meant that babies assigned and reared as girls grew up with male-sized penises, failed to develop breasts at puberty, had to shave every day or two, and so on. In other cases among the twenty-seven, boys failed to develop penises of normal size, could not urinate standing up, developed breasts at puberty, retained high-pitched voices, had little or no beard, and so on. These patients, of course, were severely distressed. Yet 23 of the 27 "established a gender role consistent with their assigned sex and rearing, despite the embarrassment and worry occasioned by hormonal contradictions. Like gonadal sex, hormonal sex *per se* proved a most unreliable prognosticator of a person's gender role and identification as man or woman, boy or girl."

Very convincing evidence came from Dr. Money's patients born with what used to be called the "testicular feminizing syndrome" but which is now also called the "androgen insensitivity syndrome." These individuals start off at conception with normal male (XY) chromosomes. Normal testes develop at the usual time in prenatal life. These testes secrete the normal amount of male hormones — androgens — at the normal time. But the growing fetus is insensitive to these hormones (probably because it lacks an enzyme necessary for androgen utilization). As a result, prenatal masculinization fails to occur. The baby is born with a clitoris instead of a penis, and with labia instead of a scrotum. The testes either do not descend at all, or else descend into the groin where they are rarely noticed. The vagina is relatively short, but that is not noticed at birth, either. "No physician would ever think of declaring one of these patients a boy," Dr. Money explains, "and none, in fact, has ever done so." These babies are invariably raised as girls.

Contrary to a widespread popular impression, normal testes and ovaries secrete both androgens and estrogens. The difference is that testes secrete larger amounts of androgens while ovaries secrete larger amounts of estrogens. At puberty, the testes of these girls, like other normal testes, secrete both in a proper ratio. Since the girls remain insensitive to the androgens, no masculinization occurs. Instead, the estrogens secreted by the testes are sufficient to achieve an almost normal female puberty. The breasts swell. Axillary and pubic hair may make their appearance—though in some cases a bit sparsely and in others not at all. In many cases neither the girls nor their parents suspect that anything is wrong until the mid-teen years, when the girl begins to wonder why she has never menstruated. Only then is it discovered that she has testes instead of ovaries.

"We have studied ten patients with the androgen insensitivity syndrome, between the ages of fourteen and thirty-one," Dr. Money reported recently. "Only one, a young girl with a highly disruptive family background, showed any disturbance of psychosexual identity." The other nine, despite their male chromosomes and male gonads, "were strongly feminine and unmistakably and immediately recognizable as such. As girls their play preference had been for dolls and other feminine toys. They had not been tomboys. In teenage they had their fair share of boy friends and dating. Marriage with fulltime homemaking was their career of choice."

A full study of these ten girls, ranging in age from fourteen to thirty-one, was published by Dr. Money with Dr. Anke A. Ehrhardt and a student, Daniel N. Masica, in September 1968. Here are the salient findings:

Homemaking. "Preference of marriage over career, and enjoyment of domestic and homemaking duties, is traditionally the stereotype of the fulfillment of a woman's role," the Money group noted. These girls fitted the stereotype. "The majority of our patients strongly desired marriage with only a minimal interest in outside jobs. . . . The strong desire in all the adult patients to be exclusively a homemaker was also reflected in their favorable outlook on domestic activities. Cooking was given special mention by six."

Marriage. Four of the girls were already married. What kinds of husbands did they pick, and what kinds of wives did they make? "These men impressed us as being in every sense psychosexually masculine," the Money group reported. "None reported any homosexual experience or inclinations. These men rated their wives, without exception, as feminine on all counts. They considered them excellent cooks, housekeepers (except for some minor pet peeves in one case), and wives. In all four cases, the marriages seemed happy and acceptably stable."

Pregnancy and Childbirth Wishes. Five of the ten girls did not know, until they reached adult life, that it would be impossible for them to have babies. Three of these five reported dreams and fantasies about pregnancy and childbirth before learning of the impossibility.

Seven of the ten patients recalled playing mother-father games frequently when they were children. "There was no ambiguity as to their role in these rehearsal games; they were always mothers exclusively. They never rehearsed the male role."

Three of the ten patients reported that they felt a sense of great loss in being deprived of the pregnancy-childbirth experience.

Breast-feeding. Ask a man whether he would breast-feed or bottle-feed his babies and he would think you were some kind of nut. All ten of these girls had ready answers. They had thought about breast-feeding and had developed definite feelings pro or con. Two wanted to breast-feed had they been physically able to. One girl said she knew she could never breast-feed and perhaps that was why she was opposed to it. The others who preferred bottle-feeding were much like women of their generation generally in this respect.

Raising a Family. "Raising her own family is all but universally the primary function of a woman in most cultures," the Money group stated. "Every one of the patients in our sample had repeated dreams and fantasies about raising a family."

Two of the four married girls in the group had already adopted two children each and planned to adopt a third. "These two women impressed us as exceptional in the skills of motherhood," the Money group reported. The other two wives were only eighteen and twenty years old when interviewed; both planned to adopt babies soon. Two other girls in the group were "going steady"; both strongly favored adoption if and when they got married. One patient was engaged. "Her fiancé knew of her infertility. She was the only patient with doubts about adoption. She felt that she could devote herself only to children she had borne, though she liked children and helped care for those of her relatives."

Dr. Money concluded:

"Nothing whatever about these women was masculine, despite their sex-chromosomal and gonadal status as males."

The studies reviewed above all began with deviations at the chromosomal, gonadal, and hormonal level and proceeded to look for psychological effects. Much the same results have been secured, however, in studies which begin at the other end. These studies start with known psychological deviants — sissies, tomboys, transvestites, transsexuals, homosexuals, and bisexuals, male and female; they seek to determine whether anatomical or physiological roots can be found for the deviations. Without reviewing the evidence here in detail, I can sum it up quite briefly. Except for a few kinds of cases to be discussed below, most sissies, tomboys, transvestites, transsexuals, homosexuals, and bisexuals appear to be essentially normal at levels 1 through 6 by all the tests now in common use. Thus the hermaphroditic findings are confirmed. Psychological maleness, femaleness, and ambiguity appear to have (at least for the most part) psychological rather than chromosomal, gonadal, or hormonal roots.

Yet a third approach to the same problem — a study of babies assigned to one sex at birth and subsequently reassigned to the other sex — also confirms the same conclusion. Scores of such cases have been studied at the Hopkins. (Some of the reassignments were made at the Hopkins, others were made elsewhere.) In most cases the reassignment was made in an effort to minimize the gap between anatomical sex and sex of rearing.

Dr. Money's findings in these cases are quite clear-cut. Before the age of eighteen months or so, reassignments are effective. The baby grows up in accordance with its newly assigned sex. The only requirements are that the parents and other relatives be firmly convinced of the new gender assignment and accept it without question; and that gossip among friends and neighbors be minimized.

After the age of four or five, however, Dr. Money reports, "reassignment of sex has proved to be a psychological failure."

The child firmly adopts the male or female role, in short, at about the time he learns to talk; and there is another parallel with talking. "Genetics and innate determinants ordain only that language can develop and differentiate . . ." says Dr. Money, "not whether the language will be Nahuatl, Arabic, English, or any other. Psychosexually, also, genetics and innate determinants ordain only that a gender role and identity shall differentiate, without directly dictating whether the direction shall be male or female." The baby ends up male, female, or mixed up, just as he ends up English-speaking, Arabic-speaking, or bilingual, depending on cultural influences in his immediate microenvironment.

Dr. Money's data indicate that there is a "critical age" at which the child's psychological male or female gender role becomes set. The critical age, of course, may vary from child to child, but it is generally between the ages of one and four or five. If sex reassignment is attempted after the critical age, Dr. Money reports on the basis of many examples, psychological problems of three different kinds may result.

> The first is that all original gender memories become dissociated or denied, with consequent vulnerability to psychopathology. The second is that the new gender role blends with the old, and the psychosexual identity becomes confused and ambiguous, perhaps with associated psychopathology. The third is that the new assignment is repudiated and the original psychosexual identity persists unchanged, creating in effect an iatrogenic homosexuality or transvestism. The latter alternative is particularly likely after school age, for psychosexual identity, like native language, becomes fixed and immutable.

There are, it is true, some exceptions — but these exceptions confirm the rule. They are the cases where the child himself feels ambiguous about his assigned sex, or actively rejects it, usually because he has been ambiguously treated at home and in the community. A few such children may spontaneously request reassignment, and others may welcome it eagerly if it is offered to them.

Two additional cases which Dr. Money studied are of special interest in this connection. Both were female with respect to their chromosomes, gonads, and internal sex organs; they had ovaries and a uterus. During fetal life, however, their bodies had for some unknown reason been flooded with androgens. These prenatal androgens masculinized their external sex organs — so completely, indeed, that both were diagnosed at birth as boys and raised as boys by their parents. The first clue these boys and their parents had that anything was wrong came at puberty (age eleven) when the boys showed menstrual bleeding through the urethra and their breasts began to swell. To reassign them as girls was unthinkable — for despite their feminine chromosomes, ovaries, and uterus, their masculine gender role and masculine gender identity were firm. "Their breast growth was alien to their body image," Dr. Money explains, "and they wanted its arrestment, which was effected by gonadectomy and androgen therapy."

Dr. Money sums up:

"To impose a reassignment of sex on a hermaphroditic child who already has a well-differentiated psychosexual identity is courting about as much psychological disaster as if an anatomically normal boy or girl were arbitrarily reassigned." The only successful solution is to alter the anatomical sex, by means of surgery and hormones, to conform to the sex of assignment, sex of rearing, gender role, and gender identity.*

Let us turn next to the trickle of recent evidence pointing in precisely the opposite direction — toward the subtle significance of chromosomal and hormonal factors in the genesis of tomboyism, sissyism, transvestism, transsexuality, heterosexuality, homosexuality, and bisexuality.

The evidence is of two kinds, animal and human. I shall review the animal evidence first.

In 1959, four researchers at the University of Kansas — Drs. Charles H. Phoenix, Robert W. Goy, A. A. Gerall, and William Caldwell Young — performed a breakthrough series of experiments on guinea pigs. Dr. Young (1899–1965), a renowned endocrinologist, was the senior member

* Remarkably effective techniques for accomplishing this are currently available at the Johns Hopkins and at several other major medical centers. Girl babies whose genitals have been masculinized before birth, for example, can have the enlarged clitoris and fused scrotumlike labia surgically corrected. Boys born with an incomplete penis can have it surgically corrected so that they can urinate normally standing up. Boys born with an empty scrotum can have plastic spheres implanted — an amazingly helpful procedure in enabling these boys to feel like boys and to socialize unselfconsciously with their fellows. Small vaginas can be enlarged and missing vaginas constructed. Malelike breasts in girls can be enlarged by estrogens as well as by plastic surgery; large breasts in boys can be flattened. Puberty can be induced by hormones. Psychological guidance and counseling in such cases, both for the children and adolescents themselves and for their parents, has also proved enormously beneficial. "Gender clinics" where these and similar kinds of therapy are available have been established at several major medical centers. A whole new medical subspecialty — pediatric endocrinology — is concerned with these and other glandular problems. Those in need of therapy or counseling or both should seek out a gender clinic or a pediatric endocrinologist at a major medical center.

The extreme cases of therapy, of course, are the male transsexuals who undergo complete hormonal and surgical reassignment so that they appear to be females with normal breast development and genitals. This reassignment (it is much more than a surgical operation) was pioneered by Dr. Christian Hamburger in Denmark, who was responsible for the Christine Jorgenson reassignment, and by Dr. Georges Burou in Morocco. It has often been performed in the United States. Females can also be hormonally and surgically reassigned as males. For details, see R. Green, and J. Money, eds., *Transsexualism and Sex Reassignment* (Baltimore: John Hopkins Press, 1969).

of the team, but Dr. Phoenix took the lead in this particular project. Drs. Young, Goy, and Phoenix later moved to the Oregon Regional Primate Research Center near Portland; for convenience I shall call their key discovery the Phoenix-Goy-Young effect.

Earlier research had shown that when male hormones are administered to pregnant female guinea pigs, the female pups are anatomically masculinized — born with penises and scrotums instead of clitorises and labia.

Earlier experiments had also shown that when female guinea pigs are spayed and later given male hormones, they display only a limited amount of malelike sexual behavior. Something more than male hormones is needed to elicit male behavior.

What the Kansas-Oregon team did was to combine these two experiments. Pregnant female guinea pigs were given male hormones — androgens — so that their female pups were born with masculinized external genitals. The ovaries were then removed after birth and androgens were given at maturity. These females behave sexually like males to a much more marked extent. Instead of arching their backs and raising their vulvas to make it easy for males to mount them (a response known in animal sex research as presenting, and also as lordosis), these females mounted other females or males and engaged in malelike copulatory movements (pelvic thrusts). In this and other ways their sexual behavior resembled neither normal females nor females spayed after birth and then given male hormones. Instead, it resembled normal male behavior. The Young-Goy-Phoenix group also showed that similar results could be secured in rats in much the same way.

Countless other experiments of this general type, performed since 1959 by many researchers at laboratories in several countries, have confirmed the Phoenix-Goy-Young effect and have provided an explanation. Male and female sexual behavior, it has been established, is controlled in a number of species by nerve centers located in and near a portion of the brain known as the hypothalamus. These centers mature before or shortly after an animal's birth. If androgens are available during the maturing process, the brain centers become masculinized. When the animal reaches puberty, its hypothalamic control centers react in a male way to male hormones and the animal displays male sexual behavior. If androgens are not available during the maturing process, the hypothalamic centers which control sexual behavior mature in a feminine manner and the animal after puberty exhibits essentially female sexual behavior — even in the presence of male hormones.

The parallel with the maturing of the external genitals is quite close. Male hormones present during one portion of the maturing process masculinize the hypothalamic sexual centers in the brain; male hormones present during another portion of the maturing process masculinize the genital tubercle to form a penis instead of a clitoris.

A detail in the Young-Goy-Phoenix series of experiments admirably emphasizes this point. When androgens were administered to pregnant female guinea pigs at just the right time and in just the right amount, it was possible to masculinize the brain centers *without* masculinizing the external genitals. These guinea pigs *looked* like normal females; yet in adult life it was possible to elicit typically masculine mounting and thrusting behavior from them. Thus they were a close animal parallel to a particular type of human Lesbian — the "dyke," who may also be completely feminine in appearance.

Can male animals be feminized in appearance and behavior in the way in which Phoenix, Goy, Gerall, and Young masculinized females?

An affirmative answer has recently come from West Berlin, where Dr. Friedmund Neumann of the German pharmaceutical firm of Schering, A.G., has developed an anti-androgen named *cyproterone.* The effect of this drug is to counteract most of the effects of androgens. If cyproterone acetate is injected into pregnant rats at about the time when the external sex organs of the fetuses are developing, Dr. Neumann reports, the males are born with completely female external sex organs. The testes are unaffected. The animals' response to female hormones *and their subsequent sexual behavior,* however, are feminized in precisely the way in which the Young-Goy-Phoenix animals are masculinized. If the feminized males are castrated and then given a normal cycle of female hormones (estrogens and progestins), their subsequent sexual behavior is female. They arch their backs and present their vulvas to the approaching male, for example. Indeed, Dr. Neumann and his associate Dr. Walter Elger report that even male stud rats fail to distinguish these *ersatz* females from true females. Normal male rats which are castrated and then given female hormones do not behave in this way. Thus once again the conclusion seems inescapable: *the availability of androgens during fetal development permanently influences not only the external sex organs but also the centers in the brain which control adult sexual behavior*—at least in certain small mammals.

I shall not trace the implications of this work in all of its fascinating details—but I shall cite one more example. At Princeton University, Dr. Robert D. Lisk is employing a technique for implanting tiny blobs of hormones directly into the brains of laboratory rats. In one of his many experiments using this technique, he implanted one female hormone (estrogen) into a small area on one side of the brain of male rats which had been castrated on the day of birth, and another female hormone (progesterone) into the same small area on the other side. Two months later, these male rats were completely bisexual. They arched their backs and raised their genitals to invite other males to mount them; they mounted available females and engaged in vigorous pelvic thrusting. "The overt response was dependent on the partners they were placed with," Dr. Lisk and an associate, Dr. A. J. Suydam, reported in 1967. During the two months between the implantation and the appearance of bisexuality, moreover, these rats were homosexual. They displayed no interest in females but arched their backs invitingly when a male approached.

Guinea pigs and rats are not humans, of course. But human beings are primates. Can primate sexual behavior also be masculinized or feminized by prenatal hormones or antihormones?

One major center for the study of primate behavior is the University of Wisconsin—where Dr. Harry Harlow, his wife Dr. Margaret Harlow, and others have long been studying the behavioral development of rhesus monkeys. In some of these experiments, monkeys were separated from their mothers at birth and raised in isolation. Dr. Harry Harlow was surprised to discover at one stage of this research that even when deprived of any opportunity to learn how older monkeys behave, "male and female infant monkeys assume quite different roles in the initiation and maintenance of play patterns. The first social play pattern to appear we call rough-and-tumble or contact play; monkey infants wrestle and roll and engage in sham biting although none is ever hurt. From its very beginning the males initiate this pattern more frequently than the females, and from 100 days onward the males more frequently engage in contact play than the females. . . . Males frequently initiate play with other males or with females, and females not infrequently initiate rough-

and-tumble play with other females but practically never with males." On other behavioral scales, too, such as grooming, the females and males were distinguishable. Females generally initiate grooming behavior.

The differences, let me stress again, cannot be attributed to learning. These infant monkeys were brought up in isolation from older animals on whom they might have modeled their behavior.

"When I first saw these data," Dr. Harlow later recalled, "I was very excited and told my wife that we had demonstrated biologically determined sex differences in infants' behavior."

Dr. Margaret Harlow, however, was not impressed.

"Child psychologists have known that for at least thirty years," she caustically informed her husband, "and mothers have known it for centuries."

The Harlow monkey colony at Wisconsin was the obvious place to try the Phoenix-Young-Goy experiment on primates. The experiment was duly performed, and the guinea pig results were confirmed. Immature female rhesus monkeys exposed to androgens before birth tended to adopt relatively masculine patterns of infant and youthful play.

Dr. Young died in 1965, but his work is being carried on at the Oregon Regional Primate Research Center, under the direction of Dr. Goy. I visited the Center in 1968, talked with Dr. Goy and Dr. Phoenix, and observed their prenatally androgenized female monkeys playing by the hour.

I am not an ethologist. But even to my untutored eye, it was easy to distinguish the behavior of monkey males from females. I made only one error. I identified as male behavior the behavior of the prenatally androgenized females.

To Dr. Money at the Johns Hopkins, all this recent animal research had a special fascination. His findings during the 1950's had seemed to indicate that human sexual behavior is determined by sex of assignment and rearing rather than by prenatal hormonal influences. Could humans really be so different from rhesus monkeys and other mammals? A startling opportunity to study the Phoenix-Young-Goy effect on *human* females presented itself to Dr. Money at precisely the right moment.

During the 1950's, when synthetic female hormones of a type known as progestins — progesterone and related "pregnancy hormones" — first became available for clinical use, many obstetricians prescribed these hormones to women who had had several miscarriages in a row, in the hope that the progestin would stave off another miscarriage. The effectiveness of the treatment remains a matter of controversy. In most cases it was apparently harmless. But in a few hundred cases out of many thousands, the synthetic progestin prescribed for these pregnant women acted like an androgen on the female fetus. Several hundred girl babies were born with enlarged clitorises, partially fused labia resembling a scrotum, and other signs of masculinization. Dr. Lawson Wilkins at the Hopkins had been among the first to identify and study this syndrome; and a number of girl babies with the syndrome were brought to his clinic for surgical correction of their genital anomalies. The operations were successfully performed and the babies went home again, presumably completely refeminized.

Just to make sure, however, Dr. Money has been following up these girls psychologically ever since. From the point of view of the scientific study of sex they are a very important population — for now that the possibility of masculinization has been discovered, very few obstetricians are prescribing the particular progestins responsible. Another crop of masculinized little girls like the crop born in the 1950's may never again be available for study.

Dr. Money and his associate Dr. Anke A. Ehrhardt have issued a preliminary report on ten of these little girls, nine of them masculinized before birth and the tenth not masculinized but born to a mother who received one of the progestins during her pregnancy. In their follow-up examinations of these girls, Dr. Money and Dr. Ehrhardt were impressed first of all by their intelligence. They seemed unusually bright and alert. Intelligence tests confirmed this initial impression. Six of the ten girls, indeed, had an IQ in excess of 130. You would expect to find six girls with IQ's that high in a crowd of 300 girls instead of among ten. High intelligence, in short, was some thirty times as common among these girls as would be anticipated. The high IQ's did not seem to be the result of any specialized talent, but to be a quite general quality. A remarkably superior school achievement level has similarly been reported by Dr. Katarina Dalton of London among English girls whose mothers were given progestins in pregnancy. (These girls were *not* masculinized genitally at birth.)

In many psychological respects, the ten girls in the Money sample — nine of them still prepubertal — were firmly feminine, as was to be expected. None of them betrayed any Lesbian tendencies, for example. Seven reported looking forward to getting married and having children. None revealed any interest or experience in childhood sexual play, but six had shown common signs of romantic play, including kissing and other usual affectionate gestures toward boys their own age. Their gender role and identity were in general conformity with their sex of assignment and rearing (level 7) rather than their fetal hormone exposure (level 3), as Dr. Money had anticipated.

And yet, there were curious details. Nine of the girls, for example, showed an interest in outdoor activities and liked to join with boys and compete with boys in their sports. Nine showed a strong interest in playing with trucks, guns, and other boys' toys; only three of these nine played with dolls and other little girls' toys even occasionally. Only one of the ten preferred dolls to trucks, guns, and other boys' toys; perhaps by coincidence, this lone exception was the only girl of the ten whose external genitals had not been masculinized before birth. None of them liked to wear boys' shirts and pants — but all of them liked to wear masculine-like clothes rather than frilly feminine dresses. Indeed, only two liked frills and furbelows even when the occasion demanded it. The others were either indifferent to feminine clothes or actively opposed to wearing them.

One difference between ordinary boys and ordinary girls is well documented in psychological studies; males are more energetic. "While boys are out staking territory claims, constructing hideouts, forts, or camps, and fending off rival intruder gangs," Dr. Money points out, "girls are expending somewhat less energy, usually closer to home, making lairs and homes for the young and raising doll babies." In this respect, the girls in Dr. Money's study group seemed to have the abundance of excess energy characteristic of boys rather than girls of their age.

Nine of the ten girls were also described as self-assertive and independent. Finally, nine of the ten were labeled "tomboys" — either by themselves, or by their mothers, or by both. The one who was not considered a tomboy and who did not consider herself a tomboy was — again, perhaps, by coincidence — the only girl whose prenatal exposure to progestins had not masculinized her genitals.

When asked to describe their daughters' most tomboyish traits, the mothers gave answers like these:

"She plays baseball with the boys. She comes home with all her clothes ripped up. She gets into fights. She is really rough."

"She would rather play baseball than dolls. She even wanted a baseball glove."

"She likes guns and soldiers."

"She is not charming, not gracious. She has really rough manners."

"She likes to run and jump. Her interest [is] in guns and cowboys."

But the girl who liked guns and soldiers also liked to cook, and the girl who played baseball and came home with her clothes all ripped up was also interested in pretty clothes and jewelry.

The outcome of this inadvertent human experiment, in short, is not very clear as yet. And it is further complicated by the fact that most of these children come from good middle-class suburban homes with educated parents; tomboyishness may be relatively common in such an environment regardless of prenatal hormones. Still, the remarkable masculinity of these children's play patterns and preferences inevitably recalls to mind that Oregon monkey playpen where I saw prenatally androgenized female monkeys also playing like males.

"What happens to *boys* whose mothers receive progestins during pregnancy?" I asked Dr. Money early in December 1968.

"No reports yet," he replied.

Before the month was out, the first study showing behavioral effects on boy babies made its appearance. *Medical Tribune* (N.Y.), which is so often the first to report discoveries of medical importance, announced on the front page of its issue for December 26, 1968:

> *Mexico City.*—Administration of progesterone during pregnancy because of recurrent abortion may have unwanted virilizing effects on male as well as female progeny, it was emphasized in a report here by Dr. Alexander Russell, chief of the department of pediatrics and child health at Hadassah University Hospital in Jerusalem.
>
> He detailed five male cases at the 12th International Congress on Pediatrics, observing that the hormone dosage was usually larger and given over a longer period than has sufficed to induce masculinization of the female. . . .
>
> All five of the boys showed hypertrophy [excessive growth] of the penis and scrotal hyperplasia at birth, and sparse pubic hair was seen in three shortly after birth. Masturbatory activity began between the fourth and sixth month.

There was characteristic behavior as well, in the form of extreme hyperactivity and "reckless adventurousness" persisting day and night.

"The child's chronic resistance to sleep would exhaust the parents at least through the first year of life," Dr. Russell observed.

Signs of sexual precocity tended to decrease with time. The behavioral pattern remained, however, and continued to present problems. "There may be many more such cases which have not been recognized," Dr. Russell suggested. . . .

Pending further information, progesterone should probably be given [to pregnant women] only in cases of demonstrated progesterone deficiency, Dr. Russell cautioned.

Girls born with a condition known as the "adrenogenital syndrome" are chromosomally female; at conception both the sperm cell and the ovum have X chromosomes, so that these girls are XX like other girls. They therefore develop ovaries instead of testes. They suffer from a glandular defect, however, which causes their adrenal glands to secrete large amounts of male hormones — androgens — both before birth and in later years.

The prenatal androgens have the usual anatomical effects. These girls are born with enlarged clitorises which look like penises, and with partially fused labia suggesting a scrotum. In extreme cases the masculinization may be so complete that the infant is diagnosed at birth as a boy.

The androgens poured out by the adrenal gland *after* birth in these girls also have very unwelcome effects if the condition is not promptly and correctly diagnosed and adequately treated. One effect is premature puberty; some untreated girls become pubertal as early as five or six years old. Worse yet, it is a masculine puberty, producing deepening of voice, masculine hair on face and body, and other familiar male characteristics. The penislike clitoris enlarges further and may be subject to erections. Masculine-type baldness may eventually develop; breasts do not grow and menstruation does not occur.*

In 1950, it was discovered that cortisone therapy will turn off the flow of androgen in this syndrome — one of the major triumphs of endocrinology. Thus two different groups of females with the andrenogenital syndrome are currently available for study. The older patients lived through puberty, and many of them into adult life, under the continuing

* Some males are also born with the andrenogenital syndrome. They suffer from premature puberty.

influence of male hormones. Many of the patients born since 1950, in contrast, had the male hormones turned off in infancy. Dr. Money and his associates published in 1968 follow-up studies on women in both groups. Let me review first the study of the older women by Drs. Ehrhardt and Money with a student, Kathryn Evers.

There were twenty-three women in the study group, aged nineteen to fifty-five at the time of last follow-up. The average age was thirty-three. They showed varying amounts of masculinization; one extreme case had been diagnosed as a boy at birth and reassigned as a girl at the age of fourteen months. But all had been raised as girls and continued to play the role of females and to think of themselves as females. Some had been followed by the Hopkins group for as long as fifteen years.

When cortisone treatment became available, all of these women received it and were thus freed from further androgenization. Breast development and menstruation began, usually within three to six months. "In the younger patients, virilism was fairly completely controlled, less so in the older women," the Money group observed. The patients were between eight and forty-seven years of age when cortisone treatment began; the average age was twenty-three. Half were over eighteen at the time treatment began. Thus these women accumulated a substantial amount of sexual experience while still under the influence of male hormones.

Intelligence. One interesting fact was the relatively high IQ's of these women. Indeed, the Money group ran IQ tests on seventy women with the adrenogenital syndrome and found high IQ's much more frequent than could be accounted for by chance alone — though the effect was not as conspicuous as in the girls masculinized before birth by progestins.

Sexual Practices. One of the twenty-three women refused to give any information about her sex life. Two reported no sexual experience whatever, not even masturbation. Two reported sexual experience limited to masturbation. One reported at the age of forty-eight that her entire sex life had been limited to one act of heterosexual coitus. "Lack of opportunity and inhibition against exposing their virilized bodies might have been part of the reason for their lack of experience," the Money group noted. Moral inhibitions against premarital intercourse was given as the reason by three of the four unmarried girls without experience; the fourth said she had had neither the opportunity nor the interest.

Of the fifteen who had had substantial sexual experience, eleven had frequent heterosexual and no homosexual contacts. Two had frequent contacts, both heterosexual and homosexual. The other two had frequent heterosexual and occasional homosexual contacts.

In addition to the four with overt homosexual contacts, however, seven women with exclusively heterosexual contacts reported homosexual dreams and fantasies. If we exclude the two women who had neither sexual experiences nor dreams nor fantasies, and the woman who refused to give information, eleven of the remaining twenty had had homosexual experience or dreams and fantasies. This is considerably higher than the roughly comparable figure reported by Kinsey for women (twenty-eight percent). It approximates the Kinsey figure for male homosexual contacts or arousals.

Note that male hormones did not *enforce* homosexuality in the cases of these women. Ten of the experienced twenty-one were completely heterosexual in fantasies, dreams, and experience alike, and not one of the twenty was *exclusively* homosexual. Still, it is hard to conclude that their male hormones, prenatal or pubertal or both, had no effect whatever on their choice of sex partners.

Dr. Money very cautiously suggests a possible interpretation. Perhaps the male hormone did not directly affect these women's homosexual, bisexual, or heterosexual choice of sexual partners at all. Perhaps, instead, it tended to give them a more masculine stance with respect to homosexuality as well as sex in general.

Certainly the data are consistent with this possibility; and some of the remaining findings point in the same direction.

Libido. Many lines of evidence indicate that while estrogens and progestins are the sex hormones which control such female phenomena as the menstrual cycle and other changes at puberty, male hormones (androgens) are the hormones affecting sexual *arousal* or libido, in females as well as males. Thus we might expect these women to show a relatively high level of libido.

Eleven of the patients rated their own sex drives as higher than that of other women. Eight thought they were average and only one considered herself below average. These estimates were made on the basis of their drives *after* cortisone treatment began. Most of them stated that their libido was even stronger *before* treatment — "in some cases so high as to have been bothersome to them."

Two patients reported experiencing orgasm in one hundred percent of their sexual contacts, heterosexual and homosexual. "Fourteen stated that they reached a climax most of the time, implying that it was the exception when they did not." Only two reported no orgasmic experience; "one was the patient who had had intercourse only once; the other was one of the married women who stated she often experienced pain and discomfort during sexual intercourse with her husband." The findings are consistent with the possibility that male hormones had some modest effect on these women's libido and orgasmic capacities — though the case is hardly proved.

Active Role in Sex. "The female role in heterosexual relations is conventionally defined as more passive and receptive," the Money group reports, "in comparison with the more aggressive, active, and initiating role of the male. Two women in our sample described themselves as predominantly initiating heterosexual behavior. One was married, the other not. Both had had homosexual experience. Among the remainder, only one patient thought of herself as reserved and passive, while eleven reported that they would feel free to initiate sex if they had the impulse to do so."

Nine out of twelve cases for whom data were available, the Money group noted, were "versatile"; that is, they "enjoyed a variety of positions in sexual intercourse rather than just one or two."

"The freedom and lack of inhibition in coitus is especially remarkable," the Money group notes, "since many of the women were insecure and ashamed of their once-virilized bodies . . . and the residual signs of virilism."

Erotic Stimuli. The Kinsey report notes that males are much more frequently aroused sexually by visual erotic material than are women. There are no striptease shows for women, for example. Men are also more arousable by narrative material, as in pornographic fiction. Men use both visual and narrative material as a prelude to masturbation; women do so much less often. Most women are sexually aroused by tactual stimuli, as in kissing, petting, and necking, rather than by visual or narrative stimuli. Their fantasies tend to be romantic rather than erotic.

Perhaps the most tantalizing of the Money group's findings concerned this phenomenon. Of the nineteen patients who reported on this point, sixteen reported sexual arousal from erotic visual stimuli and fifteen reported sexual arousal from erotic narratives.

Except in some of the bisexual cases, the *content* of the sexually exciting visual and narrative material was heterosexual and quite appropriate for a heterosexual woman. "For example, several patients stated that they were aroused by the thought or the actual sight of their husband's or boyfriend's nude body. Others gave examples of love scenes on the movie screen which would start their thinking on coitus and arouse them physically. The arousal was in the women's own genitals and was such as might lead to masturbation in the absence of a partner. It was not the sentimental arousal, more typical of the normal female, which leads to romantic longing for the loved one." Thus, while the content was appropriate to a heterosexual woman, the very existence of this type of erotic response suggested to the Money group a subtle flavor of masculinization.

In the cases we have just been considering, any masculinization which occurred might have been the result either of fetal male hormones before birth, or of pubertal male hormones later on. In these cases no distinction is possible. Let us turn next, accordingly, to the group of girls whose male hormones were turned off in infancy by cortisone therapy. These girls were also operated on in infancy so that their external genitals appeared normally feminine. Any masculinizing effect in these girls can quite unequivocally be attributed to hormonal action before birth or very shortly thereafter.

A group of fifteen such cases was described by Drs. Money and Ehrhardt plus a student, Ralph Epstein, in a 1968 paper. Much more important, these fifteen were matched with a control group of fifteen other girls selected at random except that each girl in the control group matched one girl in the patient group with respect to age, IQ, and socioeconomic level. Eleven of the girls in each group were preadolescent; the oldest girl was sixteen.

I can summarize the findings quite simply. The girls who had been masculinized before birth by male hormones from their own adrenal glands were much more tomboyish than the girls of the same age, intelligence, and socio-economic class in the control group. Indeed, they resembled quite closely the girls, described above, who had been masculinized before birth by hormones given their pregnant mothers.

Only one of the fifteen patients, for example, preferred marriage to a career. Ten of the control girls did.

Four of the patients were interested in male toys only, showing no interest in dolls. An additional eight played with dolls occasionally but preferred boys' toys. None of the control girls was interested exclusively in boys' toys, and only one preferred to play with boys' toys.

Nine of the patients reported that they were indifferent to the idea of taking care of babies, and one expressed active aversion. None of the control girls expressed either indifference or aversion.

No girl in either group wanted to dress like a boy. But nine of the patients strongly preferred wearing shirts and slacks or shorts rather than dresses. None of the control girls had this preference.

Eleven of the patients, but only five of the controls, took part in boy-like active outdoor activities.

Eleven of the patients were considered tomboys by themselves and by their mothers — not just as a passing episode but as a durable feature of their personalities. None of the girls in the control group was a tomboy in this continuing sense.

Three of the patients openly expressed a desire to be boys, and five expressed themselves as in doubt whether they would prefer to be a boy or girl. Only one of the control girls wanted to be a boy, and none was in doubt.

Several of the girls in the masculinized group recalled having "played house" as children. Two of them recalled preferring to play the papa rather than the mama role on such occasions. None of the control girls preferred the papa role.

The findings, Dr. Money concludes, *suggest* that the behavior of these girls has been modified in subtle ways by their exposure before birth to male hormones. "These modifications do not necessarily reverse the personal sense of gender identity as a female, but add a special quality to it."

At first I was baffled by an apparent contradiction in the Money data. Two of the groups of girls — the ones masculinized before birth by progestins given their pregnant mothers and the ones masculinized before birth by androgens from their own adrenal glands — displayed subtle traces of tomboyism as preadolescents. The third group — the androgen-insensitivity group of girls born with male chromosomes (XY) and with testes — also had their bodies flooded with androgens at the right time during gestation. Yet they were firmly feminine, displaying no signs of tomboyism. On reflection, the apparent contradiction soon vanished. The androgen-insensitivity girls, you will recall, did not have their genitals masculinized because they were insensitive to the androgens. A reasonable hypothesis is that the same factor which prevented the masculinization of their genitals also prevented the masculinization of their hypothalamic sex control centers.

Sex of assignment and experiences of rearing, to sum up, remain the primary determinants of human psychological maleness and femaleness — of gender role and gender identity. But in both animals and humans, hormonal influences seem also to be playing a subtle role which we have barely begun to investigate.

Equally remarkable are some recent findings concerning a chromosomal effect on adult psychosexual development.

Let's go back for a moment to boy babies born with the XXY chromosomal pattern — chromosomally hermaphroditic in the sense that they have both the XX combination characteristic of normal females and the XY combination characteristic of normal males. These individuals are anatomically males, in accordance with the rule that the presence of a Y chromosome determines anatomical and physiological maleness. Yet their condition, known as Klinefelter's syndrome, appears to have unusual psychosexual effects in adult life.

At least three sets of investigators, for example, have reported cases of XXY males who were transvestites. Others have reported on XXY cases revealing other forms of sexual pathology ranging from rape and incest through transsexualism. Dr. Money and his associate Dr. Ernesto Pollitt (now at Yale) investigated 16 cases of Klinefelter's syndrome and found among them an amazingly high proportion of sexual pathology — two transvestites, two homosexuals, and a pyromaniac. "Though actuarial statistics are grossly incomplete," Dr. Money concludes, "it nonetheless appears that psychopathology, sexual psychopathology included, has an affinity for Klinefelter's syndrome. Paradoxically, the libido is weak and erotic expression infrequent" in these XXY cases.

More recently another chromosomal condition, the XYY syndrome, has received worldwide publicity. First discovered in England in the course of a routine survey of chromosome patterns among criminals held in mental hospitals, it has since been found also in the United States and other countries.

The XYY syndrome commonly appears in tall males — typically over six feet. They commonly suffer from severe adolescent acne. A few are famous criminals.

Dr. Money, who has studied several XYY patients, is confident that the currently alleged association between XYY and criminality is imprecise and misleading. "Most XYY cases have been found in prisons and mental hospitals," he points out, "because that's where we've looked for them. Future research is almost sure to turn up many without criminal records in ordinary civilian life."

Dr. Money agrees, however, that there must be something special about these men's behavior to explain their relatively frequent appearance in prison and mental hospital populations. It may be some trait like impulsiveness, for example, or a relative inability to control casual impulses. Whatever the ultimate findings, the XYY cases resemble the XXY cases in suggesting behavioral consequences — including sexual consequences — of chromosomal patterns.

This chapter must here end abruptly, for this is as far as the currently available data carry us. Perhaps I should end it, like an installment in a serialized mystery story, with a "to be continued" tagline. For the human significance of these very recent findings remains obscure; too many pieces of the puzzle are still missing. When additional data eventually make it possible to present a full scientific account of tomboys and sissies, of hermaphrodites, transvestites, and transsexuals, of homosexuals, heterosexuals, and bisexuals, the preliminary findings here presented may prove to be little more than a modest first act. Like others, I eagerly await further developments.

8

The Falling-in-Love Experience

Dante Alighieri, Konrad Lorenz's Ducklings, and Harry Harlow's Monkeys

UNTIL quite recently in our culture, we humans used to stress the chasm dividing human sexuality from mere animal lust. In Chapter 7 I sought to show, by relating animal research to recent human findings, that the chasm is neither so broad nor so deep as Victorians like Dr. Elizabeth Blackwell supposed. In this chapter I shall be concerned with additional experiments indicating that studies of animal behavior can illuminate even those sexual phenomena which we like to think of as uniquely human — such as the falling-in-love experience.

Imprinting

During the 1930's, an eminent Austrian ethologist, Dr. Konrad Lorenz, performed a simple experiment with ducklings. Shortly after hatching, as everyone knows, baby ducklings begin to waddle along in single file behind their mothers, and they continue until maturity to follow their mothers wherever they go. Dr. Lorenz hatched a clutch of duck eggs in an incubator and then waddled past the ducklings himself, squatting low as if he were a mother duck. The ducklings promptly waddled after him in the usual way. Thereafter, despite the presence of female ducks they could have followed, these incubator ducklings continued to follow Dr. Lorenz on every possible occasion.

Dr. Lorenz gave this phenomenon a name: imprinting.* He showed that it arises only during a limited "critical period" in an animal's development. Thus mallard ducklings are not very susceptible to imprinting during the first few hours after hatching, or after the second day; the peak of imprinting sensitivity occurs between thirteen and sixteen hours after hatching.

Since Lorenz's initial reports, scientists in many countries have contributed further to the study of imprinting; notable contributions have been made by Dr. Eckhard H. Hess of the University of Chicago. Dr. Hess and others have expanded Lorenz's initial findings in two important directions:

First, they have shown that the phenomenon is not limited to birds. Imprinting has also been observed among insects, fish, guinea pigs, sheep, deer, buffalo, and perhaps other mammalian species.

Second, imprinting has been shown to determine other kinds of behavior in addition to that of the newly hatched bird following after a mother or mother substitute. Dr. Hess, for example, reports that newly hatched chicks develop three quite disparate forms of imprinted behavior during their first three days of life. On the first day, they are imprinted to follow a moving object. On the second day, they are imprinted to their immediate environment. (Thus mallard ducklings brought up in a natural nest on the ground will, as adults, build their nests on the ground; ducklings reared in an incubator box will prefer to build nests in elevated boxes.) On the third day after hatching, food imprinting occurs; chicks given access to food in a particular way on that day continue thereafter to prefer to seek food in that way.

Does imprinting also occur in the human species?

The answer depends, of course, on how we choose to define imprinting.

* Dr. Lorenz was not the first, however, to describe the phenomenon. In 1873 a British naturalist, D. A. Spalding, reported that newly hatched incubator chicks will follow the first moving object that passes by. In 1910 a German observer, O. Heinroth, reported that greylag goslings behave in the same way; indeed, if Heinroth's incubator-hatched goslings were exposed to human beings before being exposed to adult geese, they continued to follow humans in filial fashion in preference to adults of their own species. In 1908 an American, W. Craig, reported that when wild pigeon hatchlings of one species were reared by foster parents of another species, the birds so reared selected mates of the same species as the foster parents rather than their own species when they reached maturity.

If we define it in strictly Lorenzian terms as the tendency of an infant animal to follow the first moving object to which it is exposed, there is no evidence for human imprinting. A more useful definition, however, results when we contrast imprinting with ordinary kinds of learning — such as learning to run a maze, or ride a bicycle, or speak a foreign language. At least six differences between ordinary learning and imprinting can be readily distinguished:

(1) Ordinary learning occurs at almost any time between infancy and senility. Imprinting, as Lorenz perceived, occurs only during a critical period. Most of the kinds of imprinting studied to date occur in infancy; but, as we shall see, there is reason to believe that certain kinds of imprinting also occur at puberty or during adolescence.

(2) Though there are limits, the objects to which an animal can be imprinted vary widely. Thus a chick can be imprinted to follow anything from a human being to a football on roller skates. It is primarily the timing of the exposure rather than the nature of the object which determines whether a particular animal will be imprinted to object A or object B.

(3) Ordinary learning requires a series of repeated experiences to achieve perfection. An animal can become fully imprinted, however, during a single experience as brief as two or three minutes.

(4) Ordinary learning depends upon extrinsic rewards or punishments during the learning period. Imprinting does not. Indeed, a chick can be imprinted to follow a moving object even if it is being punished by a series of electric shocks during the imprinting exposure — a punishment which under any other circumstances would cause the chick to run away instead of following after.

(5) Ordinary learning depends upon extrinsic rewards and punishments for its maintenance *after* it has been learned. A rat which learns to run a maze for a food reward soon stops running the maze if it no longer finds food at the goal. Imprinted behavior is not similarly dependent; it appears to be its own reward and continues under its own steam.

(6) An animal imprinted to one object cannot in general be imprinted thereafter to another. An animal imprinted to follow a football on roller skates can, it is true, thereafter be *taught* to follow some other object by means of rewards or punishments; but imprinting is not commonly repeatable.

If imprinting is defined by these six characteristics, I see no possible room for doubt that we humans, too, exhibit a number of kinds of imprinting.

My granddaughter Thistle, for example, became imprinted in infancy to a cloth monkey named Mortimer. She would not go to sleep without Mortimer at her side; and she became alarmed and "up-tight" if she happened to notice, at any hour of the day or night, that Mortimer was not within reach. Soon Mortimer was worn out, so that it was necessary for my wife Ruth to search for and find another Mortimer identical with the original. Thistle would have none of the imposter. She clung to the tattered original until he was a mere cluster of shreds; to preserve the Mortimer effect, it became necessary to sew the shreds securely to a large patch of red velvet. Thereafter the velvet patch, with the shreds sewn on, continued to elicit the Mortimer effect.

Thistle was surrounded by a wealth of other cuddly toys, but she never became imprinted to any of them. The time for imprinting had passed — and Mortimer had filled that particular imprinting niche to the exclusion of all rivals or successors. Thistle at this writing is five years old, and is still imprinted to Mortimer — as she continues to call the patch of red velvet, though the last shreds of the original Mortimer have long since vanished.

Other infants similarly become imprinted to a doll, a "security blanket," * a rubber sheet, or some other undistinguished object. Few mothers, I am confident, will doubt that imprinting exists in the human species.

Human food preferences are no doubt imprinted in much the same way. Some people (myself among them) are imprinted to beefsteaks which have been "hung" for six weeks or more, so that they are a trifle "high"; these steaks must be seasoned with just a suspicion of garlic and served medium-rare — "like mother used to make." Others are imprinted to heavily peppered steaks served well done and soaked in Worcestershire sauce — as *their* mothers used to serve steaks. I see no reason to

* Two infant chimpanzees born in capitivity are similarly reported to have "formed intense relationships with blankets after they were separated from their mothers"; see "Sexual Behavior of the ARL Colony Chimpanzees" by Drs. Edward J. Kollar, William C. Beckwith, and Robert B. Edgerton in the *Journal of Nervous and Mental Diseases,* December 1968.

doubt that it is the *first* exposure to a new food which imprints the flavor and texture that food is subsequently expected to present. Food imprinting serves a biologically useful function in nature, of course, by keeping animals and humans away from spoiled or poisoned foods.

Dr. John Money has suggested that we are imprinted during very early childhood with our native language. At the appropriate time speech develops naturally, promptly, and with a minimum of rewards, punishments, or effort. One needs only contrast the quickness and ease with which a two-year-old learns his native language with the prolonged labor the same child at fourteen or sixteen must expend to learn a foreign language, to appreciate the difference between imprinting during the critical period and rote learning later on.

Sigmund Freud, it will be recalled, attributed human fetishism — sexual arousal by objects such as a handkerchief with a violet border or a pair of women's panties — to a process amazingly like the one we now call imprinting. The phenomenon, Freud believed, arises at a crucial period in the child's existence, when he is two or three years old. The object of the imprinting may vary widely; anything from fur or velvet to a particular kind of hairdo may function as a fetish. Once a man adopts a fetish, he does not adopt a second fetish. The imprinting occurs at a particular moment and is complete without repetition. Neither its initiation nor its survival depends on extrinsic rewards or punishments.

Dr. Money adds that sexual deviations in general may be the result of imprinting. "Whatever their other features," he points out, "aberrations like fetishism, exhibitionism, voyeurism, sadism, masochism, homosexuality, and transvestism all share one characteristic in common, namely, that the person's erotic arousal is released by an abnormal perceptual releaser." These phenomena, in short, resemble the duckling who waddles after a football on roller skates rather than a mother duck.

There is reason to believe that human beings go through a critical period with respect to sexual imprinting at about the time of puberty. Dr. Paul H. Gebhard, the anthropologist who has headed the Kinsey Institute since Dr. Kinsey's death, has presented two examples — though he cautiously refrains from using the word imprinting.

One Gebhard example concerns a man now in his thirties, whose first conscious sexual arousal occurred as he was nearing puberty. At this critical point in his life, "he became involved in a childhood tussle with a girl somewhat larger and more powerful than he. While struggling and wriggling beneath her, he experienced not only his first conscious sexual arousal but in a strong degree. This one experience has dominated his life ever since. He has [continued to be] attracted to large, muscular, dominant females; and in his heterosexual contacts he tries to arrange the same wrestling. He has, not surprisingly, developed some additional masochistic attributes."

The second Gebhard example concerns a boy who fractured his arm while he was in what Dr. Gebhard calls "the flush of sexual excitability which accompanies puberty in most males." The boy was taken to a nearby physician who noted how rapidly the broken arm was swelling and therefore decided to set the fracture at once, without anesthesia. "The physician's attractive nurse felt very sorry for the boy. During the reduction of the fracture and for sometimes afterwards she held and caressed him with his head pressed against her breasts. The boy experienced a powerful and curious combination of pain and sexual arousal.

"Considerably later in life this man began to notice that he was unusually attracted to brunettes with a certain type of hair style — attracted to an extent meriting the label of fetish. Some sadomasochistic tendencies also existed."

The hair style which so aroused this fetishist was the one worn by a well-known striptease dancer of the period, Bettie Page. The man himself was baffled at first by his fetishism, but "after much introspection" he recalled that the hair style which was his fetish was the style in which the nurse had worn her hair. "This insight did not destroy the fetish," Dr. Gebhard adds.

Dr. Gebhard labels these examples "one-shot conditioning." The term imprinting seems to me much more appropriate, since all six of the characteristics of imprinted behavior are fulfilled.

Freudians, of course, will suspect that something more lies behind the explanations of the cases here given. Perhaps the boy imprinted to the Bettie Page hairdo, for example, was really imprinted in infancy when his mother wore her hair the same way; the memory of the nurse then becomes, in Freudian terms, a "screen memory" concealing the incestuous nature of the original memory.

This possibility was raised at a 1961 conference on sex and behavior where Dr. Gebhard first presented these two cases. Dr. Gebhard was sufficiently impressed to write to the man with the hairdo fetish. Back came this answer:

> In reply to your letter of December 4th, yes, I do remember discussing my case of hair fetishism (à la Bettie Page) with you. As for the nurse resembling my mother — I'm afraid you strike out on that point. My mother was a nice little gray-haired lady who died when I was about nine years of age. I find it hard to actually picture her, but I'm quite sure that she didn't resemble our Bettie in the least.

Dr. Money suggests that some people are imprinted to a homosexual love object at a critical point in their sexual development and others to a heterosexual love object. He adds an interesting detail:

> The existence of an early imprinting period would explain why an adolescent or adult, safely past the critical period, can be forced or induced into an aberrant sexual experience without becoming a chronic practitioner of that experience. Thus an occasional adult homosexual act does not produce homosexual [imprinting].

So far we have been considering the usefulness of the imprinting concept in explaining *aberrant* human behavior — fetishism, sadomasochism, homosexuality, and so on. But imprinting is no doubt equally significant, Dr. Money believes, in *normal* sexual development.

The quite ordinary child who will grow up as a heterosexual male or female, for example, becomes imprinted to his or her appropriate gender role and gender identity between the ages of one and four. The process is rarely recognized as imprinting, Dr. Money points out, because "the imprinting that takes place in anatomically normal people is so deeply ingrained and pervasive that the average person interprets his sexual inclination as involuntary, instinctive, and inborn."

The most impressive example of imprinting in relatively "normal" humans is the falling-in-love experience.

"The critical period for this imprint," Dr. Money reports, "coincides with adolescence, though the first manifestation of falling in love may be subject to inhibition and delay, dependent on opportunity and sociocultural expectancy." Havelock Ellis's falling in love with Agnes at the age of twelve leaps to mind as an example. I should add, however, that the adolescent timing, while common, is not invariable. I have observed typical falling-in-love behavior in a few rare cases after the age of fifty.

The stimulus which triggers falling-in-love behavior, Dr. Money continues, "is usually a member of the opposite sex, but the exact characteristics of the love object are subject to extensive variation from person to person. Some of this variation is determined by fortuitous conditions at the time of falling in love, such as the availability of partners to choose from. Much of the variation, however, seems to be determined by the individuality of prior life experience." A man or woman may be so imprinted to some characteristic of a particular kind — hair of a particular shade, for example — that "only love objects possessing these characteristics can be responded to. Thus a second mate often resembles in appearance and personality a discarded one."

My own observations suggest, however, that the falling-in-love experience, especially during adolescence, is determined much more by *timing* than by the personal characteristics of the love object. Just as the mallard duckling follows the first moving object that happens by when it is thirteen hours old, so the boy or girl freshly arrived at adolescence falls in love with the first potential love object who happens past at the critical period of puberty. The object imprinted may be too old or too young, too fat or too thin, too bashful or too domineering; it doesn't much matter if he or she comes past when the moment for falling in love is ripe.

I say "comes past" because *freshness* seems to me to be one factor in falling-in-love imprinting. A rare thirteen-year-old may fall in love with the boy or girl next door; much more commonly it is the "new girl in town" who discovers to her own amazement that she has become simultaneously the love object of half the boys in town. Whether this freshness requirement is one of the reasons for the relative rarity of incestuous falling-in-love experiences is a matter of speculation. Havelock Ellis thought so, and referred to "that familiarity which inhibits the development of sexual interest." Ellis's unexpected sexual arousal at the sight of his sister, it will be recalled, occurred when he saw her again after a four-year absence. During those four years, she had been transformed from a little girl to an adolescent.

Adolescent imprinting is not limited to our own era or culture. Examples from past eras and distant cultures have been collected in a volume of autobiographical extracts entitled *The Universal Experience of Adolescence,* edited by Professor Norman Kiell.

Dr. Kiell cites, for example, the celebrated case of Dante Alighieri (1265–1321) and Beatrice (1266–1290). Dante first met Beatrice when he was nine years old and she was eight. They merely passed in the street without exchanging a word, yet Dante was so overwhelmed by the experience that he dared not allow himself to cast eyes on her again for the next nine years. Their second meeting was also a passing on the street without even a salutation. Beatrice remained Dante's love object for the rest of his life, and inspired his *Divine Comedy* — despite the fact that she had died at the age of twenty-four without the slightest suspicion of his love for her.

Similar experiences of Milton, Goethe, Davy Crockett, Hector Berlioz, Havelock Ellis, and others are presented in their own words by Professor Kiell. An extreme example was the German novelist Hermann Sudermann (1857–1928), who became imprinted and experienced the complete falling-in-love syndrome toward a girl he had not even passed on the street.

Shortly after puberty, Sudermann later recalled, he was sent to school in a village away from home, and was instructed by his mother to call on her friends, the Hornigs, who had a fourteen-year-old daughter named Klara. A cousin of Sudermann's, when she heard of this, predicted:

"You'll be captured by Klara on the spot."

That was all that was needed in Hermann's overripe state of readiness for imprinting. Shyness caused him to postpone his first visit to Klara Hornig's home from week to week; but, he recognized, "I was already head over ears in love with her."

> By day I avoided the street in which the Hornigs' house stood, although my way to school led through it. But when the dusk fell I crept gently past it, squinting sideways toward the window at which I thought my beloved one must be sitting. I had never seen her with my eyes. I did not *want* to see her, for I was afraid I should sink into the earth if I did so. My heart was already in a tumult whenever I even thought of it. But my mother began to press me. In every letter she wrote she asked me, "Why have you not yet been to see the Hornigs?" And in her last letter she had even written, "Do not write to me again until you can give me an account of your visit." I could not now postpone it any longer. And when the next Sunday afternoon came I gave my brocade cravat a rather more fashionable twist . . . and in God's name marched off to my execution. . . .
>
> Everything passed off splendidly — only Klara happened to be on a picnic

to Vogelsang, as a result of which my cousin gave me an extra pocket handkerchief when I went to bed. 'You can cry into it until it is soaked,' said this sympathetic soul. A fortnight later I received an invitation to the Sunday dinner. . . . This time *She* was there. Tall, slender, with a brilliant smile, and eyes which were incredibly blue under broad, dark brows which made the blue of the eyes under the shadow of her big eyelashes seem still more incredible. There she stood in front of me, and gave me her hand — to me, an unworthy nothing, a stupid, crooked small boy who was at the bottom of the third class. She gave me her hand as though we were comrades — she, to me; she whom the boys in the first class ran after. . . .

A flood of self-consciousness overpowered me. Yes, if it were really true that I was not despised by her, not thrown aside as being childish and of no account, then I was already the master of the situation, and in the long run I could compete even with the boys in the first class. . . .

I was in the seventh heaven. I had never felt my spirit sway so lightly above the earth. And then as the soup was being ladled out I noticed that I had forgotten my pocket handkerchief.

It was all over — my hopes and my dreams vanished. My unaccustomed joy and happiness, my self-confidence, my flood of conversation were all ruined, overwhelmed by the painful question, "How can I get a pocket handkerchief?"

But everything has an end, and so even dinner went by. Dumb, awkward, stammering stupid answers, and only concerned with one thing, namely to conceal my sniffling, I let the minutes pass by, and squinted occasionally toward the door with the hopeless wish that I could take to flight. . . . [Finally] I could stand it no longer, told my kind host that I had something very urgent to do at home, and fled as though pursued by the Furies.

And so my role in the house of my beloved came to an end. I never dared to cross its threshold again, and never again did I receive an invitation. But I still preserved in my heart, hopelessly and obstinately, my love for the most beautiful and lovely girl on earth all through the period which followed.

When I walked home at night from Biechschmidt's I used to stand for hours in front of her door, but when I saw her coming toward me on the street I turned round or ran over to the other side, and when I could not help meeting her and her smiling glance greeted me, I always had the feeling as if I had gone blind and was going to sink into the earth, so that it seemed a miracle to me afterward that I was able to pass her more or less properly. And my shame, which was thus stirred up again, raged in me for days afterward.

This went on for more than two years.

In Hermann's case, clearly, it was neither the appearance nor the personality of the stimulus — Klara — which triggered the falling-in-love;

the process was far advanced before he met Klara. It was his pubertal ripeness which mattered; a football on roller skates might almost have served his purposes. Klara merely happened to be the female within his purview at the moment. This is the essence of imprinting.

Dr. Money cites evidence pointing in the same direction. "It is possible to fall in love at first sight and at a distance," he points out. "It is even possible to fall in love with a person represented at second hand, as a movie star on a screen." Dr. Money believes, however, that in such cases it is the physical appearance which is effective. "The head and face only may be a sufficient stimulus to trigger a falling-in-love reaction. Of the remainder of the body, the hips and torso are potent stimuli, as is the chest. No one part of the body is by itself indispensable as a releaser-stimulus, however." On the basis of the Hermann Sudermann example and others, I would go further. "Love is blind." In extreme cases no body at all is needed; at the appropriate moment, the abstract concept of a fantasy partner may for some people be sufficient.

The response syndrome which follows falling-in-love imprinting is well known; as Dr. Money points out, it "has been celebrated in the declamations of love poets through the ages. There is an intense prepossession with the loved one and his or her every perceptible feature and action may become the trigger of minor raptures. This prepossession is jealously possessive and brooks no interference from a competitor. It excludes the possibility of simultaneously falling in love with a second person." Like Thistle's imprinting to the original Mortimer, even an identical twin of the beloved is excluded.

The lover wants to be with the partner all the time, to be touching and fondling in close tactile contact, and having sexual intercourse, but perhaps refraining owing to sexual inhibition.

The state of being prepossessed and engrossed in love may be of gradual or sudden onset and is enhanced if the other person responds in like fashion. The stage of maximal prepossession is of variable duration, after which it wanes. There seems to be no constant time interval before the great intensity of falling in love goes on the wane. When waning does occur, the couple may lose interest in one another, or they may find themselves in a calmer, steady love relationship in which each remains powerfully sexually stimulating to the other. It is said that the man is more likely than the woman to be inconstant and have occasional illicit affairs, but there is no conclusive evidence in this respect; it does, after all, take two to have sex, and there is no evidence that a large group of inconstant men is taken care of by a small group of promiscuous women, at least not in every community and society.

Falling in love is not a one-time thing. The spurned lover, with rare exceptions, is able to fall in love with someone else, and the widowed spouse may do likewise. The couple whose love has waned, leaving nothing, may each find another with whom to fall in love all over again. After the first big experience of adolescence, however, and especially in a couple who have kept together, an extramural sexual affair is less likely to be a falling in love than a mere perfunctory agreement to have fun with one another. In popular parlance, it is a physical relationship without the spiritual quality of falling in love.

I have quoted Dr. Money at such length because his is one of the few discussions of falling in love I have found in the whole vast scientific literature of sex research. It is certainly not a complete analysis of the behavior, and Dr. Money did not intend it to be. But it does suggest one direction strictly scientific research might take in a future study of falling in love — namely, an analysis in terms of imprinting.

Some readers, pondering the relationships between Dante and his Beatrice, Sudermann and his Klara, may smile warmly and nod approvingly; that is the way romantic love should be. Others (myself among them) must regard Dante's and Sudermann's behavior in these heterosexual relationships as aberrant and bizarre — a form of sexual perversion.* Indeed, their behavior is an illustration of precisely the evil against which Dr. Elizabeth Blackwell and other Victorians fulminated: the divorce of sex from love.

The Victorians focused their attention on only one aspect of that divorce, sexual indulgence in the absence of love — what might be called brothel behavior. They failed to recognize the close tie between brothel behavior and what I shall call "the Dante Alighieri syndrome" — sexual paralysis in the face of the most transcendent and enduring love. These are the two faces of the same coin. Both represent the divorce of love from sex. Victims of the Dante Alighieri syndrome are not only unable to achieve sexual fulfillment in the arms of the most dearly beloved; they are prevented even from *seeking* it.

What causes the Dante Alighieri syndrome? In the human case, no

* "Sexual abstinence is the most distressing of perversions" (Robert Latou Dickinson, *A Thousand Marriages*).

scientific evidence is available. But certain monkey experiments seem to me highly relevant.

At the University of Wisconsin during the 1950's, Dr. Harry F. Harlow found it necessary to raise a group of newborn rhesus monkeys in isolation — so that they could be the foundation for a breeding colony free of the diseases common among their wild monkey mothers. Seven baby monkeys were accordingly taken from their mothers at birth. Dr. Harlow and his associate, Dr. William Mason, hired an undergraduate student named Kathy, an education major, to tend them. Dr. Mason planned to study the social responsiveness of these seven infants at the age of two; hence Kathy was warned not to let them play with each other prematurely. They were to be isolated from their age mates as well as from their mothers.

One evening about 9 P.M., however, Dr. Mason unexpectedly entered the monkey nursery to find Kathy sitting in the center of the floor surrounded by the seven little monkeys. Both she and the monkeys "were having a wonderful time together." Far from showing embarrassment at being caught violating instructions, Kathy jumped up and shook her finger at her boss.

"Dr. Mason, I'm an education student and I know that it is improper and immoral to blight the social development of little children," she announced. "I am right and you are wrong."

Dr. Harlow and Dr. Mason were more amused than angry, and assigned Kathy to another job. The baby monkeys were returned to their isolation.

Five years later, when those monkeys were mature and efforts were made to breed them, the sexual results of infantile isolation became apparent. "We looked at those selfsame animals sitting in their cages," Dr. Harlow reported, ". . . staring vacantly into space or engaging in various individual, stereotyped behaviors including . . . biting and tearing at their own arms and legs. Those animals exhibited almost every kind of behavior except one — heterosexual behavior, which was conspicuous by its absence. We accepted the inevitable: Kathy had been right. . . . We had developed, not a breeding colony, but a brooding colony."

Having learned their initial lesson, the University of Wisconsin researchers next tried a less drastic experiment. They reared another batch of monkeys in isolation from their mothers, and in temporary isolation from one another, but put them together in various combinations as soon as the females began to menstruate. "We were completely unsuccessful," Dr. Harlow reported. "No normal copulatory behavior ever took place, and many pairings resulted in violent fighting and murderous aggression."

Could the monkeys raised in laboratory isolation learn how to copulate from normal monkeys raised in the wild? The answer was no. When healthy wild males were caged with laboratory-born and isolated females, no normal copulation and no pregnancies occurred.

Suspecting that the caging of the animals might be the difficulty, the Harlow group next let ten male and ten female isolation-raised monkeys, either adolescent or approaching adolescence, loose together on an island in the Vilas Park Zoo in Madison. "Within a few days," Dr. Harlow reports, "there were indications that we might be on the way to success." One of the normal preliminaries to sexual intercourse among rhesus monkeys is *grooming;* the males and females groom each other — a sort of simian equivalent of necking or petting. "Grooming had been almost nonexistent when these animals were paired in the laboratory," Dr. Harlow reports, "but patterns of normal grooming behavior quickly developed in the relatively rich environment of the Monkey Island. . . . Fighting and aggression decreased markedly, but only after one male drowned and two females were injured so badly that they had to be removed. A number of the monkeys formed friendship pairs — two large females became very attached to each other. Not only did grooming increase, but a substantial amount of play behavior developed."

Then came the anticlimax. Despite the hopeful sexual preliminaries, "no normal, adult sexual behavior followed." And no impregnations.

A photograph taken on Monkey Island dramatically illustrates the failure. Female monkeys in heat adopt a characteristic pose, tail held high, vulva fully exposed, back arched to make it easier for the male to mount and copulate. The female in the Monkey Island photograph is presenting her vulva to a nearby male almost normally. The male is obviously interested; he is staring fixedly at her exposed vulva. But instead of mounting her, he is squatting a foot or two away, and masturbating. That photograph portrays, it seems to me, the approximate simian equivalent of the Dante Alighieri syndrome among humans — sexual arousal divorced from the appropriate response.

"At this time we gambled," Dr. Harlow declares, "and added our finest, most patient, biggest, and best breeding male, Smiley, to the island population." All seventeen of the other monkeys promptly ganged up on Smiley, but "with dignity and good humor" he gradually established his dominance. "In a few days Smiley was the unchallenged and unquestioned king."

Here was the ideal situation for establishing the desired breeding colony. Smiley was the prototype of the sexually ever-eager, ever-willing, and ever-able rhesus stud male, and five or six of the females came into heat during Smiley's sojourn on the island. Yet "we never observed any really normal sexual behavior," Dr. Harlow reports, and "no female ever became pregnant."

The Harlow research also indicated that *normal play with other immature monkeys* is exceedingly important in the maturing process. Indeed, monkeys deprived of mothering in infancy grew up relatively normal and heterosexually responsive if they were allowed to play freely with other monkeys of their own age during the prepubertal period.

Monkeys are not humans, of course. Yet it is worth noting once more that we humans, like monkeys, are primates. "Parenthetically," Dr. Money remarks with respect to these Harlow experiments, "one may raise the question of whether the suppression, in our own human society, of childhood sexual play may adversely affect sexual behavior in adulthood and perhaps promote the occurrence of sexual aberration."

Eventually, after what Dr. Money has called "heroic efforts of animal husbandry," Dr. Harlow and his University of Wisconsin associates were able to get four of their reared-in-laboratory-isolation female monkeys pregnant. In due course, four baby monkeys were born. The four females who thus gave birth, it will be recalled, had been raised in isolation from their own mothers and had remained isolated until adolescence.

> After the birth of her baby [Dr. Harlow declares], the first of these unmothered mothers ignored the infant and sat relatively motionless at one side of the living cage, staring fixedly into space hour after hour. If a human being approached and threatened either the baby or the mother, there was no counterthreat. During the first week postpartum this animal was the most catatonic monkey we have ever seen. It was necessary to remove the baby and to feed it at appropriate intervals, and even these procedures elicited no response from the mother.

> As the infant matured and became mobile, it made continual, desperate attempts to effect maternal contact. These attempts were consistently repulsed by the mother. She would brush the baby away or restrain it by pushing the baby's face to the woven-wire floor. . . .
>
> The next two mothers to give birth were even more abusive to their infants than was the first. They ignored their offspring except when repelling the infants' advances. From time to time these mothers engaged in unprovoked aggression against the helpless neonates. They would beat and maul their babies, and one often hung by her feet from the ceiling of the cage and beat her infant with both hands. . . . The fourth mother resembled the first, being indifferent more often than abusive.

Dr. Harlow was particularly impressed by "the strength and persistence" of the infant's attachment to its mother. In spite of all the abuse they received, the babies continually struggled to make maternal contact. The babies learned to approach their mothers from the back, for example, and then to climb up and hang on. The mothers finally submitted to this, and even permitted occasional nursing. But "so far as infant-mother attachments were concerned," Dr. Harlow states, "it was a case of the baby adopting the mother, not the mother adopting the baby."

In a word, the way in which these monkey mothers had been reared was continuing to impair both their heterosexual responses and their maternal responses years later. (For the relationship between heterosexual and maternal responses in humans, see the research of Dr. Niles Newton in Chapter 6, above.)

Freud and almost everyone since had assumed that it is the nursing of the baby at the mother's breast which is so important in the infant's emotional development. The Harlow experiments add a further point. In some of the Wisconsin tests, baby monkeys were brought up with mother surrogates or dummies made of wire netting; the infant's milk bottle was propped so that the baby could climb up the wire frame and reach it. Other infant monkeys were reared in the same way except that the wire dummies were covered with a soft, rough terry cloth against which the infants could cuddle. The infants with terry-cloth mother surrogates did not grow up to be sexually normal — but their adult behavior was markedly less bizarre and disturbed than that of the infants brought up without the tactual experience of clinging against the terry cloth.

Dr. Mary Steichen Calderone of the Sex Information and Education Council of the U.S. (SIECUS), has suggested that an account of the Harlow monkey research be included in high school family-life and sex-education courses. I heartily agree. Moving pictures of the Harlow monkeys might also be included. Adolescents who see these movies, I suspect, may get a stronger sense of the importance of mothering and of childhood play, including childhood sex play, in the normal prepubertal development of their own children a few years hence.

9

When Sexual Inhibitions Are Cast Off

Current Studies of a Deviant Subculture: The Sexual Freedom Movement and "The Swinging Scene"

EVERYONE is not like you, your loved ones, and your friends and neighbors — and even your loved ones, friends, and neighbors may not be as much like you as you commonly suppose.

These themes, as I noted in Chapter One, were among Havelock Ellis's most fruitful contributions to sex research. They retain their significance today. We can hardly be reminded too often that human sexuality is astonishingly malleable, and that our cherished personal beliefs and behavior patterns are not universal laws of nature. This chapter, concerned with mate-swapping, group sex, and sex in public — the activities which in recent years have come to be known as "swinging" — will serve as one more reminder.

In addition, this chapter serves a second function, casting light on several issues of very broad significance:

Is it possible for ordinary men and women, brought up in the watered-down Victorian tradition so familiar today, to shuck off their taboos and inhibitions as readily as they cast off their clothes?

How do human beings behave when freed of inhibitions?

What is the effect on self-image, self-respect, self-confidence?

Is sexual jealousy an inevitable feature of the human condition, or can it also be shucked off? If not, can it be controlled? How?

I wish I could answer these questions on the basis of large-scale, technically sophisticated studies by scholars of settled repute. Unfortunately, no such studies exist. I must therefore be content to present in this chapter the preliminary, tentative findings of a few as yet unpublished investigations of "the swinging scene."

In a 1957 issue of a minor men's magazine called *MR.*, published in New York City and devoted in considerable part to seminude photos of bosomy females, there appeared a short article on wife-swapping. The term is a familiar one now, but it was fresh and attention-seizing back in 1957.

Everett Meyers, the editor of *MR.*, later claimed that it was this article which touched off a flood of similar articles on wife-swapping or mate-swapping in other semipornographic magazines. Perhaps he was right. In any event, *MR.* followed up its original article with a regular monthly correspondence column filled with alleged letters from readers reporting their own mate-swapping activities. As the months rolled by, the letters became more and more sensational. They described, for example, sex clubs at whose weekly meetings half a dozen or more couples assembled and engaged in public in coitus and other sexual activities, heterosexual and homosexual — in duos, trios, foursomes, or en masse. *MR.* prospered.

Other magazines for men, and weekly tabloids, picked up the mate-swapping and group-sex themes at about the same time or a little later, and several added a further twist: advertisements allegedly entered by "couples" or "singles" seeking partners with whom to engage in group sexual practices. Two typical ads:

A–050–C–NYC– Stunning wife, 27, 36C–24–36, and goodlooking husband, seek meetings with attractive couples. Can entertain or travel, NYC and Long Island area. Photo or phone please. Will answer all.

C–057–F–Calif.– Single, white girl, 22, very attractive, warm nature, 39–26–38, new to modern life, very interested in meeting other sincere white girls and discreet couples in Los Angeles area for exciting social fun. Have broad-minded boy friend if needed. Send photo or phone with first letter.

These advertisements were often illustrated with seminude photos of the advertisers — many of whom looked remarkably like the bosomy photographers' models already familiar in the pages of the same magazines.

The advertisements were ideally suited to stimulate the erotic imagination of males. The magazines which ran them thrived — and after 1960, at least twenty magazines devoted entirely to such advertisements, and carrying even more sensational photos of the alleged advertisers, were launched in the United States and Canada.* The style of these early advertisements was so uniform as to suggest that they had been written in the offices of the magazines running them; and the accompanying studio-posed photographs also suggested fakery — or a come-on for prostitutes.

A proportion of the men who originally bought these magazines "for kicks," however, began to take the ads seriously — and so did some of their wives. Soon much more restrained advertisements, inserted in earnest, began to be sandwiched in among the fakes:

C–020–C–NYC– Attractive white couple, 33 and 28, interested in meeting couples and bi-minded women.

F–060–M–NY– Male with prudish wife wishes to meet singles, couples, or group.

The snapshots which occasionally accompanied these ads showed people who looked much like the people who live around the corner from the rest of us.

The proprietors of the magazines, of course, quickly recognized the new trend, and capitalized on it. One enterprising proprietor announced a cocktail party to which advertisers and readers were invited; to his own amazement, scores of ordinary men and dozens of ordinary women made their appearance. Other magazines gave dinners; attendance at some of them rose into the hundreds despite admission charges as high as twenty-five dollars per couple.

Conspicuously present at these functions were respectable married couples in their twenties and thirties. ("I met two members of the Junior League and their husbands," one attender recalled recently.) Many went merely out of curiosity — but many more were in fact active participants or would-be participants in sex-in-public and group-sex activities.

* *La Plume* claims to be the oldest of these. According to a 1969 advertisement, "LA PLUME IS THE DADDY OF THEM ALL! Established about 1955, *La Plume* was, for a long time, the only 'Swinger's' magazine in existence." This priority claim, so far as I have been able to ascertain, is justified; but I doubt that *La Plume* ran advertisements by swingers as early as 1955.

To these new recruits, the term wife-swapping was objectionable because of its implication of sexual inequality and of male property rights in wives. Nor was "husband-swapping" or "mate-swapping" an adequate substitute, for much more was often involved than mere swapping — and unmarried men and women also participated. Hence the term "swinging" came into general use in the 1960's, and the subculture engaged in such activities came to be known as "the swinging scene." The ambiguity of the term swinging was no doubt one of the reasons for its popularity; one could "feel out" prospective partners by launching a casual conversation about swinging — and then switch to the more innocent meaning of the term if the response was negative.

Though most of the magazine-sponsored hotel parties for swingers were quiet affairs which would hardly have brought a blush to the cheek of Dr. Elizabeth Blackwell, they provided an opportunity for couples and singles to arrange subsequent private meetings. Later the hotel parties were superseded by motel parties where even more convenient arrangements could be made. Still later, key clubs and cocktail lounges offering opportunities for swinging contacts sprang up in a number of cities. Hosts and hostesses who enjoyed entertaining also played a major role, forming informal private groups which met in their homes occasionally or at regular, often weekly, intervals — very much on the pattern described in the early magazine articles. As Oscar Wilde so often remarked, "Nature imitates Art."

In a word, group sex "went public" during the early 1960's.*

I know of no reliable estimate of the number of couples and singles currently participating in the swinging scene. The estimate sometimes quoted in sensational paperbacks — 5,000,000 men and women — is almost certainly an exaggeration. If only one-tenth of one percent of mar-

* Group-sex activities, of course, antedated the 1957 article in *MR.* by thousands of years. The ancient Greeks and Romans were familiar with the phenomenon, and there is reason to believe that it never died out in Europe, even during the most repressive eras. The Kinsey Institute researchers found traces of group sex in the United States and reported in 1948: "Most males who have participated in sexual activities in groups have found the opportunity to do so with prostitutes."

What happened during the 1960's was that group sex in public — swinging — emerged from the brothels and became an established though minor feature of American urban and suburban life, participated in by wives and respectable girl friends.

ried couples (one couple in a thousand) swing, however, the total still adds up to some 45,000 swinging American couples.

From the point of view of the scientific study of sex, the importance of this development — and especially of parties where sexual behavior unselfconsciously proceeds in the presence of others — can hardly be overestimated. Here, for the first time in our culture, was a population ready and willing to have its sexual behavior observed in a natural setting rather than a laboratory. Here was an opportunity to make psychosexual and sociosexual field studies paralleling the Masters-Johnson physiological laboratory studies. Here at long last scientists could directly observe *how human beings behave after they have shed their inhibitions, repressions, and taboos.*

I wish I could report that departments of psychiatry, psychology, human biology, anthropology, sociology, and other medical and social sciences in our leading universities and medical research centers promptly realized the significance of this rich new research opportunity, and sent fully qualified multidisciplinary teams out into the field to make studies in depth, financed by generous grants from the National Institutes of Health and the major foundations. But that, alas, is not what happened.

Instead, the first reports from the field were an apparently endless stream of paperbacks designed to appeal to what law courts call "the prurient interest of readers" — the same interest which had launched the fake advertisements earlier. These paperbacks were often by husband-and-wife teams, or allegedly by such teams. Some sample titles: *The Velvet Underground; Mate-Swapping Syndrome; Sex Rebels; The Lesbian in Group Love; The Swinging Bi-Sexuals; Sodom U.S.A.*, and many more. None of the data in this chapter is drawn from these paperback sources.

After a lag of several years, however, a few intrepid behavioral scientists began to explore the swinging scene about 1965. Three of these researchers or research teams have recently completed studies, and have permitted me to draw freely on their as yet unpublished data: Mrs. Carolyn Symonds, whose study was centered in Southern California; Dr. Gilbert Bartell, whose study covered primarily the Middle West, with some extension into the Southwest; James R. and Lynn G. Smith, a husband-wife team whose study was centered in the San Francisco Bay area.

In addition, I have talked with one researcher and one husband-wife research team who are currently exploring the swinging scene in New York City. A sixth research project, centered in Indiana, was launched too late to be included in this review; and a seventh, in New Mexico, is at this writing still in the planning stage.

One conclusion which leaps from the studies to date is the very wide differences in swinging customs and practices. The Los Angeles scene is reported to be quite different from the San Francisco scene, and neither resembles very closely either the Chicago or New York scene. Within each city, moreover, the scene is in fact composed of a variety of contrasting subscenes.

This diversity, indeed, is the main theme of Carolyn Symonds's study. Mrs. Symonds, a young sociologist in her thirties, had for years participated with her husband in nudist activities; the two belonged to a Southern California nudist resort. The Symondses gradually became aware that some of their nudist friends were also swingers — and in 1965 it occurred to Mrs. Symonds that a study of swinging would make an excellent topic for her master's thesis in sociology at the University of California at Riverside. During the next two years she interviewed as many swingers as possible, frequented a Los Angeles area cocktail lounge catering to swingers, and made contact with a number of swinging groups. Her thesis based on this research, entitled "A Pilot Study of the Peripheral Behavior of Sexual Mate Swappers," was submitted to the university in partial fulfillment of its M.A. requirements in 1967, and accepted in 1968. So far as I have been able to ascertain, it is the first scientific study of the swinging scene to win academic recognition; I congratulate the University of California at Riverside.

California swingers, Mrs. Symonds notes, belong to two quite disparate philosophical traditions: the "Utopian swingers" and the "recreational swingers."

The Utopian swingers are in general concerned with building a better world. They see war, violence, materialism, possessiveness, jealousy, sexual exclusivity, and other common characteristics of our society as evil. Many of them are making concrete plans to establish small communes where sexual freedom can be practiced and where children can be brought up in peace, freedom and happiness; others like to think about or fantasy a communal life. Some of them, indeed, call themselves "communitarians." The acceptance of free sexual behavior is an intrinsic part of their generally Utopian approach. They believe strongly in love and in the physical expression of love. In all of this, of course, they are following a deeply rooted American tradition pioneered by the Oneida Community in upstate New York and other nineteenth-century Utopian groups.

Carolyn Symonds's "recreational swingers," in contrast, are precisely what the name implies. They are men and women, often married couples, who believe that it is much more fun for people to have sex together than to play bridge or golf together, and who practice what they believe.* Mrs. Symonds, though currently engaged in other aspects of sex research, has made some recent observations of the swinging scene in the Middle West, and plans to return to the subject for her Ph.D. thesis. The problem of financing this type of research remains a stumbling block for her as for other researchers.

Dr. Bartell's project began in a quite different way. He is a young anthropologist in his thirties, on the faculty of Northern Illinois University in DeKalb, Illinois, and his attention was first drawn to swinging in 1966 by a series of sensational articles in the Chicago *Daily News*. Out of anthropological curiosity he and Mrs. Bartell answered a few swinging ads. Since they are a very outgoing couple, they had no difficulty in establishing rapport with the couples they met in this way — and they were fascinated both by the kinds of people they met and by their accounts of the swinging scene. To extend their contacts further, the Bartells ran advertisements of their own, and frequented three cocktail lounges where Chicago swingers meet. Within a year they had established contact with and secured data from 204 swinging couples.

Dr. Bartell's study will stress, among other insights, the ways in which nonsexual patterns of behavior are carried over into the swinging scene. Some of the couples the Bartells interviewed, for example, were suburbanites living in houses of the *Better Homes and Gardens* type, surrounded by well-tended lawns and well-clipped hedges; they tended to swing in the same socially correct, formal, "up-tight" style they followed in their other activities. Bohemians, in contrast, swung in a Bohemian manner. Some swingers turned to swinging as they would turn to a country club or church couples' club for simple social support — an escape from the social isolation of Middle Western urban and suburban life.

* Though the terminology often overlaps, the term "sexual freedom movement" is more commonly applied to Utopian swingers, and "the swinging scene" to recreational swingers.

Several psychiatrists and psychoanalysts have sought to explain swinging in terms of neurosis or of the traditional perversions — especially voyeurism, exhibitionism, and "latent homosexuality." Dr. Bartell is contemptuous of such explanations. "The chief characteristic which the 204 swinging couples I talked with had in common," he told me, "was their inherent normality. They were average, commonplace, and uncomplicated in almost all respects. My data are consistent with the view that, with few exceptions, men and women who are 'sick' in the Freudian meaning of the term keep away from the swinging scene." While voyeurism and exhibitionism are no doubt features of the swinging scene, Dr. Bartell points out they are also features of our culture generally, in much the same way and to the same extent. Dr. Bartell expects to publish a full account of these and other findings in 1970.

All over the country, swinging attracts far more males than females; this almost everywhere necessitates rules limiting attendance at swinging parties to those who come as couples. Most men "dig the scene" on their first exposure to it; many women, in contrast, are "turned off." One Northern California woman who has attended several swinging parties explained why:

"I am not particularly enthused with the parties as I can find nothing I gain from them. I like sex on a more private and personal level. I like the 'relationship' of a sexual experience. I gain nothing from just the sex act in itself. I like to know and appreciate my sex partner and I can't see where this can be achieved at a one-night party."

A New York informant replies:

"At most of the swinging parties I have attended in the New York area, this unwillingness of most women — even 'swinging' women — to have sex with strangers is not only recognized but catered to. The principle that a woman must be wooed before she can be won is as fully accepted by swingers as in the wider society.

"A woman attending a party, for example, may receive tentative social overtures from half-a-dozen men in a row — most of whom make opening remarks about the weather or the hi-fi. She may ignore or repulse them all. The next man to approach may for some reason or other be allowed to strike up a casual conversation. An acquaintanceship develops, followed by simple friendship. Smiling and perhaps a touch of flirting can now be observed — commonly a series of brief eye-contacts, soon followed by the emergence of warm emotional rapport and more prolonged eye-contacts, or 'soul-searches.' The first actual physical contact — perhaps a tentative holding of hands or a shy kiss — may be delayed until this stage is reached. Thus all the traditional phases of courtship from tentative social overture to full emotional involvement are run through in the usual order and at about the usual tempo.

"But from this point on, progress is telescoped. Uninhibited sexual activity, usually including coitus, is likely to follow immediately after the establishment of rapport and initial physical contact. The whole wooing cycle is there — but it generally takes less than an hour instead of the usual days, weeks, or months."

When I called this to Dr. Bartell's attention, he was amazed. "Nothing like that goes on among the Chicago couples I talked with," he assured me. "Courtship behavior does occur when one couple is trying to recruit another couple into the swinging scene initially. But after that, wooing is dispensed with altogether. At some Chicago parties, for example, the doors are locked at 10 P.M. — and every girl or woman staying after that hour is expected simply to say yes or no immediately upon being approached and propositioned."

Carolyn Symonds also expressed surprise at the above description of courtship on the New York swinging scene, but for a different reason. "The swingers I know," she explains, "take a much more casual and relaxed attitude toward social nudity and physical contact. A man who hugs and kisses a girl, or puts his arm around her and fondles her, nude or clothed, does not necessarily expect the relationship to proceed any further in Southern California."

Further studies of the swinging scene, of course, may unearth Chicago-type behavior in Los Angeles and San Francisco-type behavior in New York. The variations may prove to be characteristic of small social subgroups rather than regional in scope. The existence of these variations, however, illustrates a significant point: human beings freed of inhibitions do not behave in one way, but in a wide variety of ways.

The Smiths' study of the sexual freedom movement and the swinging scene in the San Francisco Bay area is by far the most ambitious of the current projects. James R. Smith is a graduate student in philosophy and political science and Lynn G. Smith a graduate student in psychology at the University of California at Berkeley; they are both still in their twenties. Since 1966 they have observed at more than a hundred swinging parties in the Bay area — in each case identifying themselves openly in advance as behavioral scientists making a study of swinging. Many of the parties they attended were sponsored by the Oakland or San Francisco chapters of the Sexual Freedom League — an organization which was founded in New York in 1963 by Leo F. Koch and Jefferson Poland, but which has since flourished primarily on the West Coast, attracting both Utopian and recreational swingers. In addition to their direct observations, the Smiths have secured detailed questionnaire returns from 503 Bay area swingers. The remainder of this chapter is drawn primarily (but not exclusively) from their questionnaire materials.

What Kinds of People Swing?

When sociologists compare any two subcultures in our society — for example, Minnesota Lutherans of Finnish origin and Wisconsin Catholics of Polish origin — certain differences are found. More members of one group may attend church; more members of the other may engage in premarital intercourse. But such differences are a matter of degree, not kind; both kinds of behavior are found in both groups. The subculture observed by the Smiths — swinging members of the sexual freedom movement in the San Francisco Bay area — similarly differs from other subcultures in the relative frequency with which particular characteristics appear rather than in absolute terms. The Smith study leaves no room for doubt that most of the swingers who answered their questionnaire are not a breed apart but are human beings who resemble the rest of us in most respects.

Age: The 501 respondents who stated their age ranged from 15 to 72; the average for males was 34 and for females 28. Four percent were under 21 and seven percent were over 50.

Sex: Swinging is of greater interest to males than females. But it is not the case, as one psychiatrist I interviewed alleged, that women have no interest. The Smiths secured questionnaire returns from 140 participating females as well as from 363 males.

Race: Ninety-seven percent were white, 2 percent Negro, and 1 percent "Other."

Marital Status: Forty-four percent were married, 32 percent single, and the remainder formerly married (widowed, divorced, or separated).

Educational Status: Fifty-two percent were college graduates and 30 percent had gone on to graduate training; 8 percent already had graduate degrees. Twelve percent, moreover, were still students, so that the ultimate educational level of the group as a whole will be even higher. Only 4 percent had not finished high school.

Occupation, Social Class, Income: The Smiths' respondents ranked high on all three of these scales.

Religious Background: Fifty percent were brought up as Protestants, 20 percent as Catholics, 7 percent as Jews. The remainder belonged to minor sects or reported no religious training or affiliation during their early years.

Current Religious Affiliations: Only 16 percent state that they are currently Protestants, 5 percent that they are currently Catholics, and 2 percent that they retain their Jewish faith. Whether the departure of the others from the religion in which they were brought up preceded, accompanied, or followed their departure from conventional sexual attitudes and behavior is in most cases not known.

Number of Sexual Partners: The median number of female partners reported by male respondents was 19; the median number of male partners reported by female respondents was 15. Twenty-three percent of the males and 12 percent of the females reported more than 100 sexual partners. This is no doubt the major difference between swingers and nonswingers; but even here, the difference is one of degree.

The above figures, let me stress, are not meant to apply to swingers in general, or even to Bay area swingers. They characterize the 503 participants in swinging activities who responded to the Smith questionnaire in 1967 and 1968. But with respect to the swinging scene generally, they are by far the best statistics currently available.

I was especially interested, of course, in learning whether the "Sherfey syndrome" was observable at swinging parties the Smiths attended. Do women released from their inhibitions and taboos joyfully take on all comers one after the other, enjoying orgasm after orgasm until the supply of males runs out or exhaustion calls a halt?

The Smiths report that they have occasionally observed such behavior. One or two women may engage in it toward the end of a particular party. They add, however that such behavior was the exception rather than the rule at the more than one hundred parties they attended.*

* Dr. Bartell reports similarly that such behavior occurs occasionally in the Middle West — but only two cases were recorded in his 204 interviews.

Dr. Sherfey might argue, of course, that swinging women who do not engage in such behavior have not *really* shed their inhibitions. It seems to me at least equally reasonable to conclude that the "gang-bang" is not *the* natural mode of sexual behavior for the uninhibited human female, but one of a large number of natural modes.

What impressed me most in the Smith data was the light thrown on problems of quite general interest — problems faced by nonswingers as well as swingers.

Repressions, Inhibitions, Taboos. Many swingers, the Smiths learned, were subjected during childhood to the same repressive upbringing as the rest of us. The homes in which they were reared might be properly described as late Victorian, in spirit if not in chronology. Some retained their inhibitions and taboos until the eve of their swinging debuts. For some, the swinging experience itself was the means of freeing them from sexual taboos.

Thus one married woman, aged twenty, reported:

"Well, I was raised in a 'good' Catholic home — went to a Catholic school, etc., and was shocked at most anything I read, saw, or heard about. When I went on dates I was almost petrified to kiss the guy. Also, my parents never discussed anything with me, because everything was dirty — found out everything through jokes, friends, and then, when I got married, through books and my husband. Anyway, before I got married I had gotten raped and had really crawled in a shell of fear, etc. Going to these parties has really helped me become what I am now." *

A twenty-five-year-old married man, asked why he attended swinging parties, responded in a similar vein:

"It is easier to specify the reasons that originally prevented my attending — strict Catholic upbringing. I lost my belief in this through extensive reading in comparative religions."

This respondent thought the swinging experience had been good for him — and for his relations with his wife:

"It has increased the frequency of our sexual intercourse and also our casual sexual contacts, even around the kitchen. We are so enamored by it that we have tried to introduce our best friends to it."

* This quotation and those which follow are taken verbatim from the Smith questionnaire returns. In some cases, however, I have altered the punctuation and syntax to clarify the meaning, and I have omitted all details which might identify a respondent.

Men and women with Protestant upbringing were quite similar to the Catholic men and women in their responses. One married male respondent, aged thirty-two, reported, for example:

"Original motivation [for swinging] was from strict Puritan upbringing. This gave an abnormal degree of interest in nudity of opposite sex. Constant frustrations as child caused determination as adult to fill these needs. This led to nudism . . . which led to limited [sexual] experimenting, and that led to more total involvement."

Another Protestant, a divorced woman of thirty-two, gave her motive for swinging as a "desire to be freed from Puritan heritage."

A third, a divorced male of thirty-five, reported much more vehemently:

"I never realized [before attending first sexual freedom party] the full extent of my sexual immaturity and inhibition. The reality of my wasted youth sickens me. I realized that I had believed all of Puritan morality. I was a Puritan dupe."

Some of the women in Dr. Schaefer's sample who were adolescent during the 1940's and 1950's, it will be recalled, had engaged in premarital intercourse for the specific purpose of defying parental taboos. Parental repression in the 1960's appears to be having the same effect. One girl gave this explanation for her initial attendance at a swinging party:

"As a teen-ager it was my way of demonstrating I could defy my parents' rigid standards."

Several inhibited women noted that release from their inhibitions through swinging had made them physiologically more responsive:

"Made 'abandon' in sex more enjoyable. Made me not so 'up tight' about some aspects of sex." (Thirty-four-year-old married woman.)

"Relaxation during sex has very much improved." (Twenty-year-old single woman.)

"Have become more uninhibited. . . . Have become a freer person." (Thirty-six-year-old unmarried woman.)

A twenty-six-year-old divorcée with two children reported in more detail:

"Before attending I guess I was more or less a prude — I didn't [even] like to talk about sex." She described coitus as "just a chore." Then she joined the sexual freedom movement. "Now I enjoy it — talking about sex and discovering new, exciting, different ways to have sexual intercourse and relations."

Male respondents said much the same thing in different words:

"Beneficial in overcoming . . . hang-ups such as self-consciousness." (Married, aged forty.)

"I was sexually inexperienced and wished to gain experience and expertise. I thought it would help me to overcome my sexual frustrations and hang-ups — which it did, but not without much much work. . . . It has helped me to lose my inhibitions about sex, and satisfied my curiosity about some questions regarding sex and human interaction." (Single, aged twenty-three.)

For some individuals and married couples, the disinhibitory effect is very prompt; they almost literally shed their taboos along with their clothes at the first swinging party they attend:

"Through some very close friends of ours at a lake swimming party, [my late wife and I] participated in nude swimming — which later led to a prolonged discussion of sex and the human body, nudity, etc. This led to experimentation and games, with all that were present involved. . . . Before long most of the 'taboos' were forgotten and we all were enjoying sex as never before. We felt completely unashamed and uninhibited, and experienced a newfound *natural freedom* concerning sex. At future parties we demonstrated and tried new sex techniques, and found new pleasures that were never before experienced. . . . I have . . . come to learn that sex and love are not necessarily one item and inseparable. They can be separated without conflict to the individuals involved if they approach sex as a natural bodily function and love as an emotion." (Widower, aged thirty-seven.)

For others the process of shedding inhibitions is more prolonged:

"[My first swinging experiences] resulted in an ascetic withdrawal from much social life for several months, to 'think things out.'

"It emancipated my attitudes toward sex, giving me greater leeway in exploring life. It loosened me up.

"It presented me with a clearer understanding of my own attitudes." (Divorced male, aged twenty-four.)

One formerly very inhibited divorced male, aged forty-two, described in detail the precise process by which swinging had freed him from inhibitions two years before:

"At the first party I was invited to, I felt sick, lonely, bashful and scared. My friend . . . told his wife all about me beforehand. Upon entering their home and after introducing me around, she took over —

very, very ladylike. She paid much, much attention to me and took me under her wing, so to speak. Midway through the evening, she gently kissed her husband, got me by the arm, and walked me into their bedroom."

The remainder of his account leaves no room for doubt that this initial experience with swinging, plus a short series of subsequent sexual encounters with the same hostess, was at least as effective a form of therapy for his "sick, lonely, bashful, and scared" feelings as a prolonged series of sessions with a professional psychotherapist would have been. The Smiths report that this kind of conscious effort on the part of some experienced swingers to make the experience therapeutic for inhibited newcomers, though it is only a small factor in the total swinging scene, is observable frequently enough to be identified as an area of nonprofessional therapy warranting further study.

Not all of the Smith respondents, of course, came to their first parties full of inhibitions and taboos. Some were already "emancipated." Thus one divorcée (who did not give her age) reported that she preferred attending swinging parties instead of acquiring lovers in more conventional ways because of —

"my disgust with the narrow, uneducated, frightened approach of the average middle-class American [male] to sex and love. A desire to associate with people with more open and healthy attitudes and consequently practices. An interest in and desire for eroticism in my sex life instead of the frustration I had been experiencing at the hands and penes of my so-called lovers."

Most of these respondents, as their quoted statements show, welcomed release from inhibitions as a primary good — to be valued for its own sake. In addition, a number of the Utopian swingers identified release from sexual hang-ups with much broader and deeper ethical, aesthetic, and even mystical values. I shall cite only one example — from a twenty-four-year-old single male:

"What I have experienced is a series of real sexual relationships growing out of real interest without the usual hang-ups of a psychological nature. But these sexual relations are not mere physical gratifications; rather, they have come to foster a sense of being together, as one, moving together in a single beautiful movement. The experience of enjoying oneself while knowing you are giving pleasure to another is a great feeling. Moreover, there is a general feeling of satisfaction in knowing I am communicating with a woman on equal terms, and my general appreciation of people has commensurately increased with this feeling."

Self-Esteem and Self-Image. Several recent studies have shown that the standard methods of child rearing in our culture not only repress sexuality but also, in many cases, severely damage a child's self-image, self-confidence, and self-esteem.* An amazing proportion of children and adults, including very attractive ones, see themselves as physically ugly and socially inferior.

Studies have also shown that men and women with undamaged self-images and adequate self-esteem are more likely to achieve sexual fulfillment.†

Shakespeare's Sonnet XXIX provides the classic description of the damaged-self-esteem syndrome — as well as the classic statement of the way in which falling in love tends to repair the damage:

When in disgrace with fortune and men's eyes
I all alone beweep my outcast state,
And trouble deaf heaven with my bootless cries,
And look upon myself, and curse my fate,
Wishing me like to one more rich in hope,
Featur'd like him, like him with friends possess'd,
Desiring this man's art, and that man's scope,
With what I most enjoy contented least;
Yet in these thoughts myself almost despising,
Haply I think on thee, — and then my state,
Like to the lark at break of day arising
From sullen earth, sings hymns at heaven's gate;
For thy sweet love remember'd such wealth brings
That then I scorn to change my state with kings.

The data collected by the Smiths on the sexual freedom movement in the San Francisco Bay area suggest that, at least in some cases, swinging has a quite similar ability to repair damaged self-images and damaged self-esteem.

* See, for example, *Antecedents of Self-Esteem* by Stanley Coopersmith (San Francisco: W. H. Freeman, 1967) — or an account of Dr. Coopersmith's work by Ruth and Edward Brecher in *McCall's,* July 1966.

† See, for example, "Self-Esteem (Dominance-Feeling) and Sexuality in Women," by A. H. Maslow; "Dominance-Feeling, Security-Insecurity, and Sexuality in Women," by Manfred F. DeMartino; and other essays collected in Dr. DeMartino's *Sexual Behavior and Personality Characteristics* (New York: Citadel Press, 1963).

Consider, for example, the form of the syndrome which consists of a dislike and undervaluation of one's own body. One young woman who had previously suffered from this undervaluation reported that swinging enabled her "to accept myself (and my body) for what I am." A male twenty-year-old made the point even more bluntly:

"After my first party I didn't have any fear for sex anymore, because I discovered how wonderful it is. . . . By taking the first plunge into real sex I have developed an attitude opposite to the one I used to hold of myself — namely that I was ugly, unliked, stupid, and depressing."

The intimate relationships among sexual repression, body image, and self-esteem could hardly be more clearly expressed.

A twenty-one-year-old girl reported more briefly:

"Less self-conscious about others seeing my body; a feeling of freedom."

A twenty-five-year-old married woman wrote:

"My extramarital relations and party-attending have made me . . . much less modest (I used to feel the human body was not all that beautiful; I have changed my mind even about my own body)."

A damaged body image is only one symptom of the damaged-self-image syndrome, however. Other aspects include an undervaluation of one's own personality, behavior, and social acceptability — Shakespeare's "wishing me like to one more rich in hope . . . like him with friends possessed." The Smith data indicate that this symptom of the syndrome, too, is sometimes cured by swinging:

"People . . . seem to like me more, and more readily."

"[Swinging parties] have developed my self-confidence." (Female, married, aged twenty-four.)

"Feel considerably less self-conscious; have acquired a freer, more open attitude toward life." (Female, married, aged twenty-five.)

"I'm more pleasant, less possessive and hung-up. [I] like myself more, and accept other people more." (Female, separated, aged thirty-one.)

A thirty-six-year-old divorcée who attended her first sexual freedom event with a male friend "on a dare," and who thereafter attended again for fun, reported at greater length:

"I have gained a tremendous amount of self-confidence and emotional stability which in turn has reflected toward my attitude with other people outside [the sexual freedom movement]. I feel I am far better adjusted spiritually since I have lost the promiscuous guilt feeling. I truly believe

I am free and far more tolerant of others. . . . I am able to display my warmth and natural affection without misinterpretation of emotional involvement."

These expressions of benefit may or may not be literally true. The respondents who report "I'm more pleasant" or "people seem to like me more" may be deluding themselves. Even so, the expression of such feelings is highly significant. The heart of the matter with respect to self-image and self-esteem, expressed in varying ways by different respondents, is to be found in the quotation above: *"I like myself more."*

These findings on swinging as a cure for the damaged-self-esteem syndrome were quite unexpected. No question about self-esteem was asked in the Smith questionnaire; the quotations above were volunteered in response to an open-end question on the effects of swinging. Just why swinging should have this effect remains a matter of speculation. My own speculation is that the damaged-self-image syndrome is closely related to the guilt feelings we carry with us from childhood. We feel *guilty* of being ugly, awkward, unlovable — just as we feel guilty of masturbating. Once the feeling of sex guilt is shucked off in the swinging experience, these other damaging guilt feelings also fade away.

Several of the Smith respondents were young people engaged or "going steady." One girl who attended her first swinging parties with her fiancé didn't like them — but married the boy anyway, and continues to attend. She explained:

"Before we were married, my husband talked me into it simply because he wanted to go, so I went to please him. I enjoy being nude, but the parties are superficial — at least to my mind. Perhaps it's because I cannot get rid of my hang-ups [sufficiently] to enjoy them."

In sharp contrast, another young woman, aged twenty-one reported:

"[Swinging] has enhanced my relation with others and in specific with my steady boy friend. It has been more enjoyable, more secure, free of deception, and has brought us to a closer relationship. I have more trust, faith, and additional security. More mutual deeper love and admiration."

Swinging and the Marriage Tie. When we turn from these examples to the cases of married couples who enter the swinging scene together *after* their marriage, the Smiths' data become even richer. Let me first cite some wives and husbands who responded negatively to their swinging experiences. One thirty-five-year-old husband wrote:

"I have always enjoyed myself [at swinging parties] but my wife has gotten furious with me."

One wife, aged thirty-four, reported on her own negative reactions in more detail:

"I didn't enjoy [the swinging parties] very much myself simply because I felt awkward, out of place, etc. I feel the same way at *any* party when I don't know any people — at least not well. This usually means I watch what's going on and don't participate. As far as public intercourse goes, perhaps if I went more often to the parties I would be able to do it, but as it was I was extremely reluctant to be an actor for someone else's observing. Also the whole business of the cross-section of class, age, interests, makes friendship hard to come by. I should add that my husband wanted to go much more than I, and that probably affected my reaction to the scene profoundly."

A twenty-six-year-old wife sardonically reported:

"[My husband and I] went to two SFL parties and discontinued after we realized that we were not really in need of sexual freedom."

Most of the comments, however, were in a more favorable vein. A college instructor wrote: "Marital sexual relations have always been good — now even better." A wife, aged thirty-two, mentioned "better understandings with [my mate]." A young wife aged twenty-two thought swinging had "brought deeper meaning to my marriage." A twenty-three-year-old wife felt the parties had had little effect on her personally, but —

"My husband has solved some deep-rooted attitudes, I think. On the whole, our married relationship is very much improved since our active participation. . . . Things have been brought out to make us more secure in one another. A new honesty and communication has come to our relationship."

A thirty-one-year-old husband echoed this view:

"Our sex life has vastly improved. We are mentally closer than we were. We have rid ourselves of jealousy. . . . We now have friends with whom we can be honest, which helps bring stronger and closer relationships. We have given each other sexual freedom although we only make occasional use of it. We are generally happier than we were before and have fewer arguments."

Finding "friends with whom we can be honest" was a theme running through several other replies. "My marriage has benefited in numerous ways," one twenty-two-year-old wife commented. "My husband and I have found a source for people who think much as we do. This was formerly a problem, since 'ordinary' people are always aghast at our beliefs and morals."

A husband, aged forty-nine, whose Utopian swinging experience was with private rather than public or semipublic groups, added:

"Our marriage is more enjoyable because we have a wider, more stimulating group of friends. The warm affection among the members of our circle is a source of pleasure and emotional enrichment for us both."

One husband, aged thirty-three, wrote of the impact of swinging on his marriage in some detail:

"I believe that the harm in extramarital sex lies in the 'cheating' aspect, the necessary lying, etc. [My wife and I] decided that, since I was bound to become involved outside of marriage and since I was and am in love with my wife, she should not be denied the privileges I wanted — or left at home with the knitting while I enjoyed myself. We could not tolerate the idea of lies between us."

The result, according to this husband's account, far exceeded his and his wife's expectations.

"Fantastic effects! Our marriage is an even more total involvement with each other. . . . We wouldn't have believed what a feeling of liberation from the sexual jail of 'normal' marriages could contribute to our love for each other on all levels. We have sex with many others yet enjoy it increasingly with each other. We have a rapport and confidence that is the remark of many 'straight' people we know."

Even a twenty-five-year-old wife who had given up swinging reported that it had "matured" her marriage. She explained:

"My husband wanted me to be more sexually free (and wanted to be sexually free himself, of course) and he gradually talked me into some mate-swapping. We then became members (briefly) of [a sexual freedom group] . . . After a year or so we stopped outside sexual activity because:

"(1) My husband found new interests in community organization and grew tired of expending time in sexual parties (amazing but true).

"(2) I discovered I really enjoy sex much more if I am in love with the person. I'm glad I had all the outside activity — I learned a great deal and my present sex life is much [richer] because of it — and I still feel that it is possible that we may have sexual activity outside marriage again. At least I now realize that 'adultery' is no threat to my marriage. . . . My marriage has matured. It was based on idealism before; it is now more realistic and more exciting because my husband and I can talk about everything . . . we have realized our basic similarity in ideas."

One woman, aged thirty-two, reported that her marriage is "more honest and stronger and less possessive" since she and her husband began swinging together — and provided some fascinating details:

"In the beginning my husband and I had our difficult moments; but neither of us goes to a party unless the other is there. I find, being a woman, that my opportunities for sexual encounter are more easily found than for my husband, being a man and having to be the initiator of encounters. I feel my primary responsibility is to him. I am watchful and attentive of his mood; rather than leave him alone to sulk and feel sorry for himself (and angry at me), I would forego sexuality."

One twenty-four-year-old wife reported her discovery that, "much as I hated to admit it, I liked sex." She made this discovery "after an extramarital affair, of which I told my husband. We discussed it and decided that couple-swapping was the immediate answer. A friend introduced us to [a sexual freedom group]."

The results? "All of these things have increased my interest in sex. My marriage has [been] strengthened, for we believe, 'Those who swing together, stay together.' "

One young woman, aged twenty-one, a virgin at marriage, reported:

"I was sorry that I had not had sexual experiences with other men before I got married — it was pulling us apart — now I have an outlet for this desire along with the security of a beautiful husband. . . . I think I'm much happier now. It's healthy."

A wife who had already been married several times at the age of twenty-eight reported that she and her current husband started swinging at his insistence. "It has made me a more open person," she declared. ". . . I really feel free with my own moral standards for the first time. In my other marriages I found I wanted to run around, but this time I don't — maybe it's because my husband has given me the freedom to do this." Then a doubt intruded: "Only time will tell if this is true, though!!!"

One twenty-seven-year-old wife reported that she agreed to go swinging with her husband at his insistence — "only to discover I was more interested in participating than he." She added that her experience with her husband in swinging had "improved our relationship sexually and brought into [the] open many thoughts *re* sex. And made me more aware of myself and [my] inner drives and appetites. . . . Made me see individuals and their ideas more clearly."

One thirty-six-year-old wife and mother who had attended only one swinging party reported favorable effects — but she still had her fingers crossed:

"[Swinging] activities seem to have relieved boredom my husband has been feeling; after attending one party our sexual relationship improved greatly for a while. Now that school is out I hope to attend more parties with him and hope his arousal will remain at high level. Of course I hope that I remain his sexual object, too."

A twenty-eight-year-old husband reported:

"Marriage tensions reduced — more honesty with spouse about my sexual feeling. Feel I am experiencing life in richer, more satisfying ways. Have developed more sympathy — and perhaps more condescension toward 'straight' married men who drink too much . . . and despise themselves for wanting to screw women other than their wives. Feel I am a freer individual, living more on my own terms and by my own standards."

One fifty-year-old husband noted:

"After attending such parties . . . [my wife and I] go home [to] find we have drawn closer together and sexual relation at home is better. When you seem to think it is getting old hat at home you go to a party just to have a ball — and [discover] that what you have is better. We also have found that people who go to these parties have very little if any difficulties at home and have *no* arguments. . . . The divorce rate among these people is very likely none, or very low in comparison with other people."

No reliable data on comparative divorce rates, I regret to report, are as yet available.

In many cases, as several of the above quotations indicate, it is the husband who initiates swinging contacts and then either persuades or browbeats his wife into "going along." But this is far from being a universal pattern. One twenty-eight-year-old wife reported that she and her husband started swinging as the result of a "mutual desire of husband and me for variety in sexual life without resorting to extramarital affairs in the usual 'cheating' sense." As for the effect on her relationship with her husband —

"It certainly gives us something else to talk about over cocktails besides, 'How was your day at the office, dear?' In the atmosphere of mutual consent, my attitudes toward sexual relationships have become less . . . guilt-ridden, and I more freely [associate] with others as well as my husband."

I was astonished to discover in the Smith data a few cases in which swinging proved quite successful despite strong negative attitudes on the part of the wife before participation. Thus one twenty-six-year-old wife reported:

"I agreed to attend these parties with my husband in order to remove his desire to go out with other women and participate in sexual experiences 'behind my back.' "

To her own amazement, the swinging experience proved beneficial in other ways as well:

"My marriage is very happy. My husband and I are very close and enjoy each other more than ever, we have a new sexual interest in each other. I have changed my former Puritan attitudes about sex and marriage and have learned that it is possible to participate in extramarital sex without destroying my relationship with my husband. My experiences with other men have made me value more my husband and our sexual relationship."

Despite these positive factors, this wife made it clear she was continuing to swing for her husband's benefit:

"I am not sorry we attended these parties; however, I don't have any interest in regular attendance, and am ready to cease outside sexual activity at any time."

A faithful husband, aged fifty-two, had a poignant story to tell:

"In all my life I have had sex with only one woman, my wife. In recent years an urge has developed to do so on the sly, without my wife's knowledge. After much discussion and reading of others' experience, we decided to participate together."

Neither regretted the decision:

"My wife and I have experienced a tremendous lift which has brought us closer together, uplifted our sexual life, brought us a greater appreciation of each other, demonstrated to us perhaps our superiority to others in sexual technique. We are selecting other couples who are compatible with us, and we with them, to form a sociosexual group."

A recently widowed male, aged fifty-six and married twenty-four years, had an even more touching story to tell; his account is also unusual in describing a relatively long (twelve-year) swinging experience: "After [my first] twelve years of marital fidelity, I began increasingly to think of my marriage, however happy, as a corral. The thought of never either seducing another woman to bolster my ego or enjoying another woman sensually saddened me. . . . I was able [with difficulty] to say these and related things [to my wife], and [she] was able to say what was in her heart, and we began mutually fantasying threesomes. (Mutual fantasy is a phenomenon you should not overlook — the kind of fantasy which brings people together instead of separating them.) It wasn't easy to convert fantasy to acting out in those days [the 1950's]; and you generally associated with nicer people at the fantasy level. But there were marvellous exceptions even from the beginning; and the next twelve years were the richest we had together. . . . We talked about swinging often during her last weeks, and agreed that despite a life very rich in other respects, this was one of the things that had brought us closest."

A fifty-one-year-old wife also reported many years of swinging with her husband — beginning in 1957 in the Middle West.

"I began having sex in my teens," she explained, "and soon developed an almost nymphomaniacal type of activity. I had sex with many partners and thoroughly enjoyed it all — including homosexual sex. This pattern continued until I was married at twenty-five. For the first ten years of marriage and the birth of three children I rarely fucked anyone but my husband — though often desirous. After ten years of marriage we both began to play with others on an individual basis, but with the consent and knowledge of the other."

Individual extramarital relations led to "mate-trading" in 1957, when she was forty, "because of a desire of my husband and self for relations with a couple with whom we were friends. Over a period of years this activity expanded to group sex parties in which we presently indulge. The circumstances of mutual attraction for the other couple led us to start; the freedom of having sex with others in the presence of our spouses led us to continue."

This couple moved to San Francisco, where they had some trouble at first finding other swingers they liked. "We investigated the Sexual Freedom League but found ourselves over the age of most members and with little in common with them other than loving sex." Soon, however, they found a congenial group. "Ten married couples near our own age meet weekly for sex fun that includes [all] activities with the exception of bondage and discipline."

Many benefits, this wife believed, followed:

"My life is calmer with the present setup than it was during the period before, because there is mutual interest by the participants. It has strengthened my marriage, since neither my husband nor I now seek sex with others outside the group very often, nor do we have feelings of guilt as we once did. . . . My relations with others (nonsexual) have improved because I no longer look at an attractive male and wonder how good he would be in bed. Our sexual parties, which take place weekly, plus the almost daily attention of my husband keep me satisfied sexually."

The uses of mutual fantasy by husband and wife, jointly, as distinct from separate fantasies which keep them apart, was noted by one respondent above. Another husband, aged twenty-five, added some details:

"[My] wife's relative inexperience with other sexual partners led to mutual desire to have her experience other men. After our first group-sex experience we found the experience so satisfying that we decided to continue swinging. We enjoy group sex the most (more than swapping) but we swap, too. We transform our swapping experiences into vicarious group sex by discussing our experiences in detail while performing sexual intercourse after we return from swapping experiences. [As a result] our most powerful sexual experiences are invariably the night or day after we have swapped."

A few quarreling couples turn to swinging in desperation as a last forlorn hope for saving a marriage-on-the-rocks. A less promising approach can hardly be imagined — yet certain limited benefits are occasionally reported. One thirty-four-year-old wife stated, for example, that her husband's adulterous relations *before* they went to their first swinging party together had aroused in her "violent jealousy, suicidal and homicidal feelings, etc. He was cheating on me, embarrassing me in front of friends, rejecting me." Despite all this, she and her husband "were attracted by the idea of group sex with another couple." Attendance at several swinging parties followed.

"It has been fun and enriching and has helped my husband's and my relationship," she went on to state, "which had gotten miserable. . . . Now we share the parties and sexual experiences related to them. He has a renewed interest in me. Each other's experiences are exciting and somehow mutual. [I] still get jealous about girls he sees later as a result of parties, when I'm again left out — but not as jealous."

This wife makes it clear that all is not billing and cooing. "He has a mistress and isn't home much. Ideally I will meet someone else I can leave him for and be monogamous with. But [swinging] has greatly sweetened an unbearable situation."

A curious case involved a thirty-five-year-old wife who engaged in extramarital affairs with a clear conscience — but was worried that her husband, who had so far remained faithful to her, might engage in similar affairs later on:

"My main motivation [in having an extramarital affair] was curiosity to see if my husband's viewpoint was right — that extramarital affairs could be fun and add excitement to our marriage. [He said] we could share these experiences with one another . . . [and thus] enhance our marriage."

The result?

"Extramarital affairs have made me less [prudish] sexually. My marriage has *improved* in communication due to soul-searching on both our parts — but has been less peaceful for me as I am unable to reconcile myself to my husband's extramarital affairs (as of now, none). . . . I feel no guilt about my own as he is completely acceptable to the idea."

Here, surely, is the "double standard" in reverse.

One more example, this one also with a trace of ambivalence, will conclude this series. A thirty-five-year-old husband reported:

"I was very sexually active as a young man; my wife was a virgin. She was not an exciting female sexwise, and I could not seem to satisfy her. We grew bored. She entertained a friend one night and . . . told me about it [afterward]. . . . She felt very good and satisfied, and excited about it — as if it was twice as good because it was against what she [had been] taught. Our interest in each other grew for a while, and when we were invited to a swinging party she agreed and we got along better [afterward]."

His wife is still lukewarm about swinging. "She has refused on occasion to engage in intercourse with new men. However, [she] has not tried to harness me. We have shared a bed with another couple and she has participated and enjoyed it. However, she feels that if the occasion comes along, fine — [while] I try to make it occur more than she. Our marriage, I believe, is good and based on consideration of each other's feelings and desires."

Jealousy and Jealousy Controls. The Smiths asked respondents this question:

"If your spouse/partner has sexual relations with others (at or outside of parties), what are your reactions?"

Jealousy reactions, frequent or occasional, were reported by 34 percent of the females and 27 percent of the males.

Respondents were also asked about the reactions of their spouses or partners. Thirty-two percent of the males and 21 percent of the females reported that they perceived a jealousy reaction on the part of their partners.

What will astonish most readers, of course, is the relative *infrequency* of reported jealousy reactions in this subculture.

One way in which jealousy is controlled, the Smiths report, is by the specific agreements these couples make with one another, setting up strict rules of behavior which both agree to abide by. Among the rules which the Smiths encountered in their field study were these:

"Anything goes at parties, but nowhere else."

"Physical involvement is fine but not emotional involvement."

"What we do, we do together — no separate, outside dates."

"It's O.K. for you to have sex if I'm similarly involved."

"Only if I like the other person."

"We don't get mixed up with single people."

"When I have to be out of town we both do what we like."

"Only with people in our own little group."

"Let me know before you do anything."

"You're free to do what you like but I don't want to know about it."

"Not too often."

"Don't have *oral* sex with anyone else." Etc.

"Most such agreements seem to be in terms of time, place, person and manner," the Smiths state, "largely ignoring or attempting to ignore the specific sexual act itself. Some couples set their rules and then adhere to them; others find it necessary to retract them and further restrict themselves — having overestimated their manageable limits or having reached the conclusion that they don't need or want as much freedom as they thought they did. Still others find it desirable to extend their freedom beyond their original rules — having underestimated their own emotional or psychological tolerance, or having 'grown' so that they think they want and are capable of handling further extensions of freedom. In several cases we have found that a couple will go through a series of temporary restrictions, each designed (wittingly or unwittingly) to provide them with short-term limits which are not unmanageably threatening as they develop a deviant pattern for themselves."

Such agreements, the Smiths point out, are not new and are not limited to swingers. Robert and Frances Binkley described similar "adultery-toleration pacts" in *What Is Right with Marriage* (1929).* The violation of such a pact, of course, is very likely to give rise to an outburst of angry jealousy.

Another potential source of jealousy is the feeling that the wife's or husband's "paramount loyalty" to the marriage is threatened. Swingers reassure one another on this score by means of verbal statements and by actively demonstrating in large ways and small that the marriage still does command their paramount loyalty. Willingness to forego an attractive swinging opportunity because the spouse or lover is uninterested or opposed is one example of such a demonstration.

Deception and concealment are a source of jealousy reactions in the nonswinging world. A spouse is much more likely to resent a sexual act "done behind my back." Swingers control the "behind my back" reaction, of course, by informing one another in advance, or by limiting sexual adventure to occasions when the partner is present and participating, or in other ways which they find mutually acceptable.

* Dr. Robert Latou Dickinson also reported such a pact, entered into late in the nineteenth century and lasting many years. "The agreement of husband and wife was that each could have entire sexual freedom. She is American, wife of an able intellectual of excellent social standing. She does no work for money but does well at an avocation, has rendered important community service, is serene and untroubled." The wife first saw Dr. Dickinson at the age of twenty-six, and continued to consult him periodically for gynecological care into her sixties; she reported a hundred lovers, most of them during her marriage. Dr. Dickinson's final comment reads: "At a few years past sixty she is in fair health; she and her husband get on well. Both smoke and drink moderately, both are studious, humorous, forceful personalities with dignity and reserve of manner, expressing frank admiration and affection for each other." Dickinson and Beam, *A Thousand Marriages* (1932), Case 111 B, p. 155. This case stands out from the 999 other marriages in the Dickinson volume — most of them ranging from the boring to the intolerable.

Rivalry feelings, the Smiths report, can also be a source of jealousy reactions. "Even if the possibility of the third party being or becoming a rival [for the partner's paramount loyalty] is at a bare minimum, and even if an individual knows rationally that the third party is *not* a rival, he may still find it difficult to eliminate his unwanted rivalry feelings."

The Smiths observed a number of ways in which married, engaged, and going-steady couples minimize rivalry feelings and hence jealousy reactions. One simple way is to maintain a taboo against swinging with unattached singles — the most likely source of a genuine rival.

Another way is to make the situation clear to the third party so that he will not see himself as a rival and will make no attempt to compete, or to intrude on the couple's paramount loyalty to one another.

A third technique is one familiar in ordinary social dancing: the third party asks permission of the uninvolved partner before dancing off with the involved partner. Much the same behavior occurs at swinging parties. By asking permission, the third party concedes that he is not a rival.

The Smiths call attention to anthropological precedents for permission asking, described in Briffault's *The Mothers:* "The sanction of the husband, asked and obtained [for intercourse with his wife], pledges a tribal brother or guest not to abuse the privilege by abducting the woman."

Rivalry is also minimized, the Smiths report, in group-sex situations where there is no uninvolved partner to react jealously.

Finally, the sexually involved partner often seeks to reduce rivalry feelings by assuring the uninvolved partner — in words or through symbolic actions — that the third party is not a rival.

The Smiths perceptively point out that these various methods of jealousy control are not independent of one another. Rather, they appear to be detailed applications of a quite general principle: in order for one partner to accept the outside sexual activities of the other partner, he must *feel that he is in control of the situation.*

"What matters," the Smiths emphasize, "is the *feeling* of being in control rather than the actuality of *being* in control. It seems to be sufficient [to ward off jealousy reactions] that a person feels he is in control of a situation even though he is not — whereas it is not sufficient for him actually to be in control if he doesn't feel that he is."

The "adultery-toleration pacts" cited above give both partners the feeling that they are in control. The husband who gives up a swinging opportunity at his wife's request in order to assure her of his paramount loyalty to the marriage is assuring her that she remains in control — and the same is true of the wife who foregoes an opportunity. "Clearing" an outside sexual engagement with a spouse in advance gives the spouse a sense of control. Similarly the third party who asks the permission of the uninvolved spouse is reinforcing that spouse's sense of being in control. The ultimate demonstration of control, of course, is the exercise of a veto power over some act proposed by the spouse. But again, it is not necessary either to have veto power or to exercise it; a confidence that a veto *would* be honored may be enough.

Another factor tending to damp down jealousy reactions, the Smiths point out, is the swinging subculture's attitude toward them. In the larger American culture, jealousy is *expected* of a spouse. The jealous wife who complains of her husband's philandering is rewarded with the sympathy of her friends. The husband who fails to be jealous of his wife is ridiculed as a willing cuckold. In the swinging subculture, the reverse is true. It is the absence of jealousy which is rewarded with praise: "It's beautiful the way you two swing together so smoothly."

The faithful husband who has been longing in vain for extramarital sexual experience, perhaps for several years, feels his wife's acquiescence in the swinging scene as an invaluable boon which she has given him. His feelings toward her as a giving and understanding person rise to new heights; he expresses his gratitude and his enhanced respect in countless verbal and nonverbal ways — and she responds in kind to his new warmth. More rarely, the roles may be reversed — or each spouse may feel that the other is rendering the boon. In any event, the mutual regard thus engendered is hardly an atmosphere in which jealousy can thrive.

Finally, the Smiths call attention to a form of jealousy which they label *dyadic jealousy*. "A husband and wife, for example, may have their individual jealousy reactions to each other's behavior under control — only to find that, as a couple, they experience a jealousy reaction when another couple with whom they have been sexually intimate and involved 'swings' with with a third couple." Here is an aspect of sexual behavior which the Smiths believe should be of special interest to social psychologists, especially those concerned with small-group behavior.

The swinging scene, as noted above, was founded in considerable part on come-on advertisements:

Illinois — Attractive discreet couple in North Central Illinois, she age 45, with full figure, he 49, ht. 6–0, wt. 180, wants meetings and parties with white couples only. Candid photo with frank letter receive immediate reply. See photo. CA 9518.

Louisiana — Young couple she 21, green eyes and brown hair, 36–24–37, he 26, ht. 5–9, wt. 140, desires to meet couples 21–30 for weekends. We welcome all letters, we are very broadminded. See photo. CA 9530.

The achievement of James R. and Lynn G. Smith has been to penetrate behind the facade of such advertisements, bringing into focus the human needs and wants, the human conflicts and frustrations, and the human capacity for joy and for sexual fulfillment which attract a small minority to the swinging scene — and which lead some of those who enter the scene to like what they find there. The Smiths expect to publish a book on their study, entitled *Consenting Adults,* in 1970.

Bringing up Children. In Chapter 6, I called attention to Dr. Leah Schaefer's finding that even mothers who recognize how deeply they themselves have been harmed by their Victorian upbringings, nevertheless betray a tendency to bring up their daughters in the same damaging way. Is this also true of swinging mothers?

Two mothers in the Smith sample commented specifically on the question of bringing up children. One wrote that the sexual education of her daughters was one of the basic reasons for her decision to engage in swinging in the first place:

"I thought and do think that by attending such parties, where sex, nudity, and sexual freedom are so freely accepted, it will broaden my mind and teach me to enjoy even more my own sex life. Also [participation] will make me have a clearer concept when the time comes to teach my two daughters about 'the birds and the bees.' "

The other mother declared that her swinging experiences — in addition to teaching her that "sex handled responsibly is beautifully pleasurable and mutually rewarding" — had aroused in her a new "desire to teach my sons that sex is healthy."

A quite amusing insight into the relationship between swinging and child rearing can be found in the Sexual Freedom League's *Southern California Region Newsletter* for October 15, 1968; the passage from the newsletter which follows, describing a family outing, is also notable for its portrayal of the way in which the swinging subculture reflects the commonplace mores of the larger culture from which its members are drawn:

Despite competition with the World Series, some slight misunderstanding as how to reach the dinner location and the additional fact that many members had been out quite late on the previous night at an SFL party, between 40 and 50 members showed up at C—— and M——'s for a really heart-warming event. In addition to married and single couples there were quite a number of stag singles. But the happiest feature was that between 15 and 20 of those present were children ranging in age from infants to ten and eleven-year-olds.

Possibly because they were children from homes where the type of philosophy characteristic of the SFL prevails, they were relaxed, well-behaved, well-adjusted youngsters who quickly became acquainted with each other and played harmoniously together. The older kids took care of the younger ones and saw that they had a good time, taking all strain off the adults, who were free to enjoy the good food and stimulating conversation that abounded. However, despite the spontaneous response and enthusiastic attendance, we do not wish to leave our readers with the impression that all this has happened automatically. Rather it was the result of many persons sincerely and unselfishly cooperating and giving freely of their time, effort, and in many cases, advancing the overhead expenses out of their own pockets to provide the basics such as soft drinks, beer, coffee, paper plates, etc., to be made available by the circle in addition to the food brought by individual members. Those who attended were encouraged to donate $1.00 per each adult to defray these expenses, but everyone was welcome to share whether or not he made a contribution. In addition to expressing our appreciation to C—— and M—— for extending the hospitality of their home and to G—— and E—— and A—— and J—— for their planning and coordination, we also wish to say a big "thank you" to C—— and A—— who cranked out the invitations, and to D—— and L—— who handled the telephone inquiries about our first get-together.

Now that the ball has started rolling, we shall probably have at least one big Family Circle affair each month. In the future an effort will be made to schedule the Sunday gathering on a weekend *not* following a Saturday nite party; so even bigger turnouts can be expected. It goes without saying that the conduct of participants will be in conformity with the nature of the occasion. Nudity and sex activity will not, of course, be on the program. Thus it will be an ideal opportunity for new members or prospective members to come out without trepidation or self-consciousness to see for themselves what sort of people SFL members are. If they have any false impressions, they will lose them when they see what a "normal," happy, well-adjusted membership we have.

FAMILY CIRCLE's next event will be another Pot Luck Dinner on Sunday October 27 (to take advantage of that extra hour of time saved when the clocks go back to Standard Time).

Swinging, in short, is as American as cherry pie.

The most interesting evidence I encountered on the relationship between swinging and child rearing came from a young Utopian swinger, married several years but with no children, whom I interviewed in Berkeley.

"My wife and I felt," he explained, "that in this war-torn, hate-torn, greed-torn bigoted world there was no room for the kind of children we wanted to bring up." Upon joining a Utopian swinging group, he and his wife discovered for the first time a different sort of world, and decided to reconsider their decision to have no children. To clarify their feelings, the husband secured a tape recorder and interviewed in depth ten couples — all Utopian swingers — who were currently bringing up small children.

Most of the couples interviewed hadn't consciously thought very much about children and the swinging scene. When asked whether they wanted their children to grow up to be swingers, for example, most of them looked startled and said the question had never occurred to them. Opinions on other points varied too widely from couple to couple to be usefully summarized here. "But on one point," I was told, "all ten of the couples were agreed.

"When asked about their attitude toward their children's masturbating, they unanimously replied that they accepted it quite simply and naturally as a proper and important part of the normal process of maturation."

Future studies, of course, may reveal that the children of swingers are afflicted with many kinds of psychosexual and sociosexual inadequacies and hang-ups. Only time will tell. But the scraps of evidence so far available strongly suggest that whatever hang-ups the children of Utopian swingers may develop will *not* be the result of Victorian repressions, inhibitions, and taboos imposed upon them by their parents.

10

Sex Research and Sex Therapy

The Achievement of William H. Masters and Virginia E. Johnson

WITH the publication of their first book, *Human Sexual Response,* in April 1966, Dr. William H. Masters and Mrs. Virginia E. Johnson of the Reproductive Biology Research Foundation in St. Louis became world-renowned almost overnight. Newspapers in many countries carried accounts of their work on the day of publication, plus frequent follow-up stories. More than 250,000 copies of their book, at ten dollars a copy, were sold in the United States. It was translated into nine foreign languages. An additional 500,000 paperback copies of an account of their work by my wife and myself were also sold, and our book was also translated into nine languages. Tens of millions of readers learned of their work through magazine articles; nonreaders heard of it through gossip. Not since the Kinsey reports had sex research made such a stir in the world.

The stir was fully warranted. For *Human Sexual Response* described, in scrupulous detail, precisely how the human body responds to erotic stimulation during both masturbation and coitus. Responses of the penis, scrotum, and testes, the breasts, clitoris, labia, vagina, cervix, uterus, and other parts of the body were all presented and explained. The Masters-Johnson study made it possible to follow the entire human sexual cycle from the first stirrings of erotic desire through orgasm to ultimate subsidence as objectively as nineteenth-century physiologists had followed the digestive cycle from mastication to excretion. Their study, moreover, was authoritative; it was not based on speculation or random data but on direct laboratory observation of more than 10,000 male and female orgasms.

Scores of eminent physiologists in many countries contributed through the decades to the gradual exploration of the digestive cycle. Masters and Johnson accomplished their work on the sexual cycle alone, in twelve years of concentrated effort.

The role of Masters and Johnson in the history of science a generation hence, however, will be only partly based on this physiological achievement. Their second book, scheduled for publication in 1970, will almost certainly make a similar stir in the world, and will have an equally profound impact on our sexual insights and our culture. For in their 1970 report, Masters and Johnson will review the *psychological* aspects of sexuality with the same scientific objectivity that they brought to the physiological aspects. They will demonstrate the precise ways in which psychological hang-ups lead to the three major forms of sexual inadequacy in our culture — frigidity in the female, impotence and premature ejaculation in the male. Further, they will demonstrate that these three crippling conditions are readily correctable; and they will describe straightforward, ethically unobjectionable methods by which other therapists can effectively treat them.

Their 1970 report will be as firmly based as their 1966 report; it will draw on their ten years of experience with hundreds of troubled couples who have come to them in St. Louis for the treatment of sexual inadequacy and incompatibility. For the first time in the history of the therapy of sexual complaints, they will present follow-up reports evaluating the effects of therapy five years after its conclusion.

The significance of this clinical achievement can be illustrated by three representative examples.

Consider a man, married more than five years, who has still not succeeded in consummating his marriage. On every occasion through the years when he has tried to insert his penis into his wife's vagina, he has ejaculated semen and lost his erection before achieving entry. There are certainly tens of thousands, and probably hundreds of thousands, of such marriages in the United States today.

Masters and Johnson report that it takes two weeks or less to treat this condition. Therapy failures are exceedingly rare — perhaps one or two failures in a hundred cases. Following therapy the man is able to maintain his erection for as long as is necessary (twenty or thirty minutes, for example) in order to provide his wife with an opportunity for orgasm, or for a series of orgasms, before he reaches his climax. When interviewed five years after the termination of therapy, the man and his wife in most cases report that his sexual responses have remained under excellent control — indeed, control has further improved — through hundreds of sexual encounters. They add that the husband's ability to perform effectively and securely in the sexual sphere has also profoundly affected his ability to play the male role with confidence in the other spheres of his life, and has revolutionized the marriage relationship.

Consider next the case of a man who was formerly a premature ejaculator like the one described above, but who has now for several years been completely impotent, both with his wife and in attempted extramarital relations. Despite his own frantic efforts to secure an erection, and despite the efforts of his wife and of other women to arouse him, his penis remains limp and useless. The impact of this chronic sexual failure on the rest of his life is disastrous; his impotence haunts him by day as well as by night.

Masters and Johnson report that this condition, too, can in seven or eight cases out of ten be corrected during a course of therapy lasting two weeks or less. In most cases the patient remains fully potent on follow-up examination five years later; his wife reports that his restored self-confidence has affected his whole life stance, and hers, as well as their specific sexual enjoyment.

Finally, consider the case of a twice-married woman who knows only through her reading and through what her husbands (and perhaps a lover or two) have told her that a woman can have an orgasm. She herself has never in her life experienced one, though she has tried hard enough and often enough. A permissive psychotherapist she consulted once a week for more than a year several years ago recommended masturbation as a first step toward coital responsiveness, and described to her in full detail several masturbatory procedures which most women find effective — but to no avail in her case. She is not *psychologically* frigid. She experiences erotic desire; she is able in both masturbation and coitus to reach a stage of the most intense arousal on the very brink of orgasm, and to maintain this plateau of arousal until the strain approaches the intolerable. The anticlimax which follows is devastating and leaves her feeling angry, hurt, and irritable for days. She has learned to avoid this anticlimax by lying inert and feelingless while her husband uses her as a semen receptacle.

The outcome in such cases is variable. Sometimes the woman experiences the first orgasm in her life during the two weeks of therapy in St. Louis, and continues to be orgasmic thereafter. Interviewed five years later, she may proudly describe herself as "readily orgasmic." Some women in this group even report a capacity for occasional or frequent multiorgasmic sequences. A husband may try to explain what the change has meant to him, but words often fail him. In other cases, the outcome of therapy is described by both partners as successful, and coitus is reported as enjoyable, despite the fact that the wife still does not experience orgasm. What therapy accomplishes in such cases is to enable a couple to enjoy coitus without physiological climax for the female.

How do Masters and Johnson achieve such results?

Their 1970 report will describe their methods in detail, for use by other therapeutic teams. Like countless others, I await its publication impatiently.

The basic features of this therapy program, however, are no secret. Masters and Johnson presented their first paper on therapy, "Treatment of the Sexually Incompatible Family Unit," at the University of Minnesota back in 1961; that paper was subsequently published in *Minnesota Medicine*. During the years since 1961 they have presented additional clinical accounts before more than two hundred medical, psychiatric, and other professional audiences from coast to coast, and have answered questions from the floor. A number of these papers have also appeared in scientific publications. Physicians and other professionals visiting their center in St. Louis have been given full explanations. I have attended as many as possible of their public presentations through the years, and have followed with awe the gradual unfolding of the story. The review of their therapy program here presented is based on this public record.

In addition, it seems only fair to add, I have a warm personal regard for Dr. Masters and Mrs. Johnson. My wife and I first met them in the spring of 1966, prior to the publication of *Human Sexual Response,* and we became friends. During the intervening years I have met and talked with them in St. Louis and elsewhere. I have scrupulously refrained, however, from using my private visits with them to ferret out "inside information." Rather, I have sought to recheck my facts, to clear up ambiguities, and to gain some perspective on how they have managed to arrive at their clinical methods and findings.

Let me clear up one common misunderstanding of the Masters-Johnson clinical therapy program at the outset.

Despite their well-known concern with sexual physiology, the Masters-Johnson approach to therapy is only in small part physiological. They not only recognize but insist that the major hang-ups which impair the normal unfoldment of the human sexual response cycle are *psychological* — and must be corrected primarily through psychological methods.

It is a simple physiological fact, for example, that when a man is erotically aroused, his penis erects. This normal response is physiological. But if the penis fails to erect, the reason is rarely physiological. The problem is a psychological roadblock somewhere along the line. Under similar circumstances a woman's vagina lubricates itself — and failure to lubricate normally also results from a psychological roadblock. The goal of Masters-Johnson therapy is to eliminate these roadblocks, or detour around them, primarily by altering the partners' psychological *attitudes* toward sex in general, toward specific sexual acts, toward one another, and toward themselves.

As Dr. Masters often remarks, the therapy itself does not cure; nature does all the important work. Therapy merely establishes the psychological attitudes and the situation in which the potent forces of nature secure the erection of the penis, the lubrication of the vagina, and the subsequent physiological responses which constitute the normal sexual cycle.

Stated so bluntly, this sounds very simple. But achieving this insight wasn't simple. It took a unique chain of circumstances, and many years of experience, to enable Masters and Johnson to approach the psychology of sex in this direct and effective fashion. As a result of their work, the rest of us should be able to reach the same insights much more rapidly.

William Howell Masters was born in Cleveland in 1915, the son of parents in comfortable circumstances.* He attended Lawrenceville Preparatory School in Lawrenceville, New Jersey, and secured his bachelor of

* In what follows I have borrowed heavily from my wife's and my 1966 account of Masters and Johnson, *An Analysis of Human Sexual Response* (Boston: Little, Brown, 1966, and Signet paperback edition).

science degree from Hamilton College in 1938. During his science studies at Hamilton, or perhaps earlier, he acquired a strong dislike of mysteries. If he asked a sensible question, he wanted a sensible answer. If no clear answer was readily forthcoming, he was willing to go to considerable pains to secure one. It was this dislike of mystifications and confidence in rationality, I am convinced, which led him to decide on a career in scientific research and which has held that career on a rigidly successful track ever since.

Following graduation from Hamilton, Masters enrolled in the University of Rochester School of Medicine and Dentistry — not to prepare for the practice of medicine, but as a step toward research in the biological sciences. During his first year at Rochester, he worked in the laboratory of one of the country's foremost anatomists and authorities on the biology of sex, Dr. George Washington Corner — the first major event in the chain which was to lead to the Masters-Johnson reports.

"I remember [Bill Masters] as a very serious and intelligent young man of more independent character than many," Dr. Corner recalled in 1966. He assigned Masters to a problem in sex research — the estrous cycle in the female rabbit, and the ways in which it differs from or resembles the menstrual cycle in the human female. One stumbling block to the rabbit research was the ignorance and misunderstanding which still shrouded the *human* cycle in mystery. It was this laboratory experience, and Dr. Corner's influence generally, which led Bill Masters to narrow his goal from biological research in general to sex research in particular.

Dr. Corner approved this decision, but gave his student three often-quoted *caveats:*

He should wait until he was at least forty before tackling sex research.

He should first earn a scientific reputation in some other scientific field.

He should wait until he could secure the sponsorship of a major medical school or university.

No doubt that advice was well meant, and was warranted by the conditions of the time. The general prejudice against sex and against any exploration of sexual problems was at least as strong in scientific and academic circles as elsewhere during the 1940's; Puritanism and Victorianism still held sway in an only slightly diluted form. The few researchers who dared to tackle sexual or quasi-sexual research topics hazarded their careers; they were gossiped about and attacked. Financial support was scarce. For an unproved young M.D. to try to barge into so sensitive a field inadequately prepared would have been foolhardy indeed.

In restrospect, however, it is clear that this cautious advice to young Masters — which must also have been given to countless other highly competent young scientists throughout the first half of this century — was (and remains today) a serious stumbling block to sex research progress. Until young men and women of insight and enthusiasm, less hemmed in than their elders by post-Victorian restrictions, are not only welcomed but actively recruited into the field and amply supported in their projects, sex research will continue to lag behind other less important scientific areas.

Dr. Masters married in 1942 and received his M.D. degree in 1943. From 1943 to 1947 he was an intern, and then a resident in obstetrics and gynecology at Barnes Hospital and Maternity Hospital, Washington University School of Medicine, St. Louis. Thereafter he became successively instructor, assistant professor, and associate professor at the medical school. In 1951 he was certified as a specialist by the American Board of Obstetricians and Gynecologists. His two children, a boy and a girl, were born in 1950 and 1951. Along with his medical school assignments he served as associate obstetrician and gynecologist at St. Louis Maternity Hospital and at Barnes Hospital, and as consulting gynecologist at the St. Louis Infirmary and at Salem Memorial Hospital in Salem, Illinois; and he engaged in the practice of gynecology.

During the six years from 1948 to 1954, Dr. Masters published twenty-five contributions to the medical literature, covering a variety of obstetrical and gynecological topics. Fourteen of these papers were concerned with a single research project, pursued intensively for seven years — hormone replacement therapy for aging and aged women. The titles of these papers indicate the nature of the research: "Female Sex Hormone Replacement in the Elderly Woman" (1948); "Investigation of Sexual Regeneration in Elderly Women" (1949); "Androgen Administration in the Postmenopausal Woman" (1950); "The Rationale and Technique of Sex Hormone Replacement in the Aged Female" (1951); "Long-Range Steroid Replacement — Target Organ Regeneration" (1953), and "Estrogen-Androgen Substitution Therapy in the Aged Female" (1953).

This geriatric research program was another in the unique chain of events leading to the Masters-Johnson reports, largely through its impact on Dr. Masters's own attitudes. There are many stances or attitudes which a man may take toward sex. One is sheer sensuous enjoyment. Another is recoil in horror. A third is ethical evaluation, and a fourth is aesthetic appreciation. No doubt there are others as well. Dr. Masters's two major accomplishments to date — his studies in the physiology of sexual response and in the therapy of sexual inadequacy — resulted from his ability to set aside, at least in his professional life, all of these common reactions to sexuality, and to substitute for them the kind of attitude that scientists customarily hold toward digestion, circulation, and other physiological phenomena. Studying the effects of sex hormones on women years or even decades past the menopause was an admirable training ground for establishing precisely such an attitude in a young physician still in his thirties. Masters's work in hormone replacement therapy was important in its own right; several million menopausal and postmenopausal women today benefit from hormone replacement therapy. But it was also one more important step in the education of Dr. Masters. (Incidentally, it gave Masters a continuing concern for the long-neglected sexual problems of the aging and aged — a concern which motivates several of the studies he now has under way in St. Louis.)

Dr. Masters, as I have pointed out, hates mysteries and mystifications. Both as a medical student and as a gynecologist, he had found himself constantly hampered by lack of the simplest knowledge concerning normal sexual functions. Efforts to understand and to treat sexual complaints in pathological cases were repeatedly stymied by the mystery which surrounded the responses of normal males and normal females to normal erotic stimuli. Thus, gradually, Masters's decision to engage in sex research narrowed down further to a decision to get to the heart of the matter and study the sex act directly.

Contrary to a widespread impression, Dr. Masters was not the first to attempt such a study. Among his predecessors were the following: R. G. Bartlett, Jr. (United States), Joseph R. Beck (United States), Ernst P. Boas and Ernst F. Goldschmidt (United States), Robert Latou Dickinson (United States), Ernst Grafenberg (United States), Alfred C. Kinsey and his associates (United States), G. Klumbies and H. Kleinsorge (Germany), Hideo Mitsuya and his associates (Japan), Abraham Mosovich (United States), Paul F. Mundé (United States), Félix Roubaud (France), B. S. Talmey (United States), Theodoor Hendrik van de Velde (Netherlands), and A. Wernich (Germany). This is hardly an exhaustive list; it is merely a collection of examples with which I am personally familiar.

Félix Roubaud's description of sexual response in coitus, the earliest example in the above list, was published in 1855 in his 804-page volume entitled *Traité de l'Impuissance et de la Sterilité chez l'Homme et chez la Femme.* Nearly a century later, Roubaud's description favorably impressed Dr. Kinsey, who declared that it "has not been surpassed by later writers." This was high praise, indeed, from a man in a position to know; for Dr. Kinsey, as we shall see, had himself often observed coitus and other sexual acts directly. Despite several serious errors in Roubaud's 1855 account, it seems to me well worth quoting at some length:

> As soon as the penis enters the vaginal vestibule, it first of all pushes against the glans clitoridis, which yields and bends before it. After this preliminary stimulation of the two chief centres of sexual sensibility, the glans penis glides over the inner surfaces of the two vaginal bulbs; the collum and the body of the penis are then grasped between the projecting surfaces of the vaginal bulbs, but the glans penis itself, which has passed further onward, is now in contact with the fine and delicate surface of the vaginal mucous membrane, which membrane itself, owing to the presence of erectile tissue between its layers, is now in an elastic resilient condition. This elasticity, which enables the vagina to adapt itself to the size of the penis, increases at once the turgescence and the sensibility of the clitoris, inasmuch as the blood that is driven out of the vessels of the vaginal wall passes thence to those of the vaginal bulbs and the clitoris. On the other hand, the turgescence and the sensitiveness of the glans penis itself are heightened by compression of that organ, in consequence of the ever increasing fulness of the vessels of the vaginal mucous membrane and the two vaginal bulbs.
>
> At the same time the clitoris is pressed downward by the anterior portion of the compressor muscle, so that it is brought into contact with the dorsal surface of the glans and of the body of the penis; in this way a reciprocal friction between these two organs takes place, repeated at each copulatory movement made by the two parties to the action, until at length the voluptuous sensation rises to its highest intensity and culminates in the sexual orgasm, marked in the male by the ejaculation of the seminal fluid, and in the female by the aspiration of that fluid into the gaping external orifice of the cervical canal. . . . Whilst in one individual the sense of sexual pleasure amounts to no more than a barely perceptible titillation, in another that sense reaches the acme of both mental and physical exaltation.
>
> Between these two extremes we meet with innumerable states of transition. In cases of intense exaltation, various pathological symptoms make themselves manifest, such as quickening of the general circulation, and violent pulsation of the arteries; the venous blood, being retained in the larger

vessels by general muscular contractions, leads to an increased warmth of the body; and further, this venous stagnation, which is still more marked in the brain in consequence of the contraction of the cervical muscles and the backward flexion of the neck, may cause cerebral congestion, during which the consciousness and all mental manifestations are momentarily in abeyance. The eyes, reddened by injection of the conjunctiva, become fixed, and the expression becomes vacant; lids close conclusively, to exclude the light. In some, the breathing becomes panting and labouring; but in others, it is temporarily suspended, in consequence of laryngeal spasm, and the air, after being pent up for a time in the lungs, is finally forcibly expelled, and they utter incoherent and incomprehensible words.

Parts of these 1855 observations by Roubaud were subsequently confirmed by Masters and Johnson; other parts — notably the alleged direct frictional contact between the penis and the clitoris, and the sucking of the semen up through the cervix — were shown to be mistaken.

The first American observations of orgasm I have found were made by Dr. Joseph R. Beck of Fort Wayne, Indiana, on August 7 and 8, 1872. On August 7 Dr. Beck was consulted by a patient, Mrs. H. L——, aged thirty-two, married eight years, living with her husband, and suffering from a severe "falling of the womb" (retroversion of the uterus). Mrs. L——, Dr. Beck noted parenthetically, was "an intelligent and appreciative lady." Dr. Beck was able to correct the position of her uterus by fitting her with a mechanical support or pessary; in the course of examining her he noted signs of sexual arousal, possibly even of orgasm.

In making my visit to the residence of the patient, next day, for the purpose of adjusting the supporter, [Dr. Beck subsequently explained], I made a second examination by the touch, and upon introducing my finger between the pubic arch and the anterior lip of the prolaxed cervix, I was requested by the patient to be very careful in my manipulation of the parts, since she was very prone, by reason of her nervous temperament and passionate nature, to have the sexual orgasm induced by a slight contact of the finger, a fact which I believed had been manifested in my office examination of the previous day, and which she afterward admitted had been the case. Indeed, she stated further that this had more than once occurred to her while making digital examination of herself.

To Dr. Beck, the possibility of observing Mrs. L——'s cervix while she was actually experiencing an orgasm was of the very greatest scientific interest. Roubaud, as noted above, and other gynecologists as well, had sought to explain how the spermatozoa get from the vagina into the uterus by attributing a sucking or aspirating action to the cervix. Others had categorically denied that the cervix could suck up semen. Mrs. L——'s fallen womb made her cervix directly visible through her labia. Here was Dr. Beck's opportunity to settle the dispute —

> an opportunity never before, in so far as I knew, afforded by any one, and a chance for clearing up the hitherto . . . unknown and unknowable, which in my opinion was not to be lost under any consideration. Carefully, therefore, separating the labia with my left hand, so that the os uteri [vaginal opening of the cervix] was brought clearly into view in the sunlight, I now swept my right forefinger quickly three or four times across the space between the cervix and the pubic arch, when almost immediately the orgasm occurred, and the following is what was presented to my view. . . .
>
> Instantly that the height of the excitement was at hand, the os opened itself to the extent of fully an inch, as nearly as my eye could judge, made five or six successive gasps, as it were, drawing the external os into the cervix each time powerfully, and, it seemed to me, with a regular rhythmical action, at the same time losing its former density and hardness, and becoming quite soft to the touch. All these phenomena occurred within the space of twelve seconds of time certainly, and in an instant all was as before. At the near approach of the orgastic excitement the os and cervix became intensely congested, assuming almost a livid purple color, but upon the cessation of the action, as related, the os suddenly closed, the cervix again hardened itself, the intense congestion was dissipated, the organs concerned resolved themselves into their normal condition, and their relations to each other became again as before the advent of the excitement.

Dr. Beck initially reported his melodramatic observations in the *St. Louis Medical and Surgical Journal* for September 1872. He delivered the same paper with additions before the American Medical Association on June 2, 1874, and it was published in its expanded form in the *American Journal of Obstetrics and Diseases of Women and Children* for November 1874. From then on through the decades, Beck's findings were regularly cited as proof of the "gasping" and sucking action of the cervix at orgasm. A later American observer, Dr. B. S. Talmey, reported quite similar observations in the *New York Medical Journal* for June 23, 1917.

Van de Velde, as noted before, also made observations of female orgasm during masturbation.

The renowned American gynecologist Dr. Robert Latou Dickinson studied female sexual response during masturbation much more fully, and hence deserves a special place among Masters and Johnson's predecessors. His findings were summarized in his classic *Atlas of Human Sex Anatomy* (1933; expanded second edition, 1949).

Dickinson described, for example, one woman with "a vigorous husband who can maintain complete erection within the vagina for an hour, if desired. During any attempt on her part to bring on orgasm she has to set her diaphragm, strain down hard with her abdominal muscles in the same fashion as when expelling bowel contents with difficulty, such pressure driving the pelvic contents downward, whence they return by the elasticity of their supports, with some aid from contraction of the pelvic floor muscles. When asked to demonstrate such action, the cervix is found to be displaced one inch toward the vulva while at the same moment the anterior wall of the vagina shoots out an inch. . . . The perineum and anus make a like excursion. Such action, actually timed, occurred seventy-four times in three and a half minutes." Dr. Dickinson surmised that this curious rhythm was "a premarital [masturbatory] habit carried over into marriage."

Dr. Dickinson was concerned at one stage in his long career with the effects of masturbation on the female vulva and clitoris; he believed that certain patterns of masturbation led to greater "clitoral excursion"—that is, greater mobility of the organ. In a number of cases, he reported, he had patients demonstrate their masturbatory techniques in order to correlate the techniques used with the degree of clitoral excursion.

Dr. Dickinson was responsible (along with Dr. W. F. Robie and Dr. LeMon Clark) for the introduction into American gynecological practice of the electrical vibrator or massager. This device, applied to the mons area near the clitoris, produces intense erotic stimulation. In some cases it is capable of inducing orgasm in women previously unable to reach climax by any means whatever. Once having learned to experience orgasm with a vibrator, Dickinson, Robie and Clark all reported, a woman is more likely thereafter to proceed to orgasm during ordinary masturbation and during coitus. Demonstration of the use of the vibrator to patients gave Dr. Dickinson numerous opportunities to observe female orgasm.

Finally, Dr. Dickinson used the technique, also used later by Masters and Johnson, of observing the behavior of the vaginal lining and cervix through a glass tube resembling an erect penis in size and shape. This transparent phallus or dildo, he explained, "is passed in various directions, with the patient on the back, or better still, in the knee-chest posture. Notes are taken at once on the depth of penetration and the angle at which the tube lies. . . . The tube has a great advantage as the beam of the headlight entering it reveals what the relation of the glans penis would be to the cervix and external os when the glans passes in at various depths and angles" — data which might prove of value in cases of infertility. Dickinson's authoritative drawings of the vagina, published in his *Atlas,* were based on more than 140 such examinations. In some cases of infertility which might be due to cervical factors, moreover, Dickinson used the glass tube to observe the cervix at the moment of orgasm. The patient, he explained, "can herself employ this dummy phallus, and the observer can see whether [at orgasm] the cervix opens and shuts and mucus is extruded and drawn back." By this technique, incidentally, Dr. Dickinson was able to demonstrate that the inch-wide gaping of the cervix allegedly observed by Dr. Beck and Dr. Talmey was at best a rare and perhaps an imagined phenomenon; there may be a slight opening of the cervix at orgasm, but it is *not* a sucking-up of the semen. Dr. Dickinson's observations stripped at least some of the mystery from the inherent nature of the female orgasm. No longer was it reasonable to doubt that women really do have orgasms.

Drs. Ernst P. Boas and Ernst F. Goldschmidt at Mt. Sinai Hospital in New York recorded heart rates during coitus. "We were fortunate," they wrote in 1932, "in obtaining a record of the heart rates of a man and wife during intercourse. The couple, Cases 69 and 72, were under observation with the cardiotachometers [heart-rate recorders] for 48 hours. The record . . . shows four peaks of heart rate for the woman, each peak representing an orgasm." The wife's orgasms occurred five, eighteen, twenty-two and twenty-five minutes after her husband's penis entered her vagina. His one orgasm, as shown on the cardiotachometer record, occurred simultaneously with her fourth. "The maximum [pulse] rate was 143 in the man, and 146 in the woman." These are rates that would be expected in athletes during violent physical exertion. "In both subjects there was a rapid drop in rate after the completion of coitus." Boas and Goldschmidt did not claim priority, however. "Kolb," they declared, ". . . made pulse tracings during coitus in man and recorded maximum rates of 150."

In 1950, as Dr. Masters was actively beginning to plan his own research program, two physicians at the University Clinic in Jena, Germany — Drs. G. Klumbies and H. Kleinsorge — published detailed descriptions of physiological changes during orgasm. Their initial experimental subject was a woman capable of fantasying to orgasm "solely through mental stimulation and without any physical help." This made it possible to distinguish the direct effects of orgasm in her case from the effects of muscular exertion which ordinarily precede and accompany orgasm. Drs. Klumbies and Kleinsorge recorded the physiological changes with the aid of an electrocardiograph machine and a blood-pressure recorder. They discussed the effects of her orgasms on her pulse rate, systolic and diastolic blood pressure, cardiac volume, rhythm of heart-chamber contractions, position of the heart, respiratory movements, respiratory frequency, respiratory volume, metabolic rate, muscle irritability, and other parameters. Their published charts showed orgasmic peaks of dramatic sharpness and clarity. The woman identified some of her orgasms as more intense than others; Klumbies and Kleinsorge noted that the intensity of the orgasm as subjectively reported showed a close relation to the acuteness of the blood-pressure peak as recorded. Having concluded their studies of this woman's orgasms, they went on to record similar physiological changes in a male subject during masturbatory orgasms.

At about the same time, Dr. Abraham Mosovich recorded electroencephalograms of brain-wave patterns during sexual arousal and orgasm; some of these EEG patterns, showing remarkable changes, were published in the 1953 Kinsey report — along with reliable summaries of most of the other prior studies of sexual response.

Credit for making the most complete and thorough observations, prior to Masters and Johnson, of male and female bodily responses during masturbation and coitus almost certainly belongs to Dr. Kinsey and his Indiana University associates. This credit is rarely given; for Dr. Kinsey, no doubt prudently, decided not to publish any explanation of where, how, or by whom the observations were made. "We have had access to a considerable body of observed data," he wrote in a footnote to his 1953 report, "on the involvement of the entire body in the spasms following orgasm." The source of other observations was alluded to in similarly indirect language, without actually revealing that the observations had been made by Dr. Kinsey himself and by members of his staff. No doubt Dr. Kinsey expected his report to stir up enough of a fuss without his giving his critics added ammunition by confessing that sexual intercourse had actually been observed at Indiana University during the 1940's.

Kinsey was far too dedicated a scientist, however, to suppress the scientific findings themselves. *What* he and his associates observed — as distinct from the circumstances surrounding the observations — is quite fully set forth in Chapter 15 of the 1953 Kinsey report, "Physiology of Sexual Response and Orgasm."

These and other reports on sexual response published during the century from 1855 to 1954, however, left many important questions unanswered. Most of the reports, for example, were based on only one or a few atypical cases — a woman with a severely prolapsed uterus who was capable of reaching orgasm with three or four strokes of the forefinger, a woman who bore down with her abdominal muscles to induce orgasm, a woman capable of achieving orgasm through fantasy alone, and so on. The reports were generally fragmentary, dealing only with one or another detailed aspect rather than with the entire female response cycle. Reports on male response were even rarer. Recordings with instruments had rarely been made — and had never been correlated with simultaneous visual observations.

The alleged eyewitness accounts, moreover, were in conflict on many significant points. Were Beck and Talmey right in reporting an opening and sucking action of the cervix, or was Dickinson right in ridiculing these observations? (Dickinson scornfully remarked that the similarities between the 1872 Beck and 1917 Talmey reports "are either remarkable or suspicious.") In other branches of physiology, scientists do not rely on anecdotal data, random observations, or small samples; Dr. Masters hoped to raise sexual physiology to a level of reliability comparable to that long since achieved by cardiac and gastrointestinal physiology.

It was the predominantly favorable reception accorded the publication of the second Kinsey report in 1953 which gave Dr. Masters the courage to launch his own study the following year. He has often since expressed his indebtedness to Kinsey, whom he never knew personally, for "opening the previously closed doors of our culture to definitive investigation of human sexual response."

By 1954, in short, Dr. Masters was ready to launch his lifework. He had made a reputation for himself with his research in other fields. He had the institutional support of a major university medical center. In only one respect was he lacking Dr. Corner's specifications; he was still two years short of forty.

The 1954 Masters research plan called for a comprehensive study of physiological responses from initial erotic stimulation through orgasm to quiescence, in both masturbation and coitus, in a variety of postures, in both men and women of a wide range of ages, and at various stages in the menstrual cycle, using sophisticated instrumentation as well as direct observation and motion-picture recording on film. As a preliminary to this vast undertaking, Dr. Masters first interviewed at length and in depth 118 female and 27 male prostitutes. Eight of the women prostitutes and three of the men then participated as experimental subjects in a preliminary series of laboratory observations — a sort of "dry run" for the project.

This use of prostitutes became the subject of snide remarks and leers when the Masters studies first became known. The studies were obviously valueless, it was suggested, because prostitutes were involved in them; besides, what self-respecting scientist would demean himself by contacts with prostitutes?

It seems to me, in contrast, that Dr. Masters was either remarkably perceptive or exceedingly lucky in deciding to turn to prostitutes at this preliminary stage. They, after all, are the best-informed experts in the world on human sexual response — or were, prior to the Masters-Johnson studies. During the routine course of her work, a prostitute is typically visited by a man who has eaten too much and drunk too much to be sexually very effective. It is probably long past his bedtime; fatigue further impairs his sexual responsiveness. In some cases, he is assailed by feelings of guilt at fornication, and of shame that he must resort to a prostitute. The surroundings are hardly inspiring. The client has no affection for his partner of the moment, and usually selects her because she happens to be available rather than because of any particular attraction she might have for him. Despite many such obstacles, the prostitute is expected to and in almost all cases succeeds in arousing her client erotically and triggering his orgasm in as short a time as possible — often within a few minutes. Even a moderately competent and intelligent prostitute, after a few hundreds or thousands of such encounters, is surely a worthwhile informant concerning sexual response patterns. The prostitutes he interviewed, Dr. Masters later affirmed, "described many methods for elevating or controlling sexual tensions and demonstrated innumerable variations in stimulative technique. Ultimately many of these techniques have been found to have direct application in therapy of male and female sexual inadequacy and have been integrated into the clinical research programs." It is hardly to Dr. Masters's discredit, but rather to the discredit of his predecessors,* that he tapped and they failed to tap this rich source of clinically valuable data.

For purposes of *physiological* study, however, the St. Louis prostitute population proved to be unsuitable. Many of them were migrants, in St. Louis one month and not to be found the next; an essential feature of the Masters plan was the prolonged observation of responses as they developed through the years in individual subjects. Many of the prostitutes, moreover, exhibited substantial degrees of pelvic pathology — including a condition of chronic congestion of the pelvic region, presumably the result of frequently repeated sexual excitation without orgasmic release. Hence, despite the value of his prostitutional studies in other respects, Dr. Masters was forced to exclude most of his observations of their response patterns from his physiological findings.

The prostitutes themselves, however, provided him with a clue for finding respectable men and women willing to participate in his research project. They cited many examples of sexual activities occurring in the presence of observers. A client might engage two prostitutes, for example, or two clients might engage one or more prostitutes, and other combinations might be arranged. There were both men and women, the prostitutes reported, who enjoyed engaging in sex in the presence of others. Much more important for Dr. Masters's research program, there were respectable men and women who had no strong feeling about privacy either way; they simply lacked, for some reason or other, the strong privacy taboos common in our culture.

Dr. Masters, accordingly, took a gingerly first step toward securing respectable volunteers. He let it be known through the university and medical school community that he was planning a study of human sexual response based on laboratory observations. News such as this spreads quickly along the local grapevine. One medical school professor tells another, who tells his wife, who tells a neighbor. A medical student tells a nurse, who tells her sister-in-law.

The returns from this local gossip were of two kinds. A few of those who heard about the research via the grapevine came to Dr. Masters's

* Except Dickinson and Kinsey, who also recognized the value of data available from prostitutes.

office on the medical-school floor of the maternity-hospital building eager to volunteer "for kicks." They were promptly eliminated.

More welcome were visitors who were genuinely concerned with some important human problem which sexual research might solve, and who wanted to help solve it. Some couples were referred by their own physicians; some came because they hoped to learn ways to increase their own satisfaction and enjoyment of sex. Former patients of Dr. Masters came, and brought their husbands, when they heard he needed volunteers.

In my wife's and my 1966 account of the Masters-Johnson program, we devoted a considerable section to explaining why ordinary men and women, including the shy and the inhibited, were quite willing to be watched by scientific observers while they engaged in masturbation and coitus. We also reviewed at some length the gradual steps by which volunteers were acclimated to the laboratory situation and made to feel comfortable in it. The greater current understanding of the readily modifiable nature of sexual taboos, I trust, makes a repetition of these details here unnecessary. Certainly readers of Chapter 9, on the swinging scene and the sexual freedom movement, will have no difficulty in understanding that sexual response can proceed as normally and routinely in the presence of observers as in private.

In all, 694 individuals, including 276 married couples, participated in the Masters-Johnson laboratory program. Of the 142 unmarried participants, all but 44 had been previously married; a number of those unmarried on entering the program married during the course of their participation. The men ranged in age from twenty-one to eighty-nine; the women ranged from eighteen to seventy-eight. Of the two participants under the age of twenty-one, one was a girl of eighteen who had been married three years and had a child; she participated with her husband. The other was an unmarried twenty-year-old girl with a special vaginal condition which made her of particular value to the research program;* her participation did not include sexual intercourse.

* This young woman was born without a vagina — an unusual condition, but not as rare as is commonly supposed. In a number of such cases, Dr. Masters and others have operated and constructed vaginas; such a vagina may lubricate normally and may make possible coital orgasm for both the woman and her partner. Instead of surgery in this case, Dr. Masters successfully utilized a technique known as perineal dilation. The patient later cooperated with the Masters-Johnson research project "to the extent of [supplying] multiple vagina smears, a vaginal biopsy, cyclic vaginal pH recordings, and a detailed history."

The Masters-Johnson volunteers were on the whole highly educated; more than 200, for example, had attended graduate school following college. But another 200 had not gone to college at all, and some had not finished high school. Most of the volunteers were white, but eleven couples were black. Of special interest was the geriatric group — thirty-four married couples over the age of fifty, including some in their sixties and seventies, plus five men over fifty and their postmenopausal wives in their forties. "Their contribution has been large," Masters and Johnson acknowledged, "for their cooperation has extended over four years of concentrated investigations of geriatric sexual response."

The Masters-Johnson sample, in short, included the young and the old, the fat and the thin, the tall and the short, the rich and the poor, blacks and whites, the single, the married, the divorced, and the widowed, the circumcised and the uncircumcised, women who had never borne a child, women who had had one child, and women with two, three, and four children. Indeed, the 694 participants had only one characteristic in common: they were all able to reach orgasm during both masturbation and coitus while under observation in the laboratory setting. Applicants who could not were eliminated.

In all, the participants experienced more than 10,000 orgasms under laboratory conditions. Throughout the twelve years it lasted, this laboratory research program was kept entirely distinct from the therapy program launched in 1959; none of the 694 participants in the laboratory program were therapy patients, and none of the therapy patients participated in the laboratory research.

It was during the phase of recruiting volunteers that Mrs. Johnson came to work for Dr. Masters. Born Virginia Eshelman in the Missouri Ozarks in 1925, she had studied music at Drury College in Missouri, and later attended Missouri University — where she discovered the world of sociology and psychology. In 1950 she married; in 1952 and 1955 her son and daughter were born. Separated from her husband soon afterward, Mrs. Johnson registered for a job at the Washington University Placement Bureau at a time when Dr. Masters was seeking a woman to assist in research interviewing. For his project he had specified a woman with experience and interest in working with people. The Placement Bureau sent Mrs. Johnson to fill the job, and she has been there ever since.

This was another of the major links in the chain which led to the Masters-Johnson achievement; for by good fortune, Mrs. Johnson proved to be one of those rare human beings who sees the world as it is, undistorted by traditional ways of looking at things. She brought to the Masters-Johnson partnership, in addition to this clarity of vision, a very deep empathy with other people, especially other women. Her contribution was important in the program of laboratory observations; but it proved even more essential when the Masters-Johnson program of therapy for sexual inadequacy was launched a few years later.

Among the basic procedures for volunteers during the laboratory research program were the following:

(1) Masturbation with the hand or fingers.

(2) Masturbation (rarely) with the mechanical vibrator.

(3) Sexual intercourse with the woman on her back.

(4) Sexual intercourse with the man on his back.

(5) "Artificial coition" with a transparent probe similar to the one used by Dr. Dickinson but electronically controlled and with improved optical qualities. This was particularly useful in contraceptive studies.

(6) Stimulation of the breasts alone, without genital contact. Several of the women in the Masters-Johnson research group proved capable of reaching orgasm in this way. Observations of genital response were of course very easy in these cases, and hard-to-get data were secured.

The original Masters-Johnson sample did not include any women capable of reaching orgasm through fantasy alone, without direct contact stimulation. Masters and Johnson have since reported, however, that they have now made standard laboratory observations on three such women; the sexual response cycles in these cases proved to be identical with the cycles produced in the more ordinary ways.

It is precisely here that the most important single finding of the Masters-Johnson laboratory research comes into focus. Just as there exists a stereotyped sequence of events which comprises the normal digestive cycle, and a stereotyped normal cardiovascular cycle, so there exists in ordinary men and women a normal cycle of physiological events in response to erotic stimulation. There are, of course, minor variations from individual to individual — but the basic pattern is the same. The masturbatory cycle very closely resembles the coital cycle; the male and female cycles have many points in common. To illustrate these parallelisms *Human Sexual Response* reviews the entire cycle in terms of four successive levels or phases of arousal: excitement, plateau, orgasm, and resolution.

The Excitement Phase

The first physiological response in the male to erotic stimulation, Masters and Johnson reported (and everyone already knew), is erection of the penis — a marked increase in its size and a rise in its angle of protrusion from the body. Erection may be triggered by direct stimulation of the penis, or by a sexually stimulating sight, or an erotic train of thought. It occurs within a few seconds, regardless of the nature of the stimulus. During erection, a short penis may double in length. In a long penis, this lengthening is less marked. Thus there is less variation in length among erect than among flaccid penises.

The first sign of sexual response in women is the moistening of the vaginal lining with a lubricating fluid. This lubrication occurs quite promptly — within ten to thirty seconds of the onset of erotic stimulation. Earlier writers had assumed that the fluid comes from various glands, or from the uterus; Masters and Johnson were able to observe directly, in the course of artificial coition with the plastic artificial penis, that it actually results from a "sweating" of the walls of the vagina. Beads of moisture appear on these walls much as beads of sweat appear on the forehead — despite the fact that there are no vaginal sweat glands. As arousal proceeds, these drops coalesce to provide a lubricating film, readying the vagina for the penis. This vaginal lubrication, though different from erection of the penis, results from a similar physiological phenomenon — an increased blood supply and resulting engorgement of the tissues.

Other changes occurring during the excitement phase include erection of the female nipples and a swelling of the breasts. Nipples also erect in some males. Characteristic changes occur in the outer and inner labia, the clitoris, and the vagina.

The Plateau Phase

At this stage, the male testes increase in size about fifty percent, and they are pulled up high in the scrotum. The most dramatic change in women is the appearance of what Masters and Johnson call "the orgasmic platform." This is the engorgement and swelling of the tissues surrounding the outer third of the vagina. The result is a reduction in the diameter of the outer third by as much as fifty percent; it thus actually grips the penis, and the man's erotic arousal is notably increased. The deeper portion of the vagina, in contrast, balloons out to form a cavity. The uterus enlarges.

Another remarkable — and previously unnoted — change during the plateau phase is the elevation of the clitoris. It rises from its unstimulated position overhanging the pubic arch and seems to become retracted. The retraction draws it further away from the vaginal entrance, so that direct friction of the clitoris against the penis becomes even less of a possibility than before. The clitoral shaft is shortened by as much as fifty percent following retraction, and may seem to be lost altogether; certainly it is harder to find. Yet in its retracted position it continues to be stimulated during coitus — a mystery Masters and Johnson were the first to explain (see below).

Almost all of these and other events in the normal response cycle, Masters and Johnson explain, fall into two main classes: the engorgement of vessels and organs with excess blood, and increases in muscular tension. It is the combination of these two processes which bring both men and women to the brink of orgasm.

The Orgasmic Phase

The orgasm itself is characterized in women primarily by a series of rhythmic contractions of the orgasmic platform — the outer third of the vagina and the tissues surrounding it. These rhythmic contractions are muscular contractions.

The first few contractions occur at intervals of four-fifths of a second. Thereafter the intervals tend to become longer, and the intensity of the contractions tends to taper off. A mild orgasm may be accompanied by only three to five contractions, an intense orgasm by eight to twelve. In an extreme case, actually recorded on an automatic recording drum in the Masters-Johnson laboratory, twenty-five rhythmically recurring contractions of the orgasmic platform followed one another over a period of forty-three seconds.

The onset of female orgasm as experienced subjectively occurs simultaneously with an initial *spasm* of the orgasmic platform, preceding the rhythmic train of contractions by a few seconds.

Along with this series of contractions of the orgasmic platform, the uterus also contracts rhythmically. Each contraction begins at the upper end of the uterus and moves like a wave through the midzone and down to the lower or cervical end. The more intense the orgasm, the more severe are these contractions of the uterus. Labor contractions prior to childbirth move similarly downward along the uterus in a wavelike progression, but are more widely spaced and much stronger.

Other muscles, such as the anal sphincter muscle, may also undergo rhythmic contractions at orgasm.

Since the contractions of the uterus progress downward, Masters and Johnson point out, they are more likely to have an expulsive action than a sucking action. Nevertheless, to check the matter further, the investigators prepared a fluid resembling semen but opaque to X rays, and placed this fluid in a cap covering the cervix — so that if there were a sucking action, the fluid would be aspirated. Six women fitted with such caps masturbated to orgasm, and X-ray films were exposed at intervals. No significant gaping of the cervical opening was noted: thus the research supports Dr. Dickinson's position as against the statements of Beck and Talmey.

The male orgasm is rather similar to the female in several respects. The central occurrence is a series of rhythmic contractions or throbs of the penis, timed, as in the female, at intervals of four-fifths of a second. Following the first few contractions, in the man as in the woman, the intervals between contractions tend to become longer and the intensity of the contractions tapers off. As in the case of women, men may subjectively identify the onset of orgasm a few seconds before the occurrence of the first observable contraction.

The ejaculation of semen, which occurs during the male orgasm, is a complex process. Prior to orgasm, fluid containing millions of sperm cells from the testes has collected in the sacs known as seminal vesicles and in a pair of flasklike containers known as ampullae. At orgasm, these organs contract rhythmically, expelling their contents into the urethra. At the same time the prostate gland contracts rhythmically and expels prostatic fluid into the urethra. A bulb in the urethra near the base of the penis doubles or triples in size to receive the fluids. These changes constitute the first stage of ejaculation.

During the second stage, a series of rhythmic contractions of the urethral bulb and of the penis itself projects the semen outward under great pressure, so that if it is not contained, the semen may shoot as much as two feet beyond the tip of the penis. In older men, the contractions may be somewhat less vigorous, and the pressure of expulsion somewhat lessened. The urethra may undergo a series of minor throbs for several seconds after the contractions of the penis as a whole are no longer perceptible.

In both men and women, the events occurring in the genital organs during orgasm are accompanied by changes in the rest of the body. Pulse rate, blood pressure, and breathing rate reach a peak. There is often a "sex flush" covering much or most of the body skin. And muscles throughout the body respond in various ways.

The face, for example, may be contorted into a grimace through the tightening of muscle groups. The muscles of the neck and long muscles of the arms and legs usually contract in a spasm. The muscles of the abdomen and buttocks are also often contracted. Of special interest are the reactions of the hands and feet. Often a man or woman grasps his partner firmly during orgasm; the hand muscles then clench vigorously. If the hands are not being used in grasping, a spastic contraction of both hands and feet known as carpopedal spasm can be observed. Men and women are usually quite unaware of these extreme muscular exertions during orgasm; but it is not unusual for them to experience muscle aches in the back, thighs, or elsewhere the next day as a result.

The Resolution Phase

Following orgasm, the various organs rapidly or slowly return to their unstimulated condition, each in its proper order and at its proper pace. Indeed, a major function of the orgasm is to ensure this prompt, complete, and welcome release from sexual tension.

This is not, let me stress, a complete review of the Masters-Johnson physiological findings. Readers desiring more detail are referred to *Human Sexual Response*. But the heart of the matter should be clear from this condensed account: the human sexual-response cycle is a highly specific sequence of readily understandable events. There is nothing mysterious about it at the physiological level.

In addition to establishing the existence of this cycle, the Masters-Johnson findings clarify countless disputes which have raged for decades concerning the details. The most important of these detailed clarifications concerns the role of the clitoris.

Many young girls discover the exquisite sensitivity of this organ for themselves and masturbate by stimulating the clitoral area. Many men a generation or two ago were no doubt ignorant of its erotic function; but the word has now been spread widely through marriage manuals, pornographic fiction, male gossip, and a greater willingness of women to show men what to do.

A mystery, however, still remained when Masters and Johnson launched their study. Sigmund Freud half a century earlier had pondered the evidence available to him from patients and from other sources, and had reached the quite plausible conclusion that women have two kinds of orgasm — one kind from clitoral stimulation, the other kind from vaginal stimulation. He regarded the clitoral orgasm as immature and malelike, orgasm through vaginal stimulation as mature and superior. His successors and others carried this doctrine of two kinds of orgasm to extremes — so that some analysts, for example, described as "frigid" those women who could only reach orgasm though direct clitoral stimulation.

Much of the confusion arose from the fact that almost everybody through the decades had been comparing clitoral *masturbation* with vaginal *coitus*. The rich emotional overtones provided by the interpersonal features of coitus made such naïve subjective comparisons wholly unreliable. Masters and Johnson compared in detail orgasms following clitoral stimulation with orgasms following vaginal stimulation — *both* occurring in the absence of a partner. When studied objectively in this way, so-called clitoral and vaginal orgasms proved to be physiologically indistinguishable. (This does not mean, of course, as some critics have alleged, that Masters and Johnson think coitus with a beloved is identical with solitary masturbation. Their point is almost exactly the opposite — that the striking *differences* between the subjective experiences have heretofore masked the physiological identity.)

Studies of artificial coition with the penis substitute also made it possible for Masters and Johnson to determine for the first time *how* the clitoris is stimulated during ordinary coital thrusting.

Most prior theorists (and a few observers like Roubaud, as quoted above) had assumed that there is a direct frictional contact between the clitoris and the penis. Female frigidity was therefore attributed to too high a location of the clitoris, preventing this direct friction. Many marriage manuals (including van de Velde's) recommended that the male partner try to "ride high" — that is, press his penis and pubis (region at the base of the penis) upward to ensure contact with the clitoris. Masters and Johnson report that all this is myth. Regardless of the location of the clitoris, relatively high or relatively low, it rarely or never makes contact with the penis. What stimulates the clitoral glans during coitus is not friction against the penis or pubis, but *friction against its own hood.*

As the penis thrusts in and out of the vagina, they go on to explain, the woman's inner labia are moved in rhythm with the thrusting. These labia are attached to the hood covering the clitoris — indeed, the hood is anatomically an extension of the labia. The movement of the labia produced by each thrust is thus participated in also by the clitoral hood — and it is the rhythmic friction of the hood against the exquisitely sensitive clitoris and clitoral glans which produces the heightening of erotic tension and ultimately orgasm. To the extent that "riding high" is effective in particular cases, the effect is on the labia and hood rather than the result of direct friction against the clitoris. This is true even at the beginning of coitus; and after the clitoris has risen to its retracted position during the plateau phase, the theory of actual contact between clitoris and penis or pubis is even less tenable.

These Masters-Johnson findings also have relevance to masturbation techniques. Few women, Masters and Johnson report, masturbate by actually rubbing the clitoral glans. The stimulation is too intense. Much more commonly they massage the clitoral *shaft,* or find places close to the clitoris where rhythmic movements of the hand produce a rhythmic friction between the clitoris and its hood — precisely the stimulus which operates during coital thrusting. Thus, far from experiencing two kinds of orgasm, one clitoral and the other vaginal, women actually experience the same friction between clitoris and hood during both masturbation and coitus.

During foreplay, many men seek to arouse their partners by rubbing the clitoral glans itself. Some women, Masters and Johnson report, find the excessive stimulation thus produced quite objectionable. Rhythmic stimulation of the whole mons area above the clitoris, or of a region at the side of the clitoris, applied in such a way as to produce rhythmic friction between the clitoris and its hood, may prove much more effective as a technique of erotic arousal. Indeed, this is precisely what happens during the Helena Wright procedure when the wife places her husband's hand on her *mons veneris,* and her own hand firmly on his, and then moves her hand in ways she finds pleasurable.

The importance of these findings for marriage counseling and for sex education generally can hardly be overemphasized.

Exploring these and other aspects of sexual physiology occupied Masters and Johnson for the twelve years from 1954 to 1966. In addition to being a researcher, however, Dr. Masters is a dedicated clinician. His experience as a practicing gynecologist and as a consultant made him acutely aware of the untold accumulation of misery resulting from sexual inadequacies. The man who ejaculates prematurely, and his wife; the man whose penis will not erect, and his wife; the woman unable to enjoy sexual relations, or whose enjoyment is marred by inability to secure release from tension in orgasm, and her husband — these are seriously crippled human beings whose whole lives may be impoverished by their sexual misfortunes. Beginning in 1959, Dr. Masters and Mrs. Johnson launched a therapy program designed to help couples suffering from these conditions. Their initial hope, no doubt, was that the findings of their laboratory research could be directly applied in therapy.

It soon became apparent, however, that premature ejaculation, impotence, and frigidity are only in very rare cases physiological in origin. The cycle of sexual response fails to occur at all, or is foreshortened, or is blocked before culmination, as a result of psychological factors. Thus the Masters-Johnson emphasis expanded from a concern with the physiological events they had been studying in the laboratory to a concern with the psychology of sexual inadequacy. They structured their therapeutic program to ensure a maximum psychological impact.

The structure which they have developed through the years since 1959 is unique in the history of therapy. First of all, Masters and Johnson function as a team, both of them directly concerned with each patient and each problem. Second, they do not accept individual patients but only couples. Thus the procedure takes the form of a "therapeutic foursome." *

Most of the nearly 400 couples who have had this form of therapy since 1959 come from outside St. Louis. They register in a hotel or motel, and in effect enjoy a vacation during the therapy period. As a condition

* The therapeutic foursome itself is not unique. In the March 1968 issue of *Redbook* I described a number of other teams composed of a male and a female therapist who see patients in couples. The uniqueness lies in the combination of this foursome approach with the other features of Masters-Johnson therapy.

of therapy, patients must agree to keep in touch with the Reproductive Biology Research Foundation for five years, and cooperate in follow-up studies.

Couples see Masters and Johnson daily, including Saturday and Sunday, for the duration of the therapy. They are told in advance that therapy will last two weeks at the most and probably less.* In addition to their daily therapy sessions, they are instructed to engage in private in one or more "practice sessions" daily. A therapy session typically begins with a report of what happened during the previous practice session and ends with instructions for the next practice session.

The advantages of having a male and a female therapist jointly and simultaneously involved in the therapy became apparent very early in the Masters-Johnson program. Some women open up more freely with another woman than with a man; others are less embarrassed talking with a man, and still others find it reassuring to have both sexes present. Men vary similarly. During therapy, each member of the couple may meet with one or the other therapist, or with both, or the entire therapeutic foursome may assemble, as the progress of the therapy indicates; this flexibility has obvious advantages. At least equally important, the combination of male and female insights which a dual-sex team brings to the therapy intensifies it and hastens progress. "Sometimes I'm baffled by what the woman is trying to say," Dr. Masters declares, "but Gini knows right away." The reverse is also true.

The insistence that patients come in couples also has many advantages. Rarely are sexual problems all on one side of a marriage or affair; and even if this is true at the beginning, long years of sexual inadequacy in one partner are bound to affect the other partner as well. Learning new attitudes toward sex, moreover, necessarily involves developing new attitudes toward one's sexual partner — which can hardly be done in a vacuum. The hazard that, during therapy, one partner will "outgrow" the other is minimized.

The joint participation of the couple — usually husband and wife, though unmarried lovers may also be afflicted with sexual inadequacies — makes possible the uniquely effective *rhythm* of Masters-Johnson therapy: the daily therapeutic sessions alternating with daily practice

* The exceptions are patients living in the St. Louis area who continue their work or home activities; in such cases the therapy may be spread over a three-week period.

sessions. This enables Masters and Johnson to confront, at the beginning of each therapeutic session, not some abstract theoretical problem of sexual adjustment but what actually happened last night — as described from both of the participants' points of view. What went wrong, and what went right? If yesterday's "prescription" failed, why did it fail? On the basis of the discussion of such questions, realistic new suggestions can be offered for the next practice session.

Therapy begins, of course, with the taking of a complete medical, sexual, and psychological history from each partner by each therapist — and from the two together. What a patient hesitates to tell one therapist, he is likely to reveal to the other. Correlating the five or six histories thus secured makes possible a realistic diagnosis.

In almost all cases, the histories indicate roots of sexual inadequacy buried deep in childhood, nourished by a Puritanical upbringing and reinforced during adolescence or later. In this respect Masters and Johnson agree quite closely with the Freudians. Once full histories have been secured, however, Masters and Johnson let bygones be bygones and concentrate almost wholly on the present — the here and the now, what happened last night or this morning during the practice session.

Facing up to last night's failures can make a couple very uncomfortable. Patients — especially those with previous experience in ordinary psychotherapy — often seek to escape from this embarrassment by reminiscing instead about what happened to them when they were five years old, or six months ago. Masters and Johnson discourage such escapism — and thus save themselves and their patients endless hours of autobiographical meanderings. The target kept constantly in sight is how the couple will function and respond tonight or tomorrow morning.

The Masters-Johnson approach to this target is quite frankly directive. They don't just sit back and listen but give advice and directives ("prescriptions") freely — an approach which I personally welcome on the basis of my own experience as a patient with both directive and nondirective therapists. Certainly there is more to therapy than a mere teacher-learner relationship. But a part at least of the therapeutic experience is a learning experience. That part is diluted or lost when the approach is nondirective.

What kinds of attitude do Masters and Johnson seek to change? The same attitudes with which other therapists have wrestled through the years.

An example of a self-defeating female attitude is the woman who stretches out on the bed and announces, by her posture, gestures, and actions or even at times in words: "O.K., now give me an orgasm. I dare you. You failed last time, and you're going to fail again tonight."

Another example is the woman (also described above) who is afraid to lose control. As she feels the tide of erotic arousal rising within her, she experiences the rise as a threat, and unwittingly "turns herself off." Indeed, she may unconsciously shift position, or push her husband into a different position, in order to terminate the stimulation which is rapidly leading her toward orgasm.

A common example of the male hang-up is what Dr. Masters called "fear of performance." It is a simple fact of nature that no male through the years is fully potent at all times and places and under all circumstances. Most males, however, think of themselves as invariably potent. Thus when a man, sooner or later, unexpectedly finds himself in a position where he wants and expects to erect but fails — often because he is too tired or has had too much to drink — he becomes anxious and fearful.

The man who laughs off or shrugs off the unexpected failure regains his potency a few minutes, hours, or at worst days later. In many men, however, anxiety blocks recovery. Perhaps, a man thinks with horror, this is the end, the debacle. Anxieties left over from early childhood or from adolescence well up and attach themselves to the current impotence anxiety — and there are few things more effective than anxiety for turning off erotic response. The result is readily predictable.

During his next sexual encounter, that man is really not thinking about sex at all; he is worrying about performance. Only his body is in bed; his mind is outside somewhere, looking on to see what will happen and waiting fearfully for his penis to fail to erect. It does fail, of course, again and again and again, in the face of such anxiety. Chronic impotence is the end point.

Most readers will no doubt be able to supply from their reading or their personal experience other examples of self-defeating psychological attitudes which lead to sexual inadequacy. Dr. Albert Ellis, the New York City psychologist who founded rational psychotherapy, has explored such attitudes in depth in his *Sex Without Guilt* and other writings.

Traditional psychotherapy in many cases consists primarily in uncovering the factors in the past — perhaps in the distant past — which underlie the self-defeating current attitudes. Efforts are then made to correct the past, often by giving the patient insight into his motivations and into their distant roots. I know from my own experience as a patient how effective this kind of therapy can be. Masters and Johnson, however, offer the patient a shortcut — an opportunity to wipe the slate clean and start over. Tonight, they decree, you are going to adopt such-and-such an attitude, and your husband, too, is going to change his psychological stance. If it doesn't work tonight, let's find out why and do better tomorrow night.

Three motives secure the patients' very prompt cooperation. They know that time is short; whether it succeeds or fails, therapy will inevitably terminate in two or three weeks. They *like* Masters and Johnson, and want to do well for their sake — a phenomenon known as *transference* in traditional psychotherapy. Finally, the reward before them is a very powerful incentive — lifelong erotic enjoyment and fulfillment.

While the Masters-Johnson advice is directed primarily toward attitudes, specific procedures are recommended in selected cases as one way of effectively altering attitudes. Many of these procedures, to be described in their 1970 book, are based on the Masters-Johnson laboratory findings, adapted to therapeutic uses. Let me here describe just two therapeutic procedures, one female and one male, which are already familiar to many therapists.

The female procedure is the one described decades ago by Dr. Helena Wright in England, in which the woman's hand rests on the man's hand, the man's hand rests on the woman's mons or vulva, and the woman then moves her hand rhythmically in ways she finds erotically arousing. The impact of this procedure on psychological attitudes is clear. The woman whose responses are inhibited by her fear of "losing control" can relax in the knowledge that *she* remains in control. The woman whose sexual hang-up is an infantile need to have something magical done *to* her and *for* her finds herself in a position where she herself *must* take the lead. The man's attitudes, too, are affected in significant ways. Thus what appears at first blush to be a gimmick is in fact a procedure for the effective restructuring of a couple's attitudes.

The specific male procedure, first described in 1955 by Dr. James H. Semans of the Duke University School of Medicine, is addressed to the problem of the man who ejaculates prematurely. A leading psychiatric authority on male sexual inadequacy, Dr. Donald W. Hastings of the

University of Minnesota Medical School, has described the Semans technique as "the most successful therapy known for overcoming [premature ejaculation]."

The procedure is based on the fact that men experience a specific and readily identifiable sensation shortly before orgasm, at a moment in their response cycle which Dr. Masters calls "the point of no return" or "moment of orgasmic inevitability" — the point beyond which it is impossible to forestall ejaculation. The procedure consists in stimulating the penis until this warning feeling arises — and then stopping abruptly and immediately. It may help, too, at this point, to pinch the penis just hard enough to be slightly painful, in order to ensure erotic turnoff. If the timing is right, the sensation disappears and the ejaculation does not occur. "The erection may or may not go down," Dr. Hastings reports; "it doesn't matter. Ten or fifteen minutes later, the same procedure is repeated. Repetitions three or four times a night (or day) for three or four days running have proved highly successful in abolishing the premature ejaculation pattern."

Sometimes, of course, stimulation is continued too long and the patient does ejaculate. He can be assured not to worry; this is to be expected once in a while. No harm is done; he need merely wait until he can have another erection — perhaps a few hours later — and then try again.

Masters and Johnson have reported at medical meetings, as noted above, that their therapy for premature ejaculation (which includes the Semans procedure) is successful in 98 or 99 cases out of 100, and that in most cases ejaculatory control remains excellent five years later. This low failure rate, however, can hardly be attributed *solely* to the Semans procedure. The psychological context in which Masters and Johnson frame the procedure is also significant — indeed, it can fairly be described as inspired.

Instead of having the man stimulate his own penis, as recommended in the original Semans paper, Masters and Johnson enlist the cooperation of the wife. They teach her, too, to recognize the "point of no return" by objective signs paralleling the man's subjective sensation of "orgasmic inevitability" — so that she, too, will know when to stop. This double check makes inadvertent ejaculation less likely. Step by step, as therapy proceeds, Masters and Johnson recommend ways in which the control achieved during the wife's manual stimulation of the penis can be extended to stimulation with the penis in the vagina — by introducing it, for example, and leaving it in but refraining from coital thrusting. As confidence in the man's control grows, that confidence is shared by both partners — and both partners feel that this is their mutual achievement. The psychological advantage of this mutuality over the procedure as originally described, in which the man tries to cure himself alone, is typical of the whole Masters-Johnson therapeutic approach and of the way in which they imaginatively harness specific procedures for purposes of attitudinal restructuring.

How can psychological factors such as attitudes facilitate or block normal physiological responses such as erection, lubrication, and orgasm? Here the work of the Newtons is relevant. When nursing her baby, it will be recalled, Niles Newton's let-down reflex was inhibited by pain, embarrassment, and other psychological factors — and the evidence made it clear that the inhibition occurred in the portion of the brain known as the hypothalamus. Evidence from animal experiments indicates that the hypothalamus is involved in genital as well as breast responses, and perhaps in orgasm itself. But whether the inhibition occurs in the hypothalamus or elsewhere in the neurohormonal system, there is surely nothing mysterious about it. Interactions of mind and body are commonplaces of physiology — as when a threatening letter or an exciting moment in a bridge game raises the pulse rate and blood pressure, or sadness at a death in the family stimulates the lachrimal glands to secrete tears. No doubt future research will elucidate the sexual effects of the emotions in detail as the cardiovascular and lachrimal effects have already been elucidated.

Yet another aspect of the Masters-Johnson therapy program can best be explained in terms of a well-known nonsexual phenomenon — variations in reaction to pain.

A broken rib, as everyone who has had one knows, is excruciatingly painful. The pain sets in, ordinarily, immediately after injury, continues to be severe for hours or days unless relieved by analgesics, and then slowly tapers off. There is thus a normal pain cycle associated with a broken rib.

A soldier who breaks a rib on the battlefield, however, may feel no pain whatever and go right on fighting, oblivious of his injury. The same is true of a football player injured on the field — and there are countless other examples of psychological anesthesia as complete as any inducible by drugs.

In almost exactly the same way, the sensations which normally arise during erotic stimulation fail to reach consciousness in some people on some occasions, and in some people chronically. The patient is in some way *disconnected* from his own erotic sensations. In such cases, too, the normal physiological responses to stimulation are also interrupted; the stroked penis fails to erect or the vagina fails to lubricate. The task of therapy in such cases is to reconnect the patient, make him whole again, get him back into the marital bed instead of hovering somewhere outside, looking on but failing to *feel.*

It is this need to reconnect to which Mrs. Johnson no doubt refers when she often says, as quoted in my chapter on van de Velde: the secret is *sensate focus*. This is also the teaching of van de Velde, Kinsey, Helena Wright, and others. Forget your worries and cares, your failures last night and the night before, your hostility and guilt and shame, your wretched childhood and your miserable adolescence. Focus on the sensuous here and the sensuous now; welcome the feelings which arise during erotic arousal — the feelings you have come to therapy to experience. Then let nature take its course and do the rest.

Can the Masters-Johnson form of therapy be effectively used by other therapeutic teams?

I was delighted on my most recent visit to St. Louis to learn that the answer is yes.

A second team of therapists has been added to the Masters-Johnson staff — Dr. Richard Spitz, trained originally as a pediatrician, and Dr. Sally Schumacher, a psychologist. Using Masters and Johnson techniques, they are securing comparable results. I see no reason why, within the next few years, this form of therapy should not become available at other centers throughout the country and world.

In both their physiological research and their therapeutic program, it seems to me, Masters and Johnson represent the high point to date in the grand tradition of sex research stemming from Havelock Ellis. That tradition through the decades has been concerned with the disastrous effects of sexual repression — of sexual Puritanism and Victorianism. It has demonstrated the social roots of sexual frustration. It has not only documented these effects, but has insistently sought remedies. Indeed, sex research itself turns out to be the sovereign remedy; for by determining the facts and making them publicly known, it destroys the ignorance on which the Victorian ethic is founded.

The task remaining is to harness the power of sex research to the *prevention* of sexual inadequacies and other forms of sexual hang-ups in coming generations. And this task, too, I am delighted to be able to report, Masters and Johnson are approaching. In addition to a concern with the sexual problems of the aging and aged, the program currently under way at their Reproductive Biology Research Foundation includes work with troubled adolescents.

Epilogue: The Future of Sex and of Sex Research

In Which the Author Has the Last Word

IN RECENT YEARS it has become customary, almost obligatory, for writers to sum up their views on human sexuality in terms of a moth-eaten metaphor: the Sexual Revolution.

Some pundits allege, usually with dismay, that we are undergoing a Sexual Revolution because many college students are engaging in coitus before marriage. Others reply reassuringly that this isn't really a revolution because almost as many college students engaged in premarital intercourse in the generations Dr. Kinsey studied. The whole controversy seems to me fruitless. I shall state my own views with the aid of a less hackneyed metaphor: convalescence.

I believe that our culture is gradually convalescing from a sexually debilitating disease: Victorianism. The significant questions are the extent of our recovery to date, and the outlook for an ultimate cure.

The essence of the disease is the belief that sex is wicked, loathsome, and likely to lead to disaster. This produces a blockage of sexual response to normal erotic stimuli (see Chapter 6) — and possibly also facilitates an imprinting to perverse erotic stimuli (see Chapter 8).

Most victims of the disease, it is true, concede that some sex acts are licit — namely, coitus from time to time between a man and his wife during the first few decades of their marriage, if performed in "the missionary position," in the dark, for the purpose of procreation. But since young people raised in the Victorian tradition are not supposed to know very much about sexual intercourse, the message that sex is wicked, loathsome, and likely to lead to disaster gets through much more forcefully than this relatively minor and less frequently mentioned exception.

No doubt we are recovering from sexual Victorianism in this pristine virulent form. But the stage of convalescence we have reached varies widely from individual to individual and from social group to social group within our culture today. Next-door neighbors may be separated in their sexual attitudes and practices by a hundred years or five thousand miles. Some of us, including a surprisingly large minority of young people, continue to accept Victorianism in *almost* its pristine purity. At the other extreme are participants in the sexual freedom movement and the swinging scene described in Chapter 9. Nor is there a firm middle ground. Each of us must find his own way.

This, I think, is as it should be. My neighbor on the right should be as free to live his own life within a Victorian framework, behind the closed doors of his own home, as my neighbor on the left should be free to dance to a livelier tune.

There are difficulties associated with this diversity. It is hard for a family committed to Victorianism to raise its children in that tradition if the children next door are raised in freer ways — and it is equally hard on the family next door, whose children are quite likely to pick up sexual taboos and other destructive notions from the Victorian children. One solution is implied in Havelock Ellis's "Evolution of Modesty," with its emphasis on the ways in which people differ from one another. Children can learn that what is proper for the children next door is not necessarily proper for them. For a closely related difficulty, however, I have no solution to offer: how a public school system these days can devise a sex education program acceptable to an entire community.

Our current uneasy diversity, moreover, may even lead to a sexual turn to the right paralleling our recent political turn to the right, a ruthless repression of those who have convalesced too rapidly and too far, a sexual Joe McCarthyism — in short, a relapse into Victorianism.

Just how a society which has partially freed itself from outworn sexual taboos manages to enslave itself again is a topic about which very little is known. How, for example, did the Victorians get that way in the first place? Victoria's reign was preceded in British social history by a period of quite remarkable sexual openness. Some historians have suggested that the British upper classes accepted sexual repression for themselves, and tried to foist it on the lower classes, in order (a) to achieve the kind of labor discipline required by the Industrial Revolution — workers who showed up early Monday morning, worked faithfully and uncomplainingly until late Saturday night, and then spent Sunday soberly in church; and (b) to immunize Britain against the pernicious influences of the French Revolution and the Napoleonic reforms. The rise of religious evangelism (perhaps also politically motivated) and the personal influence of the charismatic Queen are often mentioned as well. The German repression of sexual permissiveness, beginning in 1933, was much more obviously political. Hitler and the Nazis made it clear that the needs of their Thousand-Year Reich required sexual as well as political conformity; sex research and sex education were ruthlessly repressed.

I hope historians will tackle such topics soon; for as they themselves often remark, those who fail to study history are doomed to reenact it. I would much rather study the way in which Victorianism was imposed generations ago than witness a relapse — a sexual reenslavement — during the years ahead.

In the United States, voices on the right are again angrily insisting, as in Germany in the early 1930's, that our military strength and national unity are being sapped by sexual freedom. "Impeach Earl Warren" was for years a right-wing rallying cry, based at least in part on Chief Justice Warren's willingness to let sexual matter circulate freely through the mails and be exhibited in movie theaters. The John Birch Society and other right-wing organizations have made repeated attacks on sex education in the schools. A Commission on Obscenity and Pornography was set up by Congress in 1968. President Nixon attacked the widespread distribution of sexual material through the mails in May 1969, and promised restrictive measures. But obscenity and pornography are not the true targets. A previous American drive allegedly launched against obscenity descended most harshly on Margaret Sanger and the birth control movement; no doubt the next round of victims will be chosen with equal care, and will include many schoolteachers and others concerned with sex education. It may be later than we think.

In the absence of repressive political and legal action, our further convalescence from Victorianism will largely depend on how we bring up our children — and here, it seems to me, the lessons of sex research are clear. Halfway measures are not enough. The girls whose sexual upbringing during the 1930's and 1940's was described by Dr. Leah Schaefer were subjected to far fewer restrictions than typically Victorian children, and weren't taught that sex is sinful. Yet the Victorian taint lingered; the feeling that sex is loathsome and hazardous survived — and the outcome was sexually disastrous.

Childhood masturbation is here the keystone. Researchers since Havelock Ellis have documented in limitless detail (as demonstrated throughout this volume) that the taboo against masturbation — perhaps in combination with taboos against other forms of natural childhood sex play — is the chief means by which the message is transmitted to the next generation that sex is a loathsome disease. The Victorians were shrewd enough to make enforcement of the masturbation taboo the foundation of their sexual doctrines and their child-rearing practices. Those of us who welcome the convalescence from Victorianism must place equal emphasis on masturbation as an essential phase in the normal, healthy blossoming of mature sexual responses.

The future of sex in our culture will depend only in small part on what we teach our children about sex in the sixth grade, or in high school or college. Far more important is the establishment of a milieu in which even quite young children can develop self-confidence, self-esteem, and self-acceptance — including an acceptance of their own bodies, and of their sexual feelings. This means freedom to masturbate without feelings of guilt or shame, and to play innocently rather than guiltily with other children.*

Credit for our partial sexual convalescence to date is often attributed to two purely technological advances: the discovery of the sulfa drugs, penicillin, and the other antibiotics, making it possible to cure and control the venereal diseases; and the development of the contraceptive pill. I have a third explanation.

* The most effective expression of this point of view I have found is by Dr. Kinsey's closest associate, Dr. Wardell Pomeroy, in his recent *Boys and Sex* (New York: Delacorte, 1968), a book addressed directly to teen-age boys and their parents. Dr. Pomeroy does not limit himself, for example, to assuring boys that masturbation won't drive them crazy. He suggests that they practice masturbating slowly, rather than trying to see how fast they can ejaculate — so that they will be more effective lovers and husbands later on. (Robert Latou Dickinson also made this suggestion, back in 1949.) As for frequency of masturbation, Dr. Pomeroy assures boys that desire is an adequate guide; there is nothing wrong in masturbating as often as you want to. A companion book by Dr. Pomeroy, *Girls and Sex,* is scheduled for publication late in 1969.

Sexual Victorianism, today as in the past, rests squarely and necessarily on sexual ignorance. The taboo against masturbation loses much of its obsessive-compulsive quality when people at long last learn that masturbators grow up to be prime ministers, Nobel Prize winners, and corporation presidents as well as insane asylum inmates. The Victorian custom of teaching children to put on their nightgown before taking off their underclothes, in order to spare themselves a view of their own genitals, would have lost much of its cogency if Victorians had known that their own honored grandfathers and grandmothers were accustomed to bathe nude on the beach at Brighton. The widespread Victorian belief that coitus is an ordeal which dutiful wives must occasionally endure depended upon ignorance of normal female sexual response. As the iron curtain of ignorance was slowly raised, convalescence slowly set in.

Thus we reach the surprising conclusion that much of the credit for our partial convalescence from sexual Victorianism belongs to sex research itself. Havelock Ellis, Freud, van de Velde, Robert Latou Dickinson, Kinsey, Masters and Johnson — these are the physicians who ministered to us as we recovered step by step. They and their fellow researchers supplied us with the knowledge on which our convalescence depended.

Note, however, that the impact of sex research, like the impact of Victorianism, is primarily on attitudes rather than behavior. What little evidence is available suggests that human sexual behavior has varied little through the centuries in Western countries. People have gone right on masturbating, copulating, and performing other sexual acts — heterosexual, homosexual, or otherwise — from generation to generation. Kinsey, our most reliable authority, assures us that there was masturbation, premarital intercourse, extramarital intercourse, postmarital intercourse, homosexual contacts, and other "illicit" behavior in the late Victorian generation he studied just as there was in the first post-Victorian generation. The chief difference was that Victorian frequencies were somewhat lower.

Recent publications suggest that in England, too, the Victorian repression affected what was thought, said, and openly published about sex rather than what acts were performed, when, where, and with whom. At the very height of the repression, according to recent biographies, many eminent Victorians had mistresses as well as wives, and quite a few had homosexual contacts. The anonymous Victorian author of *My Secret Life* recorded his sexual contacts with an estimated two thousand women, and several men, while Victoria sat on her throne. Victorian pornography was so frank (and some of it so delightful) that it could not be openly published in the United States until the mid-1960's and remains unpublishable in Britain. What the Victorian repression accomplished, in short, was a tainting of sexual behavior with sin, guilt, shame, and filthiness. The findings of sex research have not revolutionized behavior; they have simply made it possible for more people to enjoy sex, with fewer qualms, as a natural experience.

The Kinsey Institute, it will be recalled, reported in 1968 that girls in high school and college today are having just about the same sexual experiences as girls in the 1940's. But far more of them, the report continues, are finding the experience enjoyable. This is what sex research, through its impact on sexual attitudes, has accomplished to date. I see no reason why we should not look forward to an era when all young people will find their first coital experience, as well as subsequent sexual experiences, guilt-free, shame-free, and enjoyable.

Through the years ahead, if a new wave of repression does not inundate us, sex research will no doubt continue to contribute to our convalescence. Let me mention briefly a few of the possibilities on the horizon.

We have drugs for everything else; why not drugs for sexual inadequacy? The answer is that scientists haven't looked very hard. If a useful drug were found, moreover, there would be demands for its suppression.

This, indeed, has already happened. Among the many drugs which came into use during the 1960's for the purpose of altering mood or enhancing pleasure was the "popper" — a capsule containing a volatile chemical previously used by victims of heart disease. Poppers open the peripheral blood vessels and thus temporarily lower blood pressure. In addition, it was alleged, a whiff inhaled by a sexually aroused man or woman triggers immediate orgasm. This effect, of course, is precisely what is needed by countless young women and a considerable number of aging men who are capable of achieving a plateau of intense sexual arousal but unable to reach climax and resolution. Poppers could be purchased in drugstores without a prescription; sales soared.

Do they really work? Nobody knows. No controlled scientific study of the sexual effects of poppers has been undertaken at this writing. Instead, a 1968 United States Food and Drug Administration ruling banned over-the-counter sales of poppers. Our culture's immediate response to the possibility of an anti-frigidity drug, in short, was repressive.

Despite this repressive attitude, there is a considerable likelihood that effective drugs for the sexual inadequacies — especially for geriatric inadequacies — will in due course emerge from the laboratory. Hormone replacement therapy for menopausal and post-menopausal women is already a commonplace; Dr. William H. Masters is one of those urging similar hormone replacement therapy for aging men.

Countless small-scale experiments are also under way throughout the country on other therapeutic approaches, based neither on Freud nor on drugs. Programs at the Esalen Institute in Big Sur, California, the Aureon Institute in New York City, and the recently launched program of the Center for Marital and Sexual Studies in Long Beach, California, are examples. The latter, directed by Dr. William E. Hartman and Mrs. Marilyn A. Fithian, is the first I have found which is patterned even in part on the Masters-Johnson therapy program in St. Louis.

Only a few of these new programs are under formal medical or psychiatric sponsorship; they are designed to meet a need which medical and psychiatric centers have failed to meet. They differ widely among themselves, but most of them have one feature in common: a rejection of the orthodox view, almost universal since Freud, that therapy must be solely an exchange of words between therapist and patient. The body as well as the mind, advocates of these new approaches insist, should be involved in therapy. Emphasis is often placed on group therapy as well.

Common forms the new movement takes include sensitivity training, the therapeutic marathon (lasting twenty-four uninterrupted hours or longer), touch therapy (experience with actual physical encounters, ranging from ordinary touching to caressing, necking, and wrestling), and nude therapy.

These approaches stem in part from Dr. Wilhelm Reich, a pupil of Freud's, who broke away from orthodox psychoanalysis on this and other issues. Reich's best-known book is *The Function of the Orgasm.* In his later years Reich was a victim of paranoia; but despite that he passed on his views to a wide circle of disciples — and the Reichian approach has not only survived but flourishes in many out-of-the-way places.

I have attended sessions at several centers where bodily therapy is employed. I came away profoundly unimpressed by the theoretical underpinnings of the therapy. But I could see that something happens during these sessions — something which in selected cases may be very helpful. A man who considered himself benefited has supplied the following account of what happened to him during his first nude-therapy encounter.

"Following a dull introductory statement, a gong sounded and the woman therapist announced, 'Now we take off our clothes.' The thirty men and women present, almost all of whom had attended before, stripped quite unselfconsciously. So did I. When in Rome, do as the Romans. A 'training procedure' was then introduced. We paired up with the people who happened to be nearest; each couple sat down on the floor face to face. One partner then asked the other questions such as, 'May I touch your knee?' 'May I rub your elbow?' 'May I rub it harder?' If permitted, he did. Later the partners reversed roles. The alleged purpose was to enhance sensory awareness. I found the whole thing stupid and boring, and at one point varied the routine by asking the quite uninteresting young woman with whom I was paired, 'May I kiss your knee?' She assented, and I did — only to be interrupted by two indignant monitors who informed me that kissing was a forbidden transgression of the rules. My boredom mounted. At the intermission, I chatted with a young woman who assured me that these therapy sessions had revolutionized her life. She had been depressed, inhibited, self-conscious, self-depreciating. In therapy she had learned that a touch is not an assault, and that she was a person of dignity and worth. I concluded that she was a shill for the house, planted to engender enthusiasm. After the intermission, a second pairing occurred. There were a few more men than women present, and to my utter horror I found myself paired with another man. Almost in a panic, I was tempted to grab my clothes and bolt for the door. I had been brought up as a child to fear a homosexual attack on myself more than pain or death. At the age of three, for example, I was allowed to answer the front-door bell; but I was not allowed to go to the back door because there are tramps who come to back doors and assault little boys. If I brought a little boy home for play after school once or twice, nothing was said; but third visits were forbidden because little boys shouldn't get too close. These and countless other long-forgotten memories had flooded back into consciousness during my conventional psychotherapy sessions a few years before. Those earlier sessions had enabled me to understand my hang-up, and had made me much less tense when I accidentally found myself alone with another man in an ordinary business or social situation. Yet I now almost panicked at the thought of actual physical contact, nude, with another nude man. I recovered sufficiently to be able to state my problem to my partner. He assured me he used to have a similar problem, and that it really wasn't going to be so bad.

The next twenty-minute 'training exercise' was in fact a revolutionary experience. I learned that a touch by a man is not a homosexual assault, and that the terror I had dreaded for thirty years was just an imaginary hobgoblin. I've felt more at home in the world ever since. The experience, incidentally, was not specifically sexual. On the contrary, it enabled me to divorce the experience of casual male-to-male contact from the abnormal sexual significance my upbringing had attached to it. *Sexual* contact with another male remains as distasteful to me as ever; it just isn't threatening any more. I also changed my mind about the enthusiastic young woman I'd talked with during the intermission. She, obviously, had been brought up with the same dread of *heterosexual* contact. Touch therapy, nude therapy, really had revolutionized her life to an even greater extent."

A testimonial from one satisfied client, of course, does not certify the value of a therapy program. But I very much hope that these unorthodox therapy experiments will continue — and that their effectiveness will be objectively studied and evaluated.

Within the orthodox scientific tradition, the most impressive work currently under way (except for the Masters-Johnson program in St. Louis) is in the field of animal research. Programs under the direction of Dr. Frank A. Beach and his associates at the University of California, Berkeley, and under Charles H. Sawyer and his associates at the University of California, Los Angeles, are two examples among many. In England, the work of Dr. Joe Herbert at the University of Birmingham and of Dr. Richard P. Michael at the Primate Research Center in Beckenham, Kent, is similarly impressive. I regret that most of this current research is too complex and technical, and too remote from immediate practical application, to warrant review in detail here. Let me, however, present a few brief samples.

Dr. Paul D. MacLean and his associates at the National Institutes of Health in Bethesda, Maryland, have found more than a hundred and fifty sites in the brains of monkeys where electrical stimulation leads to erection of the penis. They and workers at other centers have also found sites where electrical stimulation of the brain leads to the ejaculation of semen without any erection.

Dr. James Olds of the University of Michigan and others have found "reward systems" in the brain where electrical stimulation leads to remarkable behavior. An animal with an electrode planted in one of these "reward" areas will press a lever to send a mild electric shock into his own brain thousands of times an hour, hour after hour. Though food and water are readily available, famished or parched rats will press the lever rather than eat or drink. Even the proximity of a female rat in heat will not deter a male rat from the happy pursuit of this electrical delight. The centers for erection and ejaculation, I need hardly add, are quite close to these reward centers. They are also quite close to oral, anal, and pain centers, leading Dr. MacLean to suggest a neurological foundation for oral, anal, and sadomasochistic sexual behavior.

At other laboratories, "copulation-reward sites" have been studied. A rat caged alone will repeatedly press the lever to stimulate himself through an electrode implanted at such a site. If a female rat is nearby, however, he will engage in copulatory behavior instead when the current is turned on — even following ejaculation, when he would otherwise be sexually unarousable. The moment the current is turned off, his sexual behavior terminates.

An amusing by-product of these laboratory studies concerns the effectiveness of a fresh stimulus. A male rat utterly exhausted following a series of copulative encounters with one female will rouse himself, copulate again, and ejaculate again if a new female is introduced.

Comparable research on the sexual neurophysiology of female animals has been delayed by the lack of a readily observable female counterpart of male erection and ejaculation. Indeed, strange as it may seem, there is almost no laboratory evidence that female animals *have* orgasms. Back in 1951, however, Drs. N. L. VanDemark and R. L. Hays of the Department of Dairy Science, University of Illinois, found that the uterus in cows undergoes a series of rhythmic contractions during coitus, reaching a climax at about the time of the bull's orgasm. The subsequent Masters-

Johnson finding of similar uterine responses during the human female orgasm suggests a way in which sexual response in female animals can now be objectively studied. So far as I have been able to ascertain, no one is as yet following up this clue.

Researchers at a number of centers are studying the relations of the sex hormones to these neurological processes. They are finding, for example, that the frequency with which an animal presses the lever to stimulate certain reward centers goes down when the testes or ovaries are removed and rises again when hormone replacement therapy is given the animal. They are achieving very curious results by implanting microscopic pellets of male hormone in the female brain, and vice versa.

Experiments such as these are casting a bright new light on the relationships between sexuality and aggression. In several series of animal experiments it has been shown that castration tames a male; hormone replacement therapy restores his aggressiveness. A dose of female hormone (estrogen) also tames a male; and male hormone produces a male-like aggressiveness in females. The human implications are not yet apparent. Some experiments at least suggest the possibility, however, that a violent, aggressive male is often a sexually frustrated male, and that sexual fulfillment as well as castration may exert a taming influence. "Make love, not war" may be more than just a slogan.

On a recent tour of centers where research of these kinds is under way, I was particularly pleased to see young men and women at work along with senior scientists. Young faces have also become more frequent in the past few years at meetings of the Society for the Scientific Study of Sex. Dr. Corner's warning to Dr. Masters to wait until he was forty before entering sex research is beginning to be honored as much in the breach as in the observance.

This, surely, is as it should be. One of the major complaints during recent campus protests has been the irrelevance of the university curriculum, and of much university-centered research, to the human condition. Throughout the 1960's, we concentrated much of our scientific endeavors on landing a man on the moon, and creating missiles which would destroy other missiles, while our mundane problems remained unsolved. The result is a growing alienation of young people — indeed, of people generally — from the scientific establishment. A vast expansion of research effort addressed to human concerns, including sexual problems, is clearly called for. I am hopeful that young scientists unwilling to dedicate themselves to designing additional weapons of destruction will be increasingly put to work on these pressing human problems.

One unanswered research question in particular fascinates me.

What happens in a society where people are sexually free, and where children are brought up without sexual taboos and inhibitions?

There are several possibilities.

It has been suggested, for example, that love will disappear and that sex will be reduced to merely an enjoyable physiological act.

It has also been suggested that even the joy of sex is dependent on setting limits. Masturbation, the Victorians alleged, leads to impotence as well as insanity. The worn-out old roué of forty, sunk into misery through his debaucheries, is a familiar figure in fiction and in antisexual gossip.*

I strongly suspect that current fears concerning sexual "excesses" are essentially hangovers from Victorianism. The threats that sex will lead to eternal damnation, to venereal disease, and to unwanted pregnancy are wearing out; hence fresh threats must be invoked.

Here, I think, is a task for sex research: an objective inquiry into the short-term and long-term effects on men, women, and children of emancipation from sexual repression, from feelings of sexual shame and guilt. Sweden and Denmark, where convalescence from Victorianism appears to have progressed the furthest, are favorable sites for such an inquiry; but much might also be learned from a comparison of the inhibited and the emancipated here in the United States or anywhere else.

In the absence of such studies, I can only conclude with a statement of personal belief.

When I began work on this book three years ago, I had a vague feeling that sexual inhibitions and frustrations have effects far broader than are realized — that much of the bigotry, hostility, and strife which character-

* Many studies have shown, however, that the worn-out roué is mythical. The men who retain full potency into their sixties and seventies are mostly those who have maintained vigorous sexual activity through the preceding decades. See Isadore Rubin, *Sexual Life After Sixty* (N.Y., Basic Books, 1965). Animal experiments help to explain these human findings; they have revealed that male sexual capacity is dependent upon use of that capacity. It is the ejaculation of sperm-laden semen which causes the hypothalamus to signal the pituitary to release gonadotrophic hormones — which in turn stimulate the testes and prostate to manufacture additional sperm cells and semen.

ize our era might have deep sexual roots. I hoped that a release from feelings of sexual guilt and shame might lead to warmer, richer interpersonal relationships — and to a relaxation of the tensions which are threatening to rend our society, perhaps to destroy mankind. A healthy society requires healthy people; perhaps, I thought, sexual fulfillment is one of the preconditions of human health.

Three years of studying the history of sex research from Havelock Ellis to date have converted these feelings and hopes into firmly held convictions.

Bibliography and References

Most of the quotations in this volume are from the "Major Sources" cited below for each chapter. Quotations from other sources are in many cases identified in the text. Additional sources are cited below under "Detailed References."

Chapter 1 Henry Havelock Ellis

Major Sources

Ellis, Havelock, *Studies in the Psychology of Sex,* in seven parts, 1896–1928. I have quoted from the definitive two-volume Random House edition now in print (copyright 1936 by The Modern Library, Inc., New York); this edition is identical in text with the four-volume Random House edition published in 1936.

Ellis, Havelock, *My Life.* First American edition, Houghton Mifflin, Boston, 1939; first English edition, William Heinemann, London and Toronto, 1940. An edition published in 1967 by Neville Spearman, London, and copyright by Alan Hull Walton, contains a foreword by Françoise Delisle (Françoise Lafitte-Cyon), and an introduction and very useful annotated bibliography by Mr. Walton.

Delisle, Françoise (Lafitte-Cyon, Françoise), *Friendship's Odyssey.* Madame Delisle first published her autobiography under this title in 1946 (Heinemann, London). Subsequently she expanded her autobiography into two volumes, illustrated — *Françoise* (Delisle, London, 1962), and *Friendship's Odyssey* (Delisle, London, 1964). I have quoted exclusively from the 1964 edition, which among other additions supplies the true names of a number of persons not named in the 1946 edition.

Detailed references

Page 30

Ellis's description of his relations with H.D. (Hilda Doolittle) is from "A Revelation," first published in Havelock Ellis, *Impressions and Comments* (Third Series). Boston, Houghton Mifflin, and London, Constable, 1924. Reprinted in Havelock Ellis, *Fountain of Life,* Boston, Houghton Mifflin, 1930.

Page 32

Ellis's letter to Joseph Wortis about H.D. is in Joseph Wortis, M.D., *Fragments of an Analysis with Freud,* New York, Simon & Schuster, 1954.

Other Publications

Ellis, Havelock, *Psychology of Sex: A Manual for Students.* N.Y.: Long and Smith, 1933. This is *not* a condensation of Ellis's *Studies* or a substitute for the *Studies.*

At least four biographies of Ellis have been published:

Calder-Marshall, Arthur, *The Sage of Sex.* N.Y.: Putnam, 1959.

Collis, John Stewart, *Havelock Ellis: Artist of Life.* N.Y.: William Sloane, 1959.

Goldberg, Isaac, *Havelock Ellis.* N.Y.: Simon and Schuster, 1926; London, Constable.

Peterson, Houston, *Havelock Ellis, Philosopher of Love.* Boston, Houghton Mifflin, 1928.

Ellis's *My Life,* however, remains the best life of Ellis.

A collection of essays about Ellis rich in eulogies is *Havelock Ellis: In Appreciation,* edited by Joseph Ishill, Berkeley Heights, N.J.: Oriole Press, 1929.

For a psychiatrist's view of Ellis, see Joseph Wortis, "Havelock Ellis," in *Recent Advances in Biological Psychiatry.* N.Y.: Grune & Stratton, 1960.

Delisle, Françoise, *The Return of Havelock Ellis,* London: Regency Press, 1968, describes communications from Ellis received by Madame Delisle since his death.

Chapter 2 Richard von Krafft-Ebing

Major Source

Krafft-Ebing, Richard von, *Psychopathia Sexualis,* first ed., Stuttgart, 1886; 12th ed. 1903. I have quoted throughout from the English translation of the twelfth edition by F. J. Rebman, first published in 1906.

Other Publications

Krafft-Ebing, Richard von, *Textbook of Insanity* (first ed. 1876), authorized translation by Charles Gilbert Chaddock. Philadelphia: F. A. Davis Co., 1904.

I have found no biography of Krafft-Ebing, and no biographical essays about him. Even the "biographical sketch of the author" published in the 1904 edition of his *Textbook of Insanity* is silent concerning his personal life. So are most of the obituary notices in German and English. Krafft-Ebing's marriage and children, however, are mentioned in the obituary published in the *Wiener Klinische Wochenschrift,* 16:21–22, 1903.

Chapter 3 Sigmund Freud

Major Sources

Freud, Sigmund, *Standard Edition of the Complete Psychological Works of Sigmund Freud.* Translated from the German under the general editorship of James Strachey in collaboration with Anna Freud, assisted by Alix Strachey and Alan Tyson. London, Hogarth Press, 23 vols., 1953–1966.

Freud, Sigmund, *Collected Papers* (1893–1938), 5 vols., authorized translation under the supervision of Joan Rivière. American edition published by Basic Books, Inc., 1959, by arrangement with The Hogarth Press and The Institute of Psycho-Analysis, London.

Freud, Sigmund, *An Autobiographic Study* (1925), authorized translation by James Strachey. Copyright 1935 by W. W. Norton Co., Inc., New York; copyright renewed 1963 by James Strachey.

Freud, Sigmund, *An Outline of Psychoanalysis* (1940), authorized translation by James Strachey. Copyright 1949 by W. W. Norton Co., Inc., New York.

Jones, Ernest, M.D., *The Life and Work of Sigmund Freud,* 3 vols. N.Y.: Basic Books, Inc., 1953–1957.

Detailed references

Page 62
"In all the cases": *Collected Papers,* Vol. V, p. 198.
Page 64
"I was born": *Autobiographical Study,* p. 13.
Page 66
To illustrate his approach. *Collected Papers,* Vol. I, p. 233.
Page 68
"Thus in one of my cases": *Collected Papers,* Vol. I, p. 212.
Page 69
"I believe this to be": Freud, Sigmund, *The Origins of Psychoanalysis: Letters to Wilhelm Fliess,* translated by Eric Mosbacher and James Strachey. London: Imago, 1954.
Page 70
"If the reader feels": *Autobiographical Study,* p. 63.
Page 70
Havelock Ellis case histories. Cases XVII, XXV: and XLII are from Part IV, "Sexual Inversion," in *Studies in the Psychology of Sex.* Other cases are from Appendix B to Part II, "Analysis of the Sexual Impulse."
Page 74
"Sexual life does not begin": *Outline,* p. 26.
Page 74
"I venture to assert": *Outline,* p. 97.
Page 75
"A child's first erotic object": *Outline,* p. 89.
Page 79
"The teachings of psychoanalysis," *Outline,* Introductory Note, p. 9.

Other Publications

The literature on Freud and psychoanalysis is enormous. As good a place as any for psychoanalytically naïve readers to begin is with a paperback by Charles Brenner, M.D., himself a Freudian psychoanalyst: *Elementary Textbook of Psychoanalysis.* N.Y.: Anchor, 1957.

Chapter 4 Theodoor Hendrik van de Velde

Major Sources

van de Velde, Theodoor, *Ideal Marriage, Its Physiology and Technique* (1926). I have quoted from the authorized translation by Stella Browne, copyright 1930 by Random House, Inc.

Detailed references

Page 85
"In my youth": van de Velde, Theodoor, *Sex Efficiency through Exercises.* London, E. Heinemann, 1933.
Page 87
"In cases where I have been consulted": van de Velde, Th., *Fertility and Sterility in Marriage,* (first ed. 1929), translation by Stella Browne, copyright by Random House, Inc., New York, 1931, pp. 242–243.

Other Publications

van de Velde, Theodoor, *Sex Hostility in Marriage.* Translated by Hamilton Marr (London: E. Heinemann, 1931). Also published as *Sex Tensions in Marriage.* N.Y.: Random House, 1931.

Chapter 5 Alfred Charles Kinsey

Major Sources

Kinsey, Alfred C., Pomeroy, Wardell B., and Martin, Clyde E., *Sexual Behavior in the Human Male.* Philadelphia and London: W. B. Saunders Company, 1948.
Kinsey, Alfred C., Pomeroy, Wardell B., Martin, Clyde E., and Gebhard, Paul H., *Sexual Behavior in the Human Female.* Philadelphia and London: W. B. Saunders Company, 1953.
Pomeroy, Wardell B., "The Masters-Johnson Report and the Kinsey Tradition," in Brecher, Ruth and Edward, eds., *An Analysis of Human Sexual Response,* Boston: Little, Brown, 1966, and Signet paperback edition.

Detailed references

Pages 105–106
The quotations from Havelock Ellis, Rabelais, Villermé, Brown, Shaw, and others will be found in Ellis, Havelock, "The Phenomena of Sexual Periodicity," *Studies in the Psychology of Sex,* Part 1, pp. 85–160.
Pages 106–109
A discussion of Kinsey's predecessors, and references to their publications, will be found in Kinsey, Alfred C., *et al., Sexual Behavior in the Human Male,* "Historical Introduction," pp. 3–34.
Page 117
Dr. Corner's view is quoted from Corner, George W., "The Origins, Methods, and Findings of the Report, *Sexual Behavior in the Human Male,*" published in *Problems of Sexual Behavior,* 1948, Pub. No. A–732, American Social Hygiene Assn., Inc., 1948.
Page 137*n*
Ellis's description of infantile female masturbation will be found in Ellis, Havelock, "Auto-Erotism," in *Studies in the Psychology of Sex,* Part 1, pp. 161–283.

Other Publications

Gebhard, Paul H., Pomeroy, Wardell B., Martin, Clyde E., and Christenson, Cornelia V., *Pregnancy, Birth, and Abortion.* N.Y.: Harper, 1958.
Gebhard, Paul H., Gagnon, John H., Pomeroy, Wardell B., and Christenson, Cornelia V., *Sex Offenders.* N.Y.: Harper & Row, 1965.

Chapter 6 Women Rediscover Their Own Sexuality

ELIZABETH BLACKWELL

Major Sources

Blackwell, Elizabeth, *Essays in Medical Sociology.* 3 vols. London, E. Bell, 1902.

A collection of Dr. Blackwell's earlier papers, including *The Human Element in Sex* (1894), from which the quotations in this book are taken.

Hays, Elinor Rice, *Those Extraordinary Blackwells: The Story of a Journey to a Better World.* N.Y.: Harcourt, Brace & World, 1967.

LEAH SCHAEFER

Major Sources

Dickinson, Robert Latou, and Beam, Lura, *A Thousand Marriages.* Baltimore, Williams & Wilkins, 1932.

Schaefer, Leah Cahan, "Sexual Experiences and Reactions of a Group of Thirty Women as Told to a Female Psychotherapist," an unpublished Ph.D. thesis submitted to Teachers College, Columbia University, 1964.

NILES NEWTON

Major Sources

Newton, Niles, *Maternal Emotions.* N.Y.: Paul B. Hoeber, Inc., Medical Book Department of Harper & Bros., 1955.

Newton, Niles, and Newton, Michael, "Psychological Aspects of Lactation," in *New England Journal of Medicine,* 277:1179–1188, 1967.

Other Publications

Newton, Niles, "Breast Feeding," in *Psychology Today,* 2:34, June 1968.

Newton, Niles, Peeler, Dudley, and Rawlins, Carolyn, "Effect of Lactation on Maternal Behavior in Mice with Comparative Data on Humans," in *Lying-In, The Journal of Reproductive Medicine,* 1:257–262, 1968.

Newton, Niles, Foshee, Donald, and Newton, Michael, "Experimental Inhibition of Labor Through Environmental Disturbance," in *Obstetrics and Gynecology,* 27:371–377, 1966; and numerous other papers by the Newtons.

For an independent report on similar phenomena, see Berry Campbell and W. E. Peterson, "Milk 'Let-Down' and the Orgasm in the Human Female," in *Human Biology,* 25:165–168, 1953.

HELENA WRIGHT

Major Sources

Wright, Helena, *The Sex Factor in Marriage.* 5th ed., 3rd impression, 1966. Ernest Benn Limited, London.

Wright, Helena, *More About the Sex Factor in Marriage.* 2nd ed., 2nd impression, London: Williams & Norgate, 1959.

Wright, Helena, "A Contribution to the Orgasm Problem in Women," in *International Journal of Sexology,* 3:8–12, 1949; reprinted in *Sex, Society, and the Individual,* edited by A. P. Pillay and Albert Ellis, Bombay, India: International Journal of Sexology, 1953.

MARY JANE SHERFEY

Source

"The Evolution and Nature of Female Sexuality in Relation to Psychoanalytic Theory," in *Journal of the American Psychoanalytic Association,* 14:28–128, 1966.

Chapter 7 John Money and Others

Major Sources

Young, William C., ed., *Sex and Internal Secretions.* 2 vols. Baltimore: Williams & Wilkins, 3rd ed., 1961. This 1609-page classic contains review articles by twenty-eight of the leading authorities on the biology of sex.

Money, John, ed., *Sex Research: New Developments.* N.Y.: Holt, Rinehart and Winston, 1965.

Money, John, *Sex Errors of the Body: Dilemmas, Education, Counselling.* Baltimore: The Johns Hopkins Press, 1968.

Green, Richard, and Money, John, eds., *Transsexualism and Sex Reassignment.* Baltimore: The Johns Hopkins Press, 1969.

Money, John, *Hermaphroditism: An Inquiry Into the Nature of a Human Paradox.* Ph.D. thesis, Harvard University, 1952. Available through University Microfilms, Ann Arbor, Mich.

Detailed references

Page 207
For review of the 76 cases, see Money, J., Hampson, J. G., and Hampson, J. L., "An Examination of Some Basic Sexual Concepts: The Evidence of Human Hermaphroditism," in *Bulletin of the Johns Hopkins Hospital,* 97:301–319, 1955.
Page 209
For cases of "testicular feminizing syndrome" or "androgen insensitivity syndrome," see Money, John, Ehrhardt, Anke A., and Masica, Daniel N., "Fetal Feminization Induced by Androgen Insensitivity in the Testicular Feminizing Syndrome: Effect on Marriage and Maternalism," in *The Johns Hopkins Medical Journal,* 123:105–114, 1968.
Page 214
For the 1959 guinea pig study of Phoenix *et al.,* see Phoenix, C. H., Goy, R. W., Gerall, A. A., and Young, W. C., "Organizing Action of Prenatally Administered Testosterone Propionate on the Tissues Mediating Mating Behavior in the Female Guinea Pig," in *Endocrinology,* 65:369–382, 1959.
Page 216
For cyproterone acetate studies, see Neumann, F., and Elger, W., "Proof of the Activity of Androgenic Agents on the Differentiation of the External Genitalia" in *Excerpta Medica Int. Cong. Ser. No. 101,* p. 168, 1965; also Neumann, F., von Berswordt-Wallrabe, R., Elger, W., and Steinbeck, H., "Activities of Antiandrogens: Experiments in Prepuberal and Puberal Animals and in Foetuses," in Tamm, J., ed., *Testosterone* (Proceedings of the Workshop Conference), April 20–22, 1967. Stuttgart: George Thieme Verlag, 1968, pp. 134–143, and papers by Neumann and others therein cited.
Page 217
For the bisexual rats, see Lisk, R. D., and Suydam, A. J., "Sexual Behavior Patterns in the Prepubertally Castrate Rat," in *Anatomical Record,* 157: 181–189, 1967.
Pages 217–218
For Dr. and Mrs. Harlow's dialogue on play patterns of monkeys, see Harlow, H. F., "Sexual Behavior in the Rhesus Monkey," in Beach, Frank A., ed., *Sex and Behavior.* N.Y.: John Wiley & Sons, 1965, pp. 234–265.
Page 219
For the follow-up study of girls masculinized before birth, see Ehrhardt, Anke A., and Money, John, "Progestin-Induced Hermaphroditism: IQ and Psychosocial Identity in a Study of Ten Girls," in *Journal of Sex Research:* 3:83–100, 1967.
Page 223
For the study of women with adrenogenital syndrome treated late, see Ehrhardt, Anke A., Evers, Kathryn, and Money, John, "Influence of Andro-

gen and Some Aspects of Sexually Dimorphic Behavior in Women with Late Treated Adrenogenital Syndrome," in *The Johns Hopkins Medical Journal,* 123:115–122, 1968.

Page 226

For the study of girls with adrenogenital syndrome treated early, see Ehrhardt, Anke A., Epstein, Ralph, and Money, John, "Fetal Androgens and Female Gender Identity in the Early Treated Adrenogenital Syndrome," in *The Johns Hopkins Medical Journal.* 122:160–167, 1968.

Page 228

For the XXY syndrome, see Money, John, "Cytogenetic and Other Aspects of Transvestism and Transsexualism," in *Journal of Sex Research,* 3:141–143, 1967.

Chapter 8 The Falling-in-Love Experience

Detailed references

Pages 230–231

For imprinting in birds and other animal species, see Hess, Eckhardt E., "Imprinting," in *Science,* 130:133–141, 1959; also "Imprinting in Birds," *Science,* 146:1128–1139; and sources therein cited.

Page 234

For John Money on imprinting and on the falling-in-love experience, see: Money, John, Hampson, Joan G., and Hampson, John L., "Imprinting and the Establishment of Gender Role," in *A.M.A. Archives of Neurology and Psychiatry,* 77:333–336, 1957; Money, John, "Components of Eroticism in Man: Cognitional Rehearsals," in *Recent Advances in Biological Psychiatry,* N.Y.: Grune & Stratton, 1961; Money, John, "The Sex Instinct and Human Eroticism," in *Journal of Sex Research,* 1:3–16, 1965; and other papers by Money.

Pages 234–236

For Gebhard's two cases of adolescent sexual imprinting, see Gebhard, Paul H., "Situational Factors Affecting Human Sexual Behavior," in Beach, Frank A., ed., *Sex and Behavior.* N.Y.: John Wiley & Sons, 1965, pp. 483–495.

Page 238

For Dante Alighieri and others, see Kiell, Norman, *The Universal Experience of Adolescence.* N.Y.: International Universities Press, 1964; paperback ed., Boston: Beacon Press, 1967.

Page 242

For Harlow's monkeys, see Harlow, Harry F., "Sexual Behavior in the Rhesus Monkey," in Beach, Frank A., ed., *Sex and Behavior.* N.Y. John Wiley & Sons, 1965, pp. 234–265.

Page 245
For Dr. Calderone on Harlow's monkeys, see Calderone, Mary Steichen, "Sex Education for Young People — and for Their Parents and Teachers" in Brecher, Ruth and Edward, eds., *An Analysis of Human Sexual Response.* Boston: Little, Brown, 1966; paperback ed., N.Y.: New American Library, 1966.

Chapter 9 When Sexual Inhibitions Are Cast Off

This chapter is based on unpublished data cited in the text.

Chapter 10 Masters and Johnson

Major Sources

Masters, William H., and Johnson, Virginia E., *Human Sexual Response.* Boston: Little, Brown, 1966.

Brecher, Ruth and Edward, eds., *An Analysis of Human Sexual Response.* Boston: Little, Brown, 1966; paperback ed., N.Y.: New American Library, 1966.

Detailed references

Pages 287–294
For the predecessors of Masters and Johnson, see Kinsey, Alfred C. *et al.*, *Sexual Behavior in the Human Female,* Ch. 14, "Anatomy of Sexual Response and Orgasm," and Ch. 15, "Physiology of Sexual Response and Orgasm," and sources there cited, Philadelphia: W. B. Saunders Co., 1953. See also Dickinson, Robert Latou, *Human Sex Anatomy,* 2nd ed., Baltimore: Williams & Wilkins, 1949, esp. Ch. VII, "Anatomy of Coitus," and sources there cited.

Page 306
The definitive account of the Masters-Johnson therapy program, *Human Sexual Inadequacy,* will be published in 1970 by Little, Brown, Boston. Some earlier accounts: Masters, W. H., and Johnson, V. E., "Treatment of the Sexually Incompatible Family Unit," in *Minnesota Medicine* (1961), 44:466–471; "Sexual Incompatibility, Diagnosis and Treatment," in

Lloyd, C. W., ed., *Human Reproduction and Sexual Behavior*, Philadelphia: Lea & Febiger, 1964, pp. 474–489; "Counseling with Sexually Incompatible Marriage Partners," in Klemer, R. H., ed., *Counseling in Marital and Sexual Problems* (A Physician's Handbook). Baltimore: Williams & Wilkins, 1965; pp. 126–137.

Index

Index